LOST IN TIME AND SPACE

An Unofficial Guide to the Uncharted Journeys of *Doctor Who*

LOST IN TIME AND SPACE

An Unofficial Guide to the Uncharted Journeys of *Doctor Who*

Matthew J Elliott

Published in 2019 by Telos Publishing Ltd
139 Whitstable Road, Canterbury, Kent CT2 8EQ

www.telos.co.uk

Telos Publishing Ltd values feedback. Please e-mail us with any comments you may have about this book to: feedback@telos.co.uk

Originally published in 2014 by Hasslein Books.

ISBN: 978-1-84583-981-9

British Library Cataloguing in Publication Data. A catalogue record for this book is available from the British Library.

This book is lovingly and respectfully dedicated to all the creative forces behind the greatest television programme in the universes of time and space, Doctor Who.

Contents

Acknowledgements

This book would not have been possible without the patience and advice of several individuals. Thanks, then, to my wife Gillian, who persevered through certain stories that really tested her patience, though they shall go unnamed here. My daughter Megan was often at my side during this adventure, her enthusiasm a constant tonic. If you ever wondered what an 11-year-old girl looks for in a *Doctor Who* story, her favourites are *The Androids of Tara* and *The Vampires of Venice*.

Gratitude also to Rich Handley and the late Paul Giachetti, who first saw the potential of the book and guided it through its original publication, and to John Rowbotham, Roger Johnson, *Who* experts David J Howe and Lars Pearson, and Big Finish scribes Ian Potter and Matt Fitton for their suggestions and observations.

The Doctor: 'Did I ever tell you that the Ship has a memory bank, hm?'

Susan: 'Yes, it records our journeys.'

– *The Edge of Destruction*

Ace: 'Doctor! Where have you been?'

The Doctor: 'Where *haven't* I been?'

– *Ghost Light*

Foreword to the 2014 edition
by Alan Barnes

From the outset, the *Radio Times* labelled *Doctor Who* a singular, ongoing 'Adventure in Space and Time'. For schoolteachers Ian and Barbara, press-ganged by an alien 'Doctor' and his weirdo granddaughter Susan into embarking on a voyage into the fourth and fifth dimensions, maybe it was – a miniseries of two years' duration, ending (as you probably know, in *The Chase*) with a hitched lift back to 1960s London in a hijacked Dalek time machine.

But there was more to it than that, of course. We may blithely nominate *An Unearthly Child* as the series' 'first episode', but one only has to watch the thing to see it's nothing of the sort. The Doctor's cosmic wanderings, we learn, began long before: forward to post-decimalisation Britain; back to the French Revolution and (arguably) ancient Greece. Before that, even, came the episode in which the Doctor and Susan became exiles, cut off from their far-distant home. If *Doctor Who* really is one big adventure in space and time, we've missed out on at least its first few seasons: *An Unearthly Child* isn't Part One – it's episode #*x* of series #*y*.

In fact, we could even say that the Doctor's continued and continuing references to his offscreen exploits are as much a hallmark of the series as Daleks, or ventilation ducts, or 'When I say run ...'. Sometimes, we might even be forgiven for thinking that what we're watching isn't the edited highlights, but the off-cuts: There's something truly perverse about a programme that tells, on the one hand, a tale as trivial as (say) *Black Orchid*, but fails to formally dramatise the Doctor's fleetingly mentioned encounters with Napoleon, Admiral Lord Nelson and/or Madame Nostradamus. Perhaps, then, we should modify that original label. 'An Adventure in Spaces Between Times'? That's got to be a better fit.

Given that almost every new television instalment causes the size of *Doctor Who*'s backstory boulder to snowball and swell, writing a definitive chronicle of the adventures we never saw is, of course, a fool's erra – sorry, a Sisyphean task. Or, indeed, a Herculean labour. Come to think of it, the Doctor(s) must surely have encountered Hercules – one incarnation per labour, perhaps? Maybe the Fourth Doctor helped him hack at the Lernaean Hydra, sprouting new heads with every swordswipe; or the Second tootled a recorder tune to assist in the capture of the Erymanthian Boar; and you just know that the man-eating, bronze-beaked Stymphalian Birds could only have been overcome with the help of a Time Lord – the big-beaked Third, perhaps?

Well, of course - and it's pretty inevitable that we'll see or hear about it, in time; either on TV or in one of *Doctor Who*'s ever-proliferating spinoff forms. Because the fact is, we'll never hear the end of the Doctor's exploits; and *that* means that the chronicler and biographer of an immortal life is on (to coin a phrase ...) an Infinite Quest. So I commend to you Matthew J Elliott's properly, classically heroic effort - not just in the pages of the volume you're holding now, but in the incalculable number of future editions he'll be now compelled to write.

Alan Barnes wrote the animated Tenth Doctor adventure The Infinite Quest, *and continues to both author and edit Big Finish Productions' audio dramas featuring five of the Doctor's earlier incarnations. His books include the highly acclaimed* Sherlock Holmes On Screen *and (with Marcus Hearn)* The Hammer Story *- the official history of Britain's foremost horror film production company.*

Introduction
By Matthew J Elliott

It's all the fault of Sherlock Holmes, really. I've gone on record elsewhere as saying that it seems as though all *Doctor Who* fans are also, for some reason, Sherlock Holmes fans. Whether it's necessarily the case that all Holmes fans are automatically *Who* fans is another matter, and one that probably doesn't merit further investigation. It was William S Baring-Gould's 1962 biography *Sherlock Holmes of Baker Street* that served as the inspiration for this book. I was especially intrigued by the author's chronology of the fictional detective's life, in particular his placement of those 'missing' cases, to which Arthur Conan Doyle tantalisingly referred in his stories - the Giant Rat of Sumatra, the Aluminium Crutch, and so on. But Baring-Gould didn't specify a precise date for any such case; rather, he'd suggest the last point at which it might have occurred, eg: 'Before Saturday, August 31, 1889 - The Bogus Laundry Affair.' And that got me thinking about *Doctor Who*.

When the music crashes in and the credits start to roll at the end of an episode, the Doctor's adventures continue. The Time Lord is, of course, an appalling name-dropper - Napoleon Bonaparte, Pablo Picasso, the Droge of Gabrieledes - and, in addition, has amassed a good deal of knowledge regarding other planets and species, including our own. How best to relay this information? It would be rather unimaginative to simply present the reader with a book of lists, even though we *Who* fans do love our lists, both reading and making them. But it's very often the Doctor's companions who hear the recollections of these unseen experiences, and in those instances, it's not too difficult to identify the latest point in the Time Lord's life when they might have happened as being immediately before the first appearance of that companion.

This isn't to say that the Seventh Doctor definitely encounters a creature known as a Stigorax in 25th Century Birmingham shortly before he met Ace in *Dragonfire*; the incident might have involved any of his six previous incarnations, but it certainly couldn't have taken place after Ace's introductory story. Where it can be said with confidence that a particular Doctor had a particular experience, I've identified that incarnation. It is undeniably the Fourth Doctor, for instance, who helped Theseus and Ariadne escape the maze of the Minotaur, a creature he encountered on two previous occasions.

Other placements have involved a certain amount of guesswork and imagination: There's no guarantee that the Ninth Doctor started work on another K-9 to relieve his loneliness after the Time War, but isn't it fun to suppose that he might have done so? No, the First or Second Doctors might never have seen Kylie perform, but, hey - fun again. Did the Fourth Doctor ever meet a Girl Guide troupe? Oh, I think you know in your single human heart that he absolutely did. And while he may simply have heard about the life and achievements of Hannibal, I don't want to live in a world where he didn't actually witness the Carthaginian general and his forces cross the Alps, Come to think of it, I *do* live in that world. Damn. The point being that it's far more enjoyable to imagine the Doctor acquiring all this information first-hand, and above all else, I'd like this book to be fun, though I can certainly see that it might serve as a useful resource for future pastiche writers, containing as it does the seeds of many hundreds of lost adventures. Treat it, if you wish, as a Wold Newtonesque approach to *Doctor Who* - speculative, fanciful, even, but always with the intent to entertain. Where someone has attempted to address one of these missing adventures in another medium - book, audio, or comic strip - I've pointed it out. I leave it up to you whether you consider it canon or not, and I have absolute faith in your judgement.

Over the course of the last 50 years, different terms have been applied to the individual segments of *Doctor Who* stories. Sometimes they're episodes, sometimes they're parts, sometimes just a number or, for much of the Hartnell series, individual titles. For the sake of consistency and my own sanity (which the ghost of Elvis informs me is hanging by a thread), I'm using the term 'episode' throughout.

The continuity set out in this book relates solely to the live-action television series, and just as the Eighth Doctor tried to avoid the Time War, I try to avoid issues of what is and isn't canon. Like him, I am destined to fail.

The spectacular minisode *The Night of the Doctor* makes it quite clear that the Big Finish audio adventures occur in the same universe as the television series, but there are even greater implications. What, for instance, of the Sixth Doctor's morphing penguin companion Frobisher, who appears in the audios *The Holy Terror* and *The Maltese Penguin*, but who originated in *Doctor Who Magazine*'s comic strip? Come to that, there's the Meep in *The Ratings War* and Time Lord agent Shayde in *No Place Like Home*. Does this mean that all the strips are canon, too? And, if so, how far back? What about the Tenth Doctor comic strip *The Lodger*, which bears as many similarities to the Eleventh Doctor episode of the same name as the Ninth Doctor strip *A Groatsworth of Wit* does to *The Shakespeare Code*? We see the image of comic book favourite Abslom Daak, Dalek Killer, in the Twelfth Doctor's TV adventure *Time Heist*, so how much of Daak's history is canon? Are the Velosians of the Twelfth Doctor TV story *The Girl Who Died* the same Velosians from the Seventh Doctor audio adventure *Starlight Robbery*, or is it just an insane coincidence?

The Seventh Doctor's archaeologist companion Bernice Summerfield appears alongside the Doctor in a number of audios, including *Shadow of the Scourge* and *The Company of Friends* (the latter also featuring the Eighth Doctor's comic strip assistant Izzy). Are the Virgin novels then canon as well? The Big Finish range includes an adaptation of the novel *Love and War*, in which Benny makes her first appearance. But there are also a couple of dramatizations of Doctor/Benny novels from which the Time Lord has been eliminated.

The Chelonians, a tortoise-like species created by Gareth Roberts for the Virgin books, get a mention in *The Pandorica Opens*, which gives the impression that, yes, those books are definitely canon, too. But where does that leave the Seventh Doctor tale *Human Nature*, remade on TV for the Tenth Doctor? Many of the BBC's later novels are connected to the earlier Virgin tales, but the Eighth Doctor audio *Zagreus* makes it plain that those books take place in another universe. Despite this, the Krill - who first appear in the BBC novel *Storm Harvest*, by Robert Perry and Mike Tucker - show up in the audio *Dust Breeding*, and the Eighth Doctor audio *The Zygon Who Fell to Earth* makes reference to the events of the book *The Bodysnatchers*. To make the lines blur yet further, several Virgin novels have been reprinted by BBC Books. It's starting to look cruel to deny anything canonicity, even *Daleks Invade Zaos* (free with your purchase of a Wall's Sky Ray ice lolly). These are all questions a better man or woman than I must tackle - this time round, at least, so you won't find them answered here. Perhaps in a sequel: *Detours in Time and Space*, maybe?

Fifty-plus years of time-travelling adventures will have to suffice, then, and fortunately, that's more than enough. Think of this book, like Baring-Gould's, as an alternative biography of the Doctor. You might have imagined you knew all there was to know about the greatest hero in all of time and space, but it turns out that the Doctor was living another life entirely while we weren't looking. This is the story of that life.

Matthew J Elliott
Lost in Time and Space

Life on Gallifrey

Not much is known about the childhood of the Time Lord known as the Doctor. His birthdate is - in Earth terms - around the year 2116.

> *Nightmare of Eden*. The Fourth Doctor says he's due to be born 'sometime quite soon.' The story is set 20 years after the liquidation of Galactic Insurance and Salvage in 2096. What qualifies as 'quite soon' for a Time Lord is anyone's guess.

Despite some questions regarding his mother's planet of origin, he is born on the Time Lord homeworld, under the sign of Crossed Computers, the symbol of the maternity service on Gallifrey, 'the Shining World of the Seven Systems', a couple of million miles from the Nebula of Cyclops and twenty-nine thousand light years from Earth. He is a Sagittarius - probably.

> The details of the Doctor's birth are given in episode three of *The Creature from the Pit*. Gallifrey is first named onscreen in *The Time Warrior*, and its reputation in the Seven Systems is mentioned in *The Sound of Drums*. Its distance from our own world is stated in episode one of *Terror of the Autons*. That same story establishes that the Time Lord Citadel is to be found on the continent of Wild Endeavour, in the mountains of Solace and Solitude. Gallifrey's distance from the Nebula of Cyclops is stated in *The Brain of Morbius*. In the novel *The Crystal Bucephalus*, the Fifth Doctor states that his homeworld is situated not too far from the Capricorn Tract. In the unscreened pilot, the Doctor's granddaughter Susan says that their era is the 49th Century, but this can't be regarded as canonical. (A lot of things can't be regarded as canonical, so get used to that.) The Eleventh Doctor makes a guess at his Terran astrological sign in *Dinosaurs on a Spaceship*.

He is an outcast, abandoned and unknown, referred to by some as 'the timeless child'.

> *The Ghost Monument*

The Doctor's true name remains undisclosed, but it is apparently 'a very difficult question' and 'more than just a secret'. He has claimed that his first name is 'Basil', and, rather less likely, that 'Bad Penny' is literally his middle-name.

> The first quote is from *Black Orchid*, the second from *The Girl in*

the Fireplace. His middle name is 'revealed' in *The God Complex*. The Twelfth Doctor gives his first name as Basil in *The Zygon Inversion* and, in fairness, that particular incarnation does kind of look like a Basil. The Sixth Doctor is apparently about to impart his real name to Peri in the first episode of *The Mysterious Planet*. River Song knows it in *Forest of the Dead*, though the precise moment he tells her has not been indicated. Clara Oswin discovers it while reading a book entitled *The History of the Time War* in *Journey to the Centre of the TARDIS*, forgets it when time is rewritten and then presumably hears it again when the invisible River Song says it in order to unlock the TARDIS in *The Name of the Doctor*. Then again, take a look at the 'Victims of the Time War' section of 'Musings' on page 266, but take something for a powerful headache beforehand. Missy, a female incarnation of the Master, is adamant in *World Enough and Time* that the Doctor's chosen name is 'Doctor Who'. The Doctor accuses her of teasing Bill, and then goes on to use the name minutes later. In *Twice Upon a Time*, the Twelfth Doctor says in private that no-one but children are capable of understanding his name, which, according to the Seventh Doctor novel *SLEEPY*, contains thirty-eight syllables. In the radio drama *Slipback*, the Sixth Doctor tells companion Peri she'd be unable to pronounce it.

Regarding his family, the Doctor speaks mostly about his father (and even then, not often). He fondly recalls watching a meteor storm with him on a warm Gallifreyan night when the skies were a burnt orange.

The Eighth Doctor talks about his father in *Doctor Who – The TV Movie* and *The Fires of Pompeii*. In *Resolution*, the Thirteenth Doctor is rather vague when recalling her 'complicated' relationship with her parent. In *The Sensorites*, Susan describes Gallifrey's night skies and silver trees. The Tenth Doctor also mentions the orange skies in *Gridlock*.

He has a total of seven grandmothers (the second of whom may or may not be a Zygon in disguise), an indolent uncle and a dull, two-headed, and presumably non-Gallifreyan godmother with double bad breath. His favourite granny (number five) tells him about the consciousness known as the Solitract, exiled to an unreachable plane and surrounded by a barrier known as the Antizone for fear that it would destroy the universe.

The Thirteenth Doctor reminiscences about her beloved Granny Five in *It Takes You Away*. In response to the observation that all motion is relative, during *Time and the Rani*, the Seventh Doctor

> remarks, 'You wouldn't say that if you met my uncle.' The godmother is recalled in *Vincent and the Doctor*. Might she have been one of the Aplans of Alfava Metraxis from *The Time of the Angels*? Or maybe she took some of the Doctor's Dalek possession medicine with alcohol.

During his eighth incarnation, the Doctor claims he is half-human on his mother's side, and his arch-enemy, the Master, notes that he has a human retinal structure. The Tenth Doctor describes his humanity as 'optional'.

> *Doctor Who – The TV Movie*. The 'optional' remark is made in *The Runaway Bride* and Ashildr questions whether the Doctor might not be half-human in *Hell Bent*. It should be noted that, in the final episode of *The Faceless Ones*, the alien species known as the Chameleons classify the Second Doctor as human, although he makes it quite clear that Earth is not his home planet. However, at the climax of *Survival*, the Cheetah People's abilities take the Seventh Doctor 'home' to Earth, rather than Gallifrey or the interior of the TARDIS. In episode three of *The Ice Warriors*, the Second Doctor is quick to take offence at the term 'only human', and in *Cold Blood*, the Eleventh Doctor states categorically that Gallifreyans are not descended from apes. The Seventh Doctor says that he is more human than he looks in the comic strip *Ground Zero*.

The Nemesis statue, constructed of the living metal Validium, apparently informs the Lady Peinforte that the Doctor's origins are by no means straightforward, and are somehow connected to the Old Time on Gallifrey, an age of chaos. What this connection might be, however, has never been revealed.

> *Silver Nemesis*. The Cybermen have the opportunity to learn this secret information about their greatest enemy, but curiosity seems to have been deleted from their databanks. Later on, though, they attempt to extract the secrets of the Time Lords from the Eighth Doctor in the comic strip *Dreadnought*.

His brother and sisters are certainly dead, but whether this occurs before his departure from Gallifrey or during the Time War is unclear.

> The Tenth Doctor says he doesn't have a brother any more in *Smith and Jones*, while in *Arachnids in the UK*, the Thirteenth Doctor recalls that she once had sisters. Perhaps their deaths happened during the Doctor's formative years – in *The Empty Child*, the Tenth Doctor says he knows how it feels to be 'the only child, left out in the cold.' He is adamant in *The Sound of Drums*

that the Master is not his brother. In the series of original novels published by Virgin, his brother is Irving Braxiatel, who features prominently in the Bernice Summerfield adventures.

He still has some family on his planet of origin when it is apparently destroyed in the Time War, though for many years he wonders about their fate.

Father's Day and *The Curse of Fenric*

If he has ever had an aunt, she is dead when he regenerates for the tenth time.

The Eleventh Hour. The Eleventh Doctor tells young Amelia Pond that he has no aunt, and considers himself lucky. Aunts, as PG Wodehouse will tell you, aren't gentlemen.

The Doctor's family dwelling is inconveniently located on the side of a mountain.

The Time Monster. In *Planet of the Spiders*, the Third Doctor notes that a hermit lived halfway up a mountain behind their house. In *State of Decay*, the Fourth Doctor states that the hermit - and, therefore, his family - were located in South Gallifrey, whatever that might mean.

The young Doctor plays with radioactive roentgen bricks in the nursery, and fantasizes about being a train driver, as well as dreaming of the stars.

The bricks are mentioned in *Smith and Jones*, while his boyhood ambition is recalled in *Black Orchid*. In *The Wedding of River Song*, the Eleventh Doctor laments never having had his own train, or his own office. He talks about his dreams during *Closing Time*.

His favourite nursery stories are *The Three Little Sontarans, The Emperor Dalek's New Clothes* and *Snow White and the Seven Keys to Doomsday.*

Night Terrors. One of these stories provides the basis for a tale his first incarnation later relates to Hans Christian Andersen, as recalled in *The Romans*. By the time of *Deep Breath* and *The Caretaker*, the Twelfth Doctor is familiar with Walt Disney's interpretation of the Snow White story.

He memorises the rhyme concerning Gallifrey's infamous and possibly mythical Dark Tower.

The Five Doctors. Oblique references are made to it in *The Age of Steel*, and the Eighth Doctor audio *Zagreus*.

He is reportedly a lonely child, but would seem to have at least one close friend - the Time Lord known in adult life as the Master.

> Madame de Pompadour sees his loneliness as she reads the Tenth Doctor's mind during *The Girl in the Fireplace.* Several original novels, beginning with the Second Doctor adventure *The Dark Path,* give the Master's true name as Koschei. In *The Magician's Apprentice,* Missy recalls them being friends when the Doctor was a little girl, and while she freely admits that this may be a lie, who am I to pretend to be an expert on Gallifreyan childhood physiology? In *World Enough and Time,* the Doctor admits that the Master was an early man-crush.

The youngsters attend the Gallifreyan equivalent of school, and often run through the red grass pastures owned by the Master's father on the slopes of Mount Perdition.

> The Tenth Doctor remembers Mount Perdition during *The End of Time.* Gallifrey's red grass is first mentioned in *Gridlock.*

Their friendship strengthens during the conflict known as the Cloister Wars.

> *The Magician's Apprentice.* This claim is made by Missy. The Wars are mentioned again in *Hell Bent,* but what actually occurred is never made clear, though it likely involved Daleks, Cybermen and Weeping Angels, examples of which are trapped by living fibre-optic cables that protect the Matrix. While the Cloister Wars definitely took place, then, it's possible that Missy is lying about their relationship at this time.

The Doctor and the Master make a pact to see every star in the Universe.

> *World Enough and Time*

At age eight, like all Time Lords, the Doctor stares into the gap in the fabric of reality known as the Untempered Schism.

> *The End of Time*

On the darkest day of his life (perhaps just after staring into the Schism), he visits the old hermit, who teaches him the secret of life through a flower. The Master, alas, does not seek the same form of emotional and spiritual solace, and thus becomes destined to grow one of the most evil beards the Universe has ever known.

> *The Time Monster*

The hermit also instructs him how to look into his own mind, but considers him slow on the uptake.

> *Planet of the Spiders.* The Third Doctor notes that some of the finest hours of his life were spent in the hermit's company. The hermit departs Gallifrey sometime before the Doctor, but such are his abilities that he has no need of a TARDIS to travel through time and space, and he considers the Doctor 'naughty' for taking one without permission. The Seventh Doctor recalls his mentor again in the novel *Timewyrm: Exodus.*

The Doctor is frightened during his youth by horror stories told to him by that hermit, one about a species of giant vampires that swarmed across the universe, others concerning the myth of the Fendahl and the break-up of the fifth planet (based on the 'official' Time Lord history), the creatures from beyond our universe known as Pantheon of Discord, and the predicted coming of a hybrid creature comprised of two warring races, which is destined to conquer Gallifrey and unravel the web of time.

> The vampire tales are recalled in *State of Decay.* The Fourth Doctor recognises depictions of embryo Fendahleen in *Image of the Fendahl.* The Pantheon of Discord are mentioned in *The Sarah Jane Adventures* story *The Wedding of Sarah Jane Smith.* Another member of the Pantheon, Krampus, appears in the Eleventh Doctor comic strip *Imaginary Enemies.* The Hybrid is first mentioned in *The Witch's Familiar.* Davros believes the being to be half-Dalek, half-Time Lord, and the Doctor confirms in *Heaven Sent* that Time Lord prophecies – *all* of them, according to *Hell Bent* – concur with his assessment.

He's less impressed, however, by the tale of the universe's self-appointed pest-controllers, the Shakri, a species he believes to be entirely fictional, invented solely to keep Gallifreyan children obedient, and by the Toclafane, a story familiar to both the Doctor and the Master.

> *The Power of Three* and *The Sound of Drums.* The Shakri are mentioned by Romana in the Fourth Doctor audio *Babblesphere.*

From boyhood, the Doctor honours ill-fated stellar engineer Omega as Gallifrey's greatest hero, though his personal idol is Time Lord criminal Salyavin – not for his crimes, but for his style and flair.

> Omega first appears onscreen in *The Three Doctors.* The Eleventh Doctor later describes Omega as a madman in *The Rings of Akhaten.* The lesson: Never meet your heroes. The Fourth Doctor's worship of Salyavin is revealed in *Shada.*

He is far from fond of Morbius, whom he regards as 'one of the most despicable, criminally minded wretches who ever lived,' and is told of the attack on the Sisterhood of Karn by Morbius' rebels, and of the renegade's eventual execution.

The Brain of Morbius. When informed by Solon that he is on the planet Karn, the Fourth Doctor says, 'I should have known.' His eighth incarnation returns to Karn at a considerable rate of knots in *The Night of the Doctor*, and at a presumably more sedate pace in *The Magician's Apprentice.*

Possessing some telepathic ability, he is able to persuade locked doors to open for him. When still very young, he sees the corpse of an old lady, covered in veils in a vain attempt to keep the flies away. The sight is the source of nightmares for some time to come.

Heaven Sent. The implication is that he later loses this telepathic gift, which explains why so much of his time away from Gallifrey involves getting locked up. He is, however, able to place a message in the subconscious of the dying Bill during *World Enough and Time.* The Seventh Doctor novel *Cat's Cradle: Time's Crucible* states that earlier generations of Time Lords possessed telekinetic abilities.

Feeling pressurized into joining the military, he takes to sleeping (and crying) in a nearby barn, so that the other boys in the house do not hear him. He eventually avoids the army and is accepted into the Prydon Academy.

Listen. The other boys are presumably the Doctor's brothers. He returns to the barn on the final day of the Time War in *The Day of the Doctor* and once again in *Hell Bent.* His Prydonian privileges (whatever they might have been) are revoked at the moment of his unauthorised departure from Gallifrey, according to Clara in *Death in Heaven,* and to the Fifth Doctor himself in the audio *Time in Office.*

At his Time Lord induction ceremony, the Doctor mouths the oath to protect the *Ancient Law of Gallifrey,* a book he mistakenly believes to be stored in the Panopticon Archives.

Shada. In the Big Finish audio version, this claim is made not by the Doctor, but by companion Romana.

As a student at Prydon Academy, he is a member of the class of '92, where he goes by the nickname Theta Sigma.

The school's name is established in *The Deadly Assassin.* In *The*

Sea Devils, the Third Doctor says of the Master 'You might almost say we were at school together,' and *The Five Doctors* confirms that he, too, attended Prydon Academy. The First Doctor fails to identify him, even though Time Lords usually seem to recognise one another despite their altered appearance. However, the Master himself points out that he hasn't exactly regenerated; even the Third Doctor isn't certain of his identity at first. It's worth noting that the War Doctor - whose regeneration was forced upon him by the Sisterhood of Karn after his death - doesn't know two of his future selves when he meets them in *The Day of the Doctor*. Several original novels state that Romana and the Time Meddler were also Prydonians. It seems, in *The Armageddon Factor*, that the Fourth Doctor is being addressed by his real name, but in *The Happiness Patrol*, his seventh incarnation explains 'My nickname at college was Theta Sigma.' River Song carves the Greek letters Theta and Sigma into a cliff-face in *The Pandorica Opens*, and the name is used again in the Sixth Doctor audio *The One Doctor* and the Seventh Doctor novels *Falls the Shadow* and *Christmas on a Rational Planet*.

He takes the tech course with fellow student Drax, though his special subject is thermodynamics.

The Armageddon Factor and *The Mark of the Rani*

In order to spoil each other's time experiments, the Doctor and his fellow students often construct time flow analogues from whatever is handy.

The Time Monster

He is familiar, at this time, with the female Gallifreyan calling herself the Rani, whose special field of study is neurochemistry. He considers her to have 'a brilliant but sterile mind,' and condemns her experiments as unethical. She is exiled after her experiments turn mice into monsters, which eat the Lord President's cat. The Doctor, however, thinks the Rani ought to be committed.

The Mark of the Rani. In episode four of *The Deadly Assassin*, the Fourth Doctor cracks a joke about subsidence in the Capitol caused by a plague of mice. The Fifth Doctor novel *Divided Loyalties* claims that the Rani's true name is Ushas, an assertion repeated in the Sixth Doctor audios *The Rani Elite* and *Planet of the Rani*. Her giant mice are mentioned again in the Seventh Doctor comic strip *Party Animals* and the Eighth Doctor audios *Nevermore* and *The Man Who Wasn't There*.

He studies under Borusa, whom he is never able to deceive, and who is fond of saying 'only in mathematics will we find truth,' as well as 'there's nothing more useless than a lock with a voice print.'

The Deadly Assassin and *The Invasion of Time*

Borusa repeatedly informs the Doctor that he will never amount to anything in the galaxy as long as he retains a propensity for vulgar facetiousness.

The Deadly Assassin

The Doctor has a happier relationship with Azmael, whom he considers his mentor and the finest teacher he ever had. Azmael thinks the Doctor always full of good intentions.

The Twin Dilemma. The novelization states that Azmael actually assassinated the High Council of Time Lords, something the Valeyard never managed to do.

Another of his teachers is exactly like future companion Clara Oswald.

The Caretaker. Very likely, the teacher *is* Clara, having hurled herself into the Doctor's timeline at the climax of *The Name of the Doctor*.

A professor (perhaps either Borusa or Azmael, or even Clara) is unsuccessful in explaining the nature of Artron energy to him.

Four to Doomsday. The Fifth Doctor says that only his professor at the Academy really understood the subject.

He is disappointed not to be taught a course in interspatial geometry.

The Stones of Blood. The Fourth Doctor bemoans the fact that the Gallifreyans gave up teaching the subject 2,000 years earlier.

He takes a cybernetics course, and is instructed by his tutor always to ensure that Arrow A is pointing to the front when replacing an artificial brain.

Destiny of the Daleks. The Seventh Doctor imparts this advice to Ace in the audio *The Silurian Candidate*.

He learns about tachyonics, but since Gallifrey abandons them in favour of warp matrix engineering, he forgets what he knows.

The Leisure Hive

For reasons unknown, he is never taught about quasitronics or the twin planets of Atrios and Zeos.

The Invasion of Time and *The Armageddon Factor*. Romana criticizes the Fourth Doctor's education, but it's entirely likely that he just wasn't paying attention.

Many of his teachers resign in frustration, usually complaining 'I don't have to answer all these questions.'

The Battle of Ranskoor Av Kolos

One of his fellow students, Runcible – whom he calls 'Runcible the Fatuous' – is present when the Doctor is involved in a scandal. This involves his rash decision to venture into the Cloisters, where many unwary beings attempting to gain access to the Matrix found themselves trapped. The Doctor is lost there for four days, during which time the Cloister Wraiths speak to him, advising him of a way out via the primary service hatch which will take him to an entirely different part of the city. They also apparently inform him of the true nature of the legendary Hybrid. The incident affects the Doctor profoundly, causing some to believe he has gone mad, after which he is rumoured to have stolen both the moon and the wife of the president.

In *The Deadly Assassin,* Runcible believes the Doctor was expelled. The scandalous indiscretions of his youth are recalled by Missy during *The Magician's Apprentice,* who freely admits she's probably lying. She also doesn't specify which moon, or the president of what, which isn't particularly helpful. How like Missy. In *Hell Bent,* the Doctor states that he actually stole the president's daughter, and that the moon in question was not so much purloined as mislaid. The Fifth Doctor visits the Cloisters in the comic strip *Ophiuchus.*

Scraping through with 51 percent on the second try, he is granted an honorary doctorate.

In *The Ribos Operation,* the Fourth Doctor is horrified that Romana knows this 'confidential information' regarding his grades. In *The Armageddon Factor,* Drax says that these events occurred 450 years prior (by his time). The Doctor states, in *The Ark in Space,* that his doctorate is purely honorary, though in *Spearhead from Space,* his third incarnation claims to be a doctor of 'practically everything' (an assertion he repeats in *The Mutants, Utopia* and the Second Doctor novel *World Game*). In *Four to Doomsday,* the Fifth Doctor modestly drops the 'practically.' He is simply a doctor of 'many things' in *Underworld.*

The Doctor's success is due, in part, to his mastery of three-dimensional graph geometry.

The Dalek Invasion of Earth

He earns compliments regarding his sophisticated prose style, but fails to earn a medical degree.

> *The Keeper of Traken* and *The Rescue*. In *The Ark*, the First Doctor describes himself as 'a bit of a quack.' In *An Unearthly Child, Marco Polo* and the Fourth Doctor short story *Frayed*, he insists that he is not a doctor of medicine. This deficiency has apparently been rectified by the time he regenerates (although see companion Rory's remarks in *Amy's Choice*, as related in 'The Doctor's Doctorate' section of 'Musings' on page 273). In the audio adaptation of the unmade First Doctor story *Farewell, Great Macedon*, he claims to have studied medicine for a couple of years, and to have taken his planet's equivalent of the Hippocratic Oath.

He is similarly unsuccessful when it comes to his TARDIS pilot's licence, as he never learns to take the brake off - a common complaint among renegade Time Lords.

> *The Shakespeare Code* and *The Time of the Angels*. The Seventh Doctor audio *The Grand Betelgeuse Hotel* provides some details of the written portion of the TARDIS driving test.

His degree in cosmic science is lower than the Master's - which he ascribes to his being a late developer.

> *Terror of the Autons*

Despite this, he considers himself a slightly better mathematician than his arch-enemy.

> *The Deadly Assassin*

He, does, however, achieve a first in jiggery-pokery, while excelling at recreational mathematics.

> Presumably, the Ninth Doctor is being facetious about his first in *The End of the World*, but, hey, who knows? Perhaps it's the qualification you achieve for retaining a propensity for vulgar facetiousness. In *42*, his subsequent incarnation laments the fact that recreational mathematics, like interspatial geometry, is no longer being taught, suggesting that he studied it once.

He discovers some details of Gallifrey's Dark Days (as does the Time Lord who takes the post of Castellan during the Doctor's fifth incarnation), in particular the conflicting accounts of the deadly games fought in the Death Zone. These include some mention of the Cybermen and the Daleks. In the case of the latter race, he learns more than is covered in his beloved nursery story - enough, at least, to realize that the Time Lord prediction that they will one day become the dominant species is correct. He formulates a plan which is entirely at odds with the Gallifreyan non-intervention policy (but less extreme than the one forced upon his fourth incarnation in *Genesis of the Daleks*).

> In *The Tenth Planet,* the First Doctor is interrupted just as he begins to relate the story of Earth's twin planet, Mondas. The First Doctor short story *The Golden Door* has it that the Time Lord saw a televised news report on the Cybermen's invasion and filed the information away for future use, and the First Doctor audio *The Alchemists* implies that Susan knows about their aversion to gold. The Cybermen of *Earthshock* are certainly familiar with the Time Lords, mentioning their policy of non-interference and ability to regenerate. By comparison, Romana states in *Destiny of the Daleks* that she knows nothing of the Daleks (yet in the same episode, she notes they were once human). Though unfamiliar with their appearance during their first meeting in *The Daleks,* the First Doctor tells companion Ian with confidence, in *The Dalek Invasion of Earth,* that they are witnessing the middle period of Dalek history. In *The Five Doctors,* the Fifth Doctor states that the Daleks, like the Cybermen, were never included in the Death Zone games, suggesting he has some knowledge of their involvement - or lack of it - in Gallifrey's past, and the presence of both in the Cloisters seems to confirm this. His first incarnation certainly has no knowledge of the existence of the Thals in their first televised encounter. The story *Time and Relative* implies that certain information regarding the Daleks has been deleted from the minds of both the Doctor and his granddaughter. It is clear, from the Master's description of the Death Zone as the Time Lord's 'black secret,' that certain elements of the story of the Dark Days are not generally known beyond the nursery rhyme concerning Rassilon's Tower. The Fifth Doctor says he has known the Castellan for 'too long,' and that he was filled with horror by any mention of this shameful period of Gallifreyan history. That events at this time are contradictory is illustrated by the fact that Rassilon is supposed to have put a stop to the cruel contest, but that it is also sometimes referred to as the Game of Rassilon.

Investigation of Gallifreyan history, and the interference of its people in the lives of other species, piques the Doctor's interest. He thus finds out about the unfortunate results of Time Lord involvement in the lives of the Minyans (including their development of the Pacifier Ray and the toothbrush).

> *Underworld*

He also learns of the schism in the College of Cardinals, which led to a rival president setting up shop on the planet Drornid.

> *Shada.* In the final scene, the Fourth Doctor tells Romana that the villain Skagra hails from Drornid.

He grows interested in humanity, but notes that there are strict laws regarding investigating their fate after the point at which their home planet is totally destroyed.

> In *Frontios,* the Fifth Doctor is extremely anxious that the Time Lords should never know of his presence on the human outpost, and in *Utopia,* the TARDIS breaks the rules regarding humanity's destiny while attempting to shake off Captain Jack.

Upon reading of the destruction of the planet Ravalox in the Stellian Galaxy, he notes its many similarities to Earth. It is several hundred years, however, before he has the opportunity to investigate that apparent coincidence.

> *The Mysterious Planet.* A deleted scene has the Sixth Doctor claiming to have read about Ravalox in the book *Extinct Civilizations,* written by Warris Bossard. In the novel *The Eight Doctors,* it is stated that the Time Lords alter history to ensure that Earth does not eventually become the ravaged Ravalox.

He also learns of the Dark Times, billions of years before our current Earth date. Huon particles were plentiful during this period, before Time Lords in some way 'got rid of them,' along with the Racnoss.

> *The Runaway Bride.* The Tenth Doctor explains Huon energy (mentioned again in the novel *Shining Darkness*) to Donna and Lance, telling them that the particles now only exist at the heart of the TARDIS.

So angered is the Doctor at the offence against the dignity of sentient life forms that is the Wallarian peep-show device known as a miniscope that he petitions the High Council to have such devices outlawed. He becomes such a nuisance that the Time Lords ultimately abandon their pretence at non-interference and have all the machines recalled (save for one that has fallen into the hands of a non-Wallarian).

> *Carnival of Monsters.* The Third Doctor is quite satisfied that this adventure occurs after the recall, and that Vorg's miniscope is one that was somehow missed. Another rogue miniscope

appears in the Fifth Doctor novel *Goth Opera*. The Twelfth Doctor theorises that he and companion Clara might be trapped in one during *Robot of Sherwood*.

He sees Gallifreyan lighthouses, three-dimensional paintings created via computer (with which he is unimpressed), the gem known as a white-point star, a Time Lord hard drive known as a Matrix data-slice, and a metaphoric symbiosis regenerator, used by a Time Lord experiencing an acute regenerative crisis which cannot be aided by the Sisterhood of Karn's famed elixir.

In *The Brain of Morbius*, the Fourth Doctor is familiar with the elixir's properties. Lighthouses are mentioned in *Horror of Fang Rock* and computerised paintings in *City of Death* (the multi-dimensional element of Time Lord art is revealed in *The Day of the Doctor*). During *The End of Time*, the Tenth Doctor tells his companion Donna's grandfather Wilf that white-point stars are only found on a single planet. In *Mawdryn Undead*, the Fifth Doctor identifies a regenerator on Mawrdyn's spaceship. In *Dark Water*, Missy uses a stolen Matrix data-slice to store the consciousness of Earth's deceased before downloading them into cyber-bodies.

The Doctor hears of the remarkable healing properties of the polygonal zero room under the junior senate block.

Castrovalva. This therapy technique is also mentioned in the Seventh Doctor novel *Timewyrm: Exodus*.

He witnesses - and possibly participates in - mind-bending contests, also known as Time Lord Wrestling. Extreme bouts end in deathlock.

The Brain of Morbius. The Fourth Doctor engages in a similar duel with Megron, Chief of the Carions, in the educational radio programme, *Exploration Earth: The Time Machine*.

He becomes a husband, a parent to more than one child, and a grandparent while on Gallifrey. His parenting skills include the ability to insert dreams into the minds of children with just the touch of his finger. By his own admission, he is 'rubbish' at his wedding.

The Doctor's very first companion is, of course, his granddaughter Susan. He does not mention his children until *The Empty Child*, and then in an indirect manner. The Tenth Doctor is more specific about parenthood in *Fear Her*. In *The Doctor's Daughter*, he makes it plain that he fathered multiple children. He tells companion Donna Noble that his children are dead, but if their deaths are supposed to have occurred during the Time War, it could be that he simply imagines them to be dead. Strangely, after showing such candour during this incarnation, his next self is rather cagey when the subject comes up in *The Beast Below*. He demonstrates his dream-planting gift in *Listen*. He talks about his wedding in *Blink*. In the novel *Only Human*, the Ninth Doctor states that he was at one time married to Lady Mary Wortley Montague.

He is permitted to leave Gallifrey occasionally, in order to complete small errands for the Time Lords. At the tender age of ninety, he visits the centre of a rift in time and space known as the Medusa Cascade and seals it single-handedly.

The Stolen Earth and *Last of the Time Lords*. The Tenth Doctor tells companion Donna about the fifteenth broken moon of the Medusa Cascade in *The Sontaran Stratagem*. The Cascade is also mentioned in *The Fires of Pompeii* and *Midnight*. The sealing of the rift is depicted in the comic book *The Forgotten*.

On one top-priority mission, the Doctor delivers a sealed container that will only open for the correct recipient.

The Mutants. The Third Doctor recognises such a container in episode one.

He is sent to attend the inauguration of Space Station Chimera, a small scientific research vessel in the Third Zone, located a mere twelve days from Earth as the Hyperdrive ship flies. There, he befriends Joinson Dastari, Head of Projects and a pioneer of genetic engineering. The Doctor is in Dastari's office when the scientist works out the Theory of Parallel Matter in pen and ink, and hears about his study of rho mesons as the unstable factor in pin galaxies. He also encounters the servitor species known as the Androgums.

The Two Doctors. The Station is called J7 in Robert Holmes' novelization. Androgums are mentioned again in the novels *Shakedown* and *Snowglobe 7*.

Before his flight from Gallifrey, he meets the Time Lord later known as the War Chief.

The War Games. It is not impossible that the War Chief is an incarnation of the Master; certainly, they share many characteristics, including a love of villainous-looking facial hair. Though the War Chief seems to have been killed by the War Lord's men in episode nine, he may, in fact, have been on the brink of regeneration. Then again, he reappears in the novel

> *Timewyrm: Exodus*, and is depicted in his younger days (where his true name is given as Magnus) in the novels *Divided Loyalties* and *Invasion of the Cat-People*, as well as the comic strip *Flashback*.

He presents Missy with a brooch formed from dark star alloy on the occasion of something to do with her daughter.

> *The Witch's Familiar*. While *Last of the Time Lords* depicts the young Master as male, but a brooch is a more traditional gift for a woman (on Earth, admittedly), suggesting that at least one early incarnation of his frenemy was female.

Though considered a pioneer, the Doctor decides to leave his home planet and his fellow Time Lords, having grown 'tired of their lifestyle' and bored with their (contradictory) policy of non-intervention, as well as their lack of humour.

> The term 'pioneer,' used in *The Daleks*, is the Doctor's own, and it's one he repeats in the First Doctor audio *The Destination Wars*. In *The Brain of Morbius*, however, the Fourth Doctor refers to himself as 'a mere nobody' among the Time Lords, so take your pick. In the novel *World Game*, the Second Doctor states that he almost became Lord President while living on Gallifrey, and the Seventh Doctor comic strip *Time and Time Again* shows his first incarnation reaching that position in an alternative timeline where he never left his homeworld. His fifth self describes his disillusionment in *Resurrection of the Daleks*. In episode three of *The Hand of Fear*, the Fourth Doctor recalls a rule stating that Time Lords are pledged to prevent alien aggression 'only when such aggression is deemed to threaten the indigenous population.' The Second Doctor laments their humourlessness in *The War Games*.

There are pressing reasons for the Doctor's departure, though he considers that he has 'every right to leave.' He remains terrified of what the Cloister Wraiths told him in his youth, despite the fact that he can no longer remember what it was, and is anxious to discover why good prevails in the universe when might should be on the side of evil.

> The term 'pressing reasons' is used by the Fourth Doctor in *Logopolis* and the First in *Twice Upon a Time*. He asserts his justification in *The War Games*, but finally admits during *Heaven Sent* that he lied to himself about being bored. The details of his encounter with the Cloister Wraiths are given in *Hell Bent*.

Half a Century prior to the flight from Gallifrey of the renegade unpopularly known as the Meddling Monk, and without stopping to question his actions, the 236-year-old Doctor and his granddaughter, Susan, steal a faulty TARDIS from a repair shop.

> *The Time Meddler* and *Mindwarp*. In *The Ribos Operation*, the Fourth Doctor is said to be 759 years old – he protests at the time, but admits it a few stories later in *The Power of Kroll*. In *The Pirate Planet*, he's been piloting the TARDIS for 523 years. The Eleventh Doctor, in *The Snowmen*, says he's been saving the universe for more than a thousand years, confirming that he was about 200 when he left Gallifrey (assuming he's telling the truth in *A Town Called Mercy*, when he says he's 1,200 years old). Then he spoils it all by claiming to be only 1,000 in *The Bells of Saint John*, although the Tenth Doctor played his part by giving his age as 906 in *The End of Time*. The actual theft of the TARDIS is seen in *The Name of the Doctor*. The novel *Lungbarrow* claims that the Doctor was, in fact, 430 at the time of his departure.

Not only is it far from 'the latest model' of TARDIS, but the Type 40 – one of 305 such registered vehicles – is considered a museum piece, having been originally manufactured during the boyhood of Professor Chronotis (AKA Salyavin). Its prime flaw is considered the intolerable distance of the kitchens from the main Control Room.

> *Frontier in Space, The Deadly Assassin* and *Shada*

The fact that its navigation system is (according to a mysterious young woman who speaks to the Doctor moments before his flight) knackered is also not much of a selling point.

> *The Name of the Doctor*. The Doctor's conversation with Clara is related from Susan's perspective in the audio *The Beginning*, and recalled by the Fifth Doctor in the audio *Zaltys*.

In its favour, however, the craft is unlocked at the time. Upon entering and touching its console, the Doctor declares it to be the most beautiful thing he has ever known, despite the fact that it lacks an automatic drift control, a proper stabiliser and the Stattenheim Remote Control he has long coveted. What's more, it has not had the necessary chameleon conversion, it has a fault in its time mechanism and it uses the old Mark One dematerialisation circuit.

> His declaration of affection is recalled in *The Doctor's Wife*. In *The Time Meddler*, the Monk boasts about his Mark IV craft's automatic drift control. In *The Two Doctors*, the Sixth Doctor tells

> the Second he's always wanted a Stattenheim. It seems, from remarks made in *The Mark of the Rani*, that the device was created by the female renegade (so why isn't it called a Rani Remote Control?). The Sixth Doctor complains that he has long-since lost the handy device in the audio *The Lure of the Nomad*, but he has it in the audio *The Hourglass Killers*, as does the Seventh Doctor in the novel *Infinite Requiem*. The Seventh Doctor novel *Christmas on a Rational Planet* states that the real Stattenheim lived in 16th Century Berlin. The chameleon conversion is discussed in *Logopolis*, but the Fourth Doctor never goes into any great detail about what that actually means. In episode three of *Terror of the Autons*, the Third Doctor discovers that the Master's Mark Two circuit is incompatible with his own TARDIS. The Master laments the absence of a proper stabiliser in episode three of *The Claws of Axos*, causing him to brand the Type 40 a 'museum piece.' In the Second Doctor novel *The Dark Path*, the Master's TARDIS is a Type 45. The First Doctor originally mentions the ship's faulty (but repairable) time mechanism during the second episode of *The Keys of Marinus.*

It is at least preferable to the Type 706, which he feels has no character, and it possesses – as do all Type 40s – a molecular stabiliser.

> *The Invasion of Time* and *The Stones of Blood*

His intended theft of the vehicle is by no means easy, given that it is designed for six pilots rather than just one.

> *Journey's End*. This certainly gives the lie to the Fourth Doctor's claim, in episode four of *Pyramids of Mars*, that the TARDIS controls are isomorphic (one-to-one). Over the years, many other characters are seen piloting the TARDIS, including several of the Doctor's enemies (Skagra in *Shada*, and the Master in *Utopia*, for example). Moreover, in *A Christmas Carol*, the Eleventh Doctor states bluntly that there is no such thing as isomorphic controls, only to discover that there actually is. Then again, one incarnation earlier, in *Last of the Time Lords*, he learns that the Master's laser screwdriver is isomorphic, too, so he should really know better.

He takes with him his cot, the component parts of a Hypercube (should he ever wish it to regain contact with his people), the Gallifreyan last will and testament known as a confession dial, and the remote Stellar manipulator known as the Hand of Omega, which he intends to hide away until he can use it against the Daleks.

The cot is first seen in *A Good Man Goes to War*. This might seem to be an indication of his granddaughter Susan's age when they fled, were it not that she is seen fully grown as they steal the ship in *The Name of the Doctor* (without the Hand of Omega, seemingly). In addition, she recalls Gallifrey very well in the final episode of *The Sensorites*. The cot appears again in *Journey to the Centre of the TARDIS*. The Hypercube is first featured in *The War Games*, but is not named as such until the Seventh Doctor novel *Love and War*. The term is eventually uttered onscreen in *The Doctor's Wife*. Others appear in the audios *The Dying Light*, *Last of the Cybermen*, *Shockwave*, *Washington Burns* and *The Time Machine*, and in the Eleventh Doctor novel *The Dalek Generation*. The confession dial, which allows Time Lords to make their peace before their consciousness is uploaded into the Matrix, is first seen in the online prequel to *The Magician's Apprentice*. Episode three of *Remembrance of the Daleks* suggests that the First Doctor might have been involved with the prototype stellar manipulator, but this point is never pursued. Had the Seventh Doctor's reign continued past his third season, we would certainly have learned about both this and his connection with the being known as the Other (who is not referenced onscreen, only in some novelizations). In the fourth episode, the Doctor says that the Hand has returned to Gallifrey – the destruction of the Daleks' home world Skaro was, then, the only reason he needed it. Strangely, no mention is made of the Hand of Omega at the Second Doctor's trial, to say nothing of his theft of a TARDIS and the existence of Susan. That's just what the Time Lords do: Say nothing.

His intended destination appears to be the planet Earth.

The Name of the Doctor. Both the First Doctor and Susan are seen wearing Earth clothing before taking the TARDIS. It is entirely possible that he wishes to acquire the human DNA he will require in order to alter his species via the Chameleon Arch, should the need arise (as it finally does in *Human Nature*). What more natural way than to select a species who 'look Time Lord,' as the Tenth Doctor says in *Planet of the Dead*?

To prevent the Time Lords from tracking him, the Doctor removes the Mark 3 emergency transceiver from the TARDIS, assuming incorrectly that it will never be needed.

The Creature from the Pit

At first, he believes that he will one day be permitted to return to Gallifrey, though he abandons such hopes following his first regeneration.

The First Doctor voices this opinion in *100,000 BC, The Sensorites* and *The Massacre*. In the final episode of *The Faceless Ones*, the Second Doctor laments the fact that he, unlike companions Ben and Polly, has been unable to return to his home planet.

He is saddened by the loss of his family, but eventually learns to let their memory sleep in his mind.

The Tomb of the Cybermen

The Doctor's journeys across time and space become legendary - in fact, the rest of the universe takes the name 'Doctor' from this one remarkable individual.

A Good Man Goes to War. In *The Return of Doctor Mysterio*, the Twelfth Doctor says 'I started it, they're all based on me.'

The First Doctor
William Hartnell
1963-1966

Prior to *100,000 BC*

The First Doctor acquires a ring that possesses unspecified but remarkable properties.

> In his original incarnation, the Doctor wears this ring at all times, and it may in fact come from Gallifrey. The first indication that it is in any way unusual comes in *The Web Planet*, when he uses it to operate the TARDIS doors after the ship is drained of power, and elsewhere to control a docile Zarbi. Later, in *The Daleks' Master Plan*, it is able to override the Time Meddler's sabotage. Immediately after his first regeneration, the Doctor simply throws the ring away as it no longer fits (despite his deeming it valuable enough to have demanded its return from the Menoptera in *The Web Planet*). By the time of his third incarnation, he no longer knows where it is, or he would have used it when the TARDIS once again experiences a power drain in *Death to the Daleks*. In the audio *The Sleeping City*, the Doctor uses the ring to revive Ian from a trance. His seventh incarnation eventually discovers it lodged in the ship's console during the strip *The Chameleon Factor*.

On the run from his own people in a rackety old TARDIS, the Doctor installs a Time Path Detector on the console in order to ensure that he and Susan are not pursued by his fellow Time Lords.

> *The Chase*. Companions Ian, Barbara and Vicki have never noticed the Time Path Detector because it has never activated before. The device appears in the novels *Timewyrm: Genesis*, *Timewyrm: Exodus* and *The Dark Path*.

He and Susan fall afoul of the telepathic plants on the planet Esto, which emit a psychic screech when anyone stands between them.

> Susan recalls the psychic jungle in *The Keys of Marinus*. The fact that she doesn't know where she first heard the screeching suggests it was quite early on in their travels. She eventually identifies the planet by name in episode two of *The Sensorites*. Esto is also mentioned in the Eighth Doctor novel *The Tomorrow*

Windows and in the Tenth Doctor short story *Number 1, Gallows Gate Road.*

The two visit Britain sometime after February 14, 1971.

100,000 BC. Susan correctly predicts that the country will go decimal, which it did on February 15, 1971.

They witness the French Revolution - which the Doctor considers his favourite period of Earth's history - and he learns how to cook at that time, though he still prefers to rely on the TARDIS' food machine.

Susan considers her schoolbook about the French Revolution to be historically inaccurate in *100,000 BC,* and informs Barbara and Ian of her grandfather's fondness for that period (!) in episode one of *The Reign of Terror.* He talks about the Revolution again in the novel *The Eight Doctors* and *The Clockwise Man.* The Seventh Doctor novel *Just War* states that the incident represents his very first visit to Earth. His culinary baptism is mentioned in *The Lodger.*

Circa 1881, they are with a Native American when he sees his first steam train, and they hear of the activities of the notorious Clanton brothers. The Doctor and Susan acquire costumes appropriate to the period - which the Doctor considers absurd - but their presence nevertheless causes considerable comment, and the Time Lord decides that if he should travel to that period again, he'll use an alias.

The steam train incident is mentioned in *100,000 BC.* In *The Gunfighters,* it's revealed that there are male and female clothes suited to the American West in the TARDIS. The Doctor recognises the name Clanton in episode two. He evidently doesn't know the details of the famous shootout at the OK Corral, however, since, at the climax of episode four, he attempts to prevent it. In the audio *Upstairs,* the First Doctor knows a Comanche war cry, the Seventh recalls learning the tracking skills of the Arapaho in the audio *A Thousand Tiny Wings.* In the Fourth Doctor audio *Hornets' Nest: The Dead Shoes,* it's said that he learned to handle a lasso in the Old West.

Landing in ancient Greece (where the TARDIS takes the form of an ionic column), he and Susan make the acquaintance of sceptic philosopher Pyrrho and sculptor Praxiteles. They see indications of the Daemons' involvement in human history and learn of their home planet Daemos, 60,000 light-years away.

In *100,000 BC,* Susan tells Ian and Barbara that the TARDIS

> once disguised itself as an ionic column. In *The Daemons,* the Third Doctor mentions that alien species' planet of origin and presence in ancient Greece. The First Doctor recalls meeting Pyrrho in the final instalment of *The Keys of Marinus.* The Fifth Doctor identifies a kouros as the work of one of Praxiteles' students in episode one of *Planet of Fire,* while the same incarnation recalls meeting the man himself in the audio *Omega.* In *Enlightenment,* he notes that everything on Critas the Eternal's Greek barge is historically accurate. It's interesting that the Fourth Doctor's unconscious mind - as revealed in episode three of *The Invisible Enemy* - is filled with ionic columns. In episode five of *Marco Polo,* the First Doctor cries 'Great Olympus!' upon discovering that his granddaughter is missing. The Sixth Doctor recalls seeing the building of the Parthenon in the audio *The Spectre of Lanyon Moore.*

On a trip to Victorian England, he is given an improbably large Ulster by Gilbert and Sullivan.

> *Inside the Spaceship.* In episode two of *The Evil of the Daleks,* the Second Doctor is able to identify furniture from the Victorian era.

He becomes a skilled backgammon player.

> *Marco Polo.* The Doctor plays against Kublai Khan for extraordinarily high stakes in episode seven, and challenges one of the Celestial Toymaker's henchmen to a game in the unmade story *The Nightmare Fair.* He still has Khan's Key to the World on his keyring in the Fourth Doctor novel *Eye of Heaven.*

Before companions Ian and Barbara enter the TARDIS, the scanner malfunctions and no longer shows images in colour. It is some considerable time before the Doctor is able to fix it.

> *The Keys of Marinus.* Barbara complains that the scanner is in black and white. By a fortunate coincidence, it is repaired by the time the show itself goes into colour. The novelization of *The Day of the Doctor* states that his first two incarnations could only see in monochrome.

Leaving Susan behind in the ship, the Doctor mingles with the Aztecs, and learns some of their customs (though not the one about the grinding of cocoa beans signifying a proposal of marriage), as well as the basic design of their tombs and some of their nastier habits. He studies a plant, the sap of which causes temporary loss of consciousness.

The Aztecs. Unlike her grandfather, Susan doesn't know anything of Aztec culture. The Doctor says he thinks he knows the plant used to render companion Ian senseless in episode three.

During Earth's First World War, the two travellers are caught in a Zeppelin raid.

Planet of Giants. The incident is mentioned again in the audio *The Alchemists*.

The Doctor programs the TARDIS food machine with the flavour of English bacon.

The Daleks. Companions Barbara and Ian eat bacon and egg-flavoured food bars in episode one.

On a trip to the planet Venus during the 25th Dynasty, Susan sees the metal seas, while her grandfather is taught the native forms of karate and hopscotch, and a charming lullaby which, by a staggering coincidence, has the same melody as *God Rest Ye, Merry Gentlemen*. An order of nuns teach him Venusian aikido, at which he attains the level of Grandmaster Pacifist. He learns the proverb, 'If the Thrashkin puts his fingers in his ears, it is polite to shout.' He acquires a device he later cannibalizes to track time distortions, as well as a toothbrush. He learns from painful personal experience never to trust a Venusian Shanghorn with a Perigosto stick.

The metal seas are mentioned in *Marco Polo*. Susan apparently tells David Campbell about Venus in an offscreen moment during *The Dalek Invasion of Earth*. In his third incarnation, the Doctor displays his martial artistry many times, beginning with *Inferno* (in the original script, it was 'Feltian karate'). In *The Green Death* and *World Enough and Time*, he practises Venusian aikido, a skill for which four arms are usually the bare minimum. The training process is described by the Thirteenth Doctor in *The Ghost Monument*. The Doctor's initiation to the Venusian martial arts is described in both the novel *The Eight Doctors* and the short story *Prisoners of the Sun*. The First Doctor boasts of his skill at hand-to-hand combat in *The Smugglers* and claims, in *The Romans*, to have taught the Mountain Mauler of Montana everything he knows (though, in *Thin Ice*, the Twelfth Doctor declares zero-gravity wrestling his favourite version of the sport). In the novel *The Devil Goblins from Neptune*, the Third Doctor is revealed to be a master of Saturnian kung-fu. He recites the first line of the Venusian lullaby to Bok the gargoyle during *The Daemons*. It is sung in full by the Third Doctor in both *The Curse of Peladon* and *The Monster of Peladon.* In the audio *Little Doctors,* the Second Doctor says that it was sung to him during his childhood, implying previously unknown links between Gallifrey and Venus. The Seventh Doctor novel *Lucifer Rising* states that the lullaby's lyrics are actually pretty racy. In *The Time Monster,* he tells his companion Jo that the word Thrashkin has not been used on Venus since the 25th dynasty. The Time Sensor's measurements are all Venusian. The Sixth Doctor uses an entirely different device to perform the same function in *The Mark of the Rani.* Perigosto sticks are mentioned in *The Green Death,* the novelization of *The Daemons* and the novels *Love and War* and *Seeing I.* A Shanghorn appears in the Sixth Doctor audio *Voyage to Venus.* The Third Doctor displays his skill at Venusian hopscotch in episode four of *Death to the Daleks,* and the Fourth makes a flippant reference to Venus in *The Stones of Blood.* The Fifth Doctor recognises Venus from space in *Enlightenment,* and the Tenth gives Martha a toothbrush containing Venusian spearmint during *The Shakespeare Code.* Depictions of his visits to this world can be found in the novel *Venusian Lullaby* and the audio *Voyage to Venus* (the latter revealing that the similarities between the melodies of the lullaby and the Earth Christmas carol are no coincidence). The Seventh Doctor novel *Strange England* states that the Doctor once trained with the Venusian State Circus, while the Eleventh Doctor has a copy of *The Venusian Book of Calm* in the novel *Touched by an Angel.*

The wanderings of the Doctor and Susan take place over the course of several years, during which they have numerous homes in many places.

In episode six of *The Dalek Invasion of Earth,* the Doctor notes that he has been taking care of Susan for years. She recalls their multiple homes in episode one of *Marco Polo.* They cannot have been travelling together for a great many years, however, for though she is only seen from behind in *The Name of the Doctor,* Susan does not look noticeably younger than she is in *100,000 BC.* Furthermore, although Time Lords have famously elongated lifespans, she confirms in *Marco Polo* that she is indeed 16, rather than simply appearing to be a teenager, a claim refuted by the audio *Here There Be Monsters.*

The Doctor studies the Earth creatures known as cats, and deems it a fallacy that they can see in the dark.

The Sensorites. The Sixth Doctor is particularly fond of cats, even to the point of considering eating one during episode three of *The Two Doctors*.

Dining with Henry VIII proves to be a hazardous affair: The monarch throws a parson's nose at the Doctor, who immediately throws it back, and is taken to the tower as punishment. Luckily, that is where he wants to be, because the TARDIS is already there. He receives fashion tips from famous dandy Beau Brummel.

The Sensorites. The Doctor informs his companions that Brummel told him he looked better in a cloak. His newly-regenerated sixth incarnation talks about him in episode one of *The Twin Dilemma*, and later in the the audio *The Red House*. The First Doctor says that the nose incident was long before companions Ian and Barbara joined the TARDIS crew. Susan remembers it, but what part she played is unknown. She may have been inside the inaccessible TARDIS. Being locked in the Tower of London is something of a hobby for the Time Lord; he remembers being imprisoned there in *The Mind of Evil* and a daring escape is described in *The Impossible Astronaut*. By the time the Eleventh Doctor gets put in there during *The Day of the Doctor* (along with two of his former selves), he even knows what time they serve breakfast. He also visits there as a free man during *The Power of Three*. The Seventh Doctor's companion, Ace, fears being locked in the Tower during episode one of *Silver Nemesis*. Other Tower-related shenanigans occur in the audios *The Devil's Armada*, *Circular Time: Summer*, *The Marian Conspiracy*, *Jubilee* and *The Crimes of Thomas Brewster*, and in the novel *The Roundheads*. The Tenth Doctor plans to introduce Martha to Henry VIII at the end of *Last of the Time Lords*, and the Eleventh Doctor meets him on a couple of occasions. In the novel *Tragedy Day*, the Seventh Doctor claims to have assisted him in the writing of *Greensleeves*. In the Sixth Doctor comic strip *The Gift*, we learn that the Time Lord has been invited to all Henry's weddings. Henry becomes the Tenth Doctor's father-in-law following his marriage to Elizabeth I in *The Day of the Doctor*. He and the Doctor meet in the short story *God Send Me Well to Keep* and the audio *Recorded Time*. The Tenth Doctor recalls dining with Henry in the story *Revenge of the Judoon*.

The Doctor embarks upon a study of clocks, including wall quartz clocks, grandfather clocks, cuckoo clocks and atomic clocks (the latter being particularly useful when he visits Earth on New Year's Eve, 1999).

The Fourth Doctor talks about the study of clocks in *The Sontaran Experiment* and *The Armageddon Factor*. His first incarnation displays his horological knowledge in episode one of *The Sensorites*, and his second in episode five of *The Space Pirates*. There is a carriage clock on display in the TARDIS during the early stories (notably *Inside the Spaceship* and *The Time Meddler*), and many more in *Doctor Who - The TV Movie*.

The TARDIS takes the Doctor and Susan to Dido, a planet with a very distinctive odour, and a friendly population of approximately one hundred. They enter the Hall of Judgement and learn that the people have just perfected a ray to be used in construction work.

The Rescue. The Doctor says it has been years since he was last on Dido. What use a peaceful people would have for a Hall of Judgement, complete with weaponry, is unclear. Talent contests? Dido is mentioned in the novels *The Empire of Glass* and *The Tomorrow Windows*, as well as the Seventh Doctor audio *Maker of Demons*.

The pair see aqueducts in 3rd Century Rome, and are under the mistaken impression that they have wiped out the cult of Demnos. It is probably at this time that the Doctor learns of the insanity of the legendary Emperor Nero.

In *The Romans*, the Doctor remembers thinking that pipes are preferable to aqueducts. In the unscreened pilot, he and Susan talk about ancient Rome. The Fourth Doctor is already familiar with the Cult of Demnos in *The Masque of Mandragora*. In the audio *The Alchemists* - set before the TARDIS' arrival in 1960's London - the First Doctor makes use of a trunkful of golden coins given to him by the Emperor Augustus. The Fifth Doctor mentions Nero in the audio *The Eye of the Scorpion*, while the Eighth recalls the historic blaze in the audio *The Natural History of Fear*.

The Doctor places two Atmospheric Density Jackets with respiratory compensators inside the TARDIS. He lands on the planet Pictos, in the Isop Galaxy, and is told of the species known as the Menoptera, living on the moonless planet Vortis.

The Web Planet. Companion Ian has never seen the jackets before (they appear in several novels and comic strips, but never again on television). The Doctor knows of both the planet Pictos and the Menoptera. The fact that he believes Vortis to be moonless shows that his visit occurred prior to this story's events.

He and Susan briefly visit Genoa sometime after the Crusades.

> *The Crusade.* The Doctor says he knows Genoa well. He also knows the Saracen name for King Richard, and that the monarch will not win the campaign. The fact that he doesn't pick up any clothes appropriate to the period and location, and so is forced to steal some, suggests that he and Susan were not there for an extended length of time. Companion Ian discusses the Crusades with Marco Polo, but the Doctor is not present at the time. In *Robot of Sherwood*, the Twelfth Doctor claims to have fenced with Richard the Lionheart.

The Doctor sees a Time-Space Visualizer in operation. In the 18th Century, he shares a hot beverage with James Watt when the boiling kettle gives the inventor the idea to use steam as a power source.

> *The Space Museum.* The meeting with Watt is before companions Ian and Barbara set foot inside the TARDIS. The Time-Space Visualizer may be a piece of Gallifreyan equipment; the Doctor is very surprised to find one in the Moroks' museum. The device is still in the TARDIS in the Third Doctor novel *The Eye of the Giant*, the Sixth Doctor audio *The One Doctor*, the Eighth Doctor comic strip *Happy Deathday* and the Eighth Doctor audio *Relative Dimensions.* The First Doctor is looking for the manual in the audio *The Doctor's Tale.* The Seventh Doctor novel *Infinite Requiem* states that the device has made a recording of all his adventures, so there's hope for recovering those lost episodes yet.

He sees vampire bats in South America and studies the architecture of Eastern Europe.

> *The Chase.* The Fourth Doctor and Romana fall afoul of vampire bats in *State of Decay*.

He stops using the ship's Time Scanner due to its unreliability.

> *The Moonbase.* The Second Doctor says he has not used the Time Scanner in a long time. Had it been functioning at the time of *The Chase*, he would surely have used it rather than the Time-Space Visualizer.

During an emergency, he discovers that the ship's fail-safe measures - which cause it to lock onto the nearest spacecraft in the event of impending breakup - have ceased to function.

> *Terminus.* The TARDIS faces breakup many times onscreen (*Inside the Spaceship* being the first), but the fail-safe is never

shown to work until the Fifth Doctor's era, and never again thereafter.

He and Susan visit the Rings of Akhaten during the Festival of Offerings. They encounter a number of species, including the Panbabylonians, the Lugal-Irra-Kush, the Lucanians, the Hooloovoo, the increasingly rare Terraberserkers of the Kodion Belt, the Ultramancers and a moped saleswoman called Dor'een.

The Rings of Akhaten. The Eleventh Doctor tells companion Clara that he's been there before, in the company of his granddaughter. The beings he identifies all hail from the local system, and were undoubtedly present at the earlier Festival. The Hooloovoo share their name with the hyperintelligent shade of the colour blue from Douglas Adams' novel *The Hitchhiker's Guide to the Galaxy* – a work with which the Doctor is familiar (see *Ghost Light* and *The Christmas Invasion*) – but are not actually related to them.

Shortly before their arrival on Earth in the 1960s, the two travellers nearly lose the TARDIS on the planet Quinnis, in the Fourth Universe (which is possibly where the Second Doctor considers taking companions Victoria and Jamie in *The Evil of the Daleks*).

Inside the Spaceship. Susan says the Quinnis incident happened 'four or five journeys back.' The Doctor seems to acknowledge the existence of other universes here, but has forgotten all about them by the time his third incarnation arrives on an alternative Earth in *Inferno.* The Quinnis trip is depicted in the fittingly titled audio *Quinnis,* and the Third Doctor claims to have trained there to become a ninja in the novel *The Devil Goblins from Neptune.* The First Doctor short story *64 Carlysle Street* features a criminal who hails from Quinnis. That same incarnation of the Doctor mentions the planet in the comic strip *A Religious Experience,* where it is incorrectly spelled 'Quinnus.'

For some time, the Doctor uses the wood-panelled Secondary Control Room when piloting the TARDIS. He is subsequently unable to remember why he stopped.

The Masque of Mandragora. Although this is never seen onscreen, the Second and Third Doctors have also visited the Secondary Control Room (Sarah discovers their possessions). Technically, according to *The Invisible Enemy,* it is the main Control Room, and the one with which we are more familiar is the No 2 Room (which is not a euphemism for the TARDIS toilet, although the vessel has at least one of those). This alternative control room is seen again in the Sixth and Seventh Doctor strips *Changes* and *Distractions.*

The TARDIS finally arrives in London in the year 1963. The Doctor and his granddaughter take up residence in a junkyard located at 76 Totters Lane. Perhaps because it is on the regular beat of a uniformed policeman, the ship's chameleon circuit transforms the exterior into the form of a police box, though without a door handle.

100,000 BC. The year is established in episode two, and confirmed in *The Chase, The Reign of Terror* and *Remembrance of the Daleks.* The chameleon circuit is not named until *Logopolis* (it would seem that the reptiles are not unique to Earth, and *The Faceless Ones* confirms this). The TARDIS door handles reappear over the centuries - in the first episode of *Full Circle,* companion Adric notes that they aren't on the same level. It is perhaps through the Doctor's seemingly psychic relationship with his craft that he learns what a police box is. Then again, he might just have read the words on the front.

The Doctor is fearful of what might happen if they remain in one era for too long, and objects to Susan attending nearby Coal Hill High School - with, it seems, good reason.

100,000 BC. The Doctor's frequent return trips to the area cause the fabric of time to wear thin around Coal Hill, according to the *Class* episode *For Tonight We Might Die.*

He nevertheless befriends café owner Harry, and gains a passing familiarity with the music of the Beatles.

Harry appears in *Remembrance of the Daleks,* while the Doctor's knowledge of the Beatles is acquired at different points in time. He has heard of them in *The Chase,* and his second incarnation doesn't recognise the lyrics of *I Am the Walrus* in *The Three Doctors,* but he hears *Paperback Writer* playing in *The Evil of the Daleks.* The Seventh Doctor mentions *A Hard Day's Night* in *Ghost Light,* while the Tenth references *Here Comes the Sun* in *42* (although he doesn't know whether they had more pre-download Number Ones than Elvis Presley, an artist of whom he is also fond - see *Time and the Rani, The Christmas Invasion, The Idiot's Lantern* and *Rosa*). In the First Doctor story *Time and Relative,* Susan admits to having a crush on John Lennon, whose assassination the Seventh Doctor witnesses in the novel *The Left-Handed Hummingbird.* In the audio *The Little Doctors,* the

Second Doctor expresses a fondness for the song *Can't Buy Me Love.* The Tenth Doctor and Donna see the Fab Four perform in the strip *The Time of My Life* and he and Martha are on their way to see the Beatles' last live gig in the comic book *Black Death, White Life.* The audio *The Havoc of Empires* ends with the Third Doctor promising to take Jo to see the boys playing at The Cavern, while the Fifth Doctor hopes to introduce Nyssa to them in the audio *1963: Fanfare for the Common Men.* In the Eighth Doctor audio *The Resurrection of Mars,* the Meddling Monk claims to possess lost footage of the Beatles' appearance on *Juke Box Jury.*

The Doctor purchases a functioning Geiger counter, and briefly takes up smoking.

The Geiger counter is first mentioned (and later destroyed) in episode two of *100,000 BC,* in which the Doctor is also seen to smoke a pipe. Being whacked on the head by a caveman proves to be an unconventional but effective cure for this nasty habit. He loses not only his pipe, but his matches, though by the time of *The Creature from the Pit,* he has bought another box, and he is later seen to strike a match in the final episode of *The Greatest Show in the Galaxy.*

Drawing his inspiration from his granddaughter's favourite pop music band, he uses the name 'Dr J Smith' when applying for a library card, though he never bothers to get a spare in any of his later incarnations.

The Vampires of Venice. The Eleventh Doctor produces the library card, which has a photograph of his first incarnation and the Totters Lane address (establishing that he used the John Smith alias before companion Jamie apparently selected it for him during *The Wheel in Space*). He goes by Smith in the First Doctor novel *The Witch Hunters,* while his second incarnation selects the name in order to qualify for a bank account in the audio *The Selachian Gambit,* and chooses the French equivalent, Jean Dupont, in the novel *World Game.* In the comic book *The Forgotten,* the Fourth Doctor uses the name Jean Forgeron. Multiple incarnations of the Doctor use the alias Johann Schmidt in the novels *The Shadow in the Glass, Timewyrm: Exodus* and *Borrowed Time,* as well as in the audios *The One Doctor, Storm Warning* and *Klein's Story,* and the comic strip *The Instruments of War.* The Doctor has been seen with many books over the course of thirteen incarnations, including the rather far-fetched *Monsters From Outer Space* (as seen in *The*

> *Chase*), the book concerning myths and superstitions to which his second incarnation refers in *Fury From the Deep*, *Decline and Fall of the Roman Empire* (*The Mutants*), *The Prisoner of Zenda* (with which his fourth self is familiar in *The Androids of Tara*), *Peter Rabbit*, *Everest in Easy Stages* and *Teach Yourself Tibetan* (*The Creature From the Pit*), *Principia Mathematica* (*Four to Doomsday*), *Moby Dick* (which he didn't enjoy, according to *Extremis*), *The Water Babies* (*The Mysterious Planet*), *Juggling for the Complete Klutz* (*The Greatest Show in the Galaxy*) and the novels of Edith Wharton (*Arachnids in the UK*). In *100,000 BC*, Susan listens to John Smith and the Common Men on her transistor radio, and the Fifth Doctor meets the lads themselves in the audio *1963: Fanfare for the Common Men.*

Though anxious to avoid attention on Earth, the Doctor nevertheless makes the acquaintance of a Major Green (later in charge of security on the WOTAN project) while involving himself in a matter relating in some way to computers. Anxious to protect his 'Smith' alias, the Time Lord presents himself to Green as 'Doctor Who,' the same name he uses when corresponding with the eminent scientist Zaroff.

> In *The War Machines*, Green already knows the Doctor and introduces him to Professor Brett as a specialist in computer development. It is surely from him that WOTAN learns the name 'Doctor Who.' Any knowledge Green might have of the Time Lord, however, is wiped from his memory during this story; when he is revived from his hypnotic trance, he no longer recognises the Doctor. The Second Doctor's note to Zaroff in *The Underwater Menace* is signed 'Dr W.'

Whatever his business with Green might be, it most likely concerns the Fylingdale installations, the Royal Observatory and a cyclotron. Given his connection with computer technology, it is perhaps from Green that the Doctor acquires a replacement for the 'faulty filament' he mentions in episode one of *100,000 BC.*

> In *Remembrance of the Daleks,* the sites instantly spring to the Seventh Doctor's mind when he thinks of 1963. His first incarnation recognises an illusory cyclotron in episode two of *The Keys of Marinus*. In episode three of *The Invasion*, the Second Doctor notes that the structures at Tobias Vaughn's plant resemble a 'deep-space radio communications system.' The First Doctor story *Time and Relative* ends with the TARDIS filament burning out after a journey to Pluto.

He makes arrangements to hide the Hand of Omega in a nearby graveyard, with the assistance of an undertaker and a blind vicar.

Remembrance of the Daleks

In addition to visiting Nelson's Column, the Doctor makes a study of Earth insects, including grasshoppers, bees and spiders. He places aspirin and antiseptic in the TARDIS' first-aid kit.

> During *The Web Planet,* the Doctor terrifies the Zarbi with a spider from his insect collection. He is familiar with the behaviour of bees in *The Robots of Death, The Armageddon Factor* and *Delta and the Bannermen.* The Fourth Doctor refers to them as 'Terran insects,' so at that point he has yet to learn about their planet of origin, Melissa Majoria (see *The Stolen Earth*). In *The Name of the Doctor,* the Eleventh Doctor says he thought about keeping bees when he retired (perhaps he was more impressed with Goronwy than we imagined). In episode five of *Planet of the Spiders,* the Third Doctor compares the habits of the Metebelis 3 arachnids to that of their Earth cousins. In episode one of *The Web Planet,* he remarks that the statue of the Menoptera on Vortis cannot be Nelson because of the lack of pigeons. Clara Oswald and the Twelfth Doctor are almost crushed by Nelson's falling statue during *In the Forest of the Night,* while the Fifth Doctor scales the Column in the audio *The Lions of Trafalgar.* In *The Sea Devils,* the Third Doctor claims to have known the admiral (the Second Doctor meets him in both the comic strip *HMS TARDIS* and in the novel *World Game*). In episode three of *100,000 BC,* Susan says that they have a lot of antiseptic onboard the TARDIS.

The Daleks

Inside the Spaceship

Marco Polo

Prior to *The Keys of Marinus*

The Doctor learns the skills of the pickpocket.

> In episode two of *The Reign of Terror,* he deftly steals a coin from the purse of the Overseer. In the final part of *The Highlanders,* the Second Doctor removes the contracts from Solicitor Grey's pocket without anyone noticing, as the Sixth Doctor does with a leaf from Investigator Hallet's pocket during *Terror of the*

Vervoids, and the Eighth with Dr Bowman's security pass in *Doctor Who – The TV Movie*.

He meets storyteller Hans Christian Andersen, and gives him the idea for *The Emperor's New Clothes*, based on a popular Gallifreyan bedtime story. He passes on his self-defence skills to the Mountain Mauler of Montana.

The Romans. The Eleventh Doctor mentions *The Emperor Dalek's New Clothes* in *Night Terrors*. The meeting between the Mountain Mauler and the First Doctor is related in the short story *Bear Paw Adventure*.

He places a recording compound in a white box near the TARDIS' first-aid kit.

The Web Planet. The Doctor has moved the first aid kit by the time of *Shada*. Note that throughout *The Keys of Marinus*, companion Ian is in the same clothes he wore during *Marco Polo*, but both Susan and Barbara have changed, suggesting space for additional adventures.

He travels by penny-farthing bicycle, and spends some time studying the habits of sea lions.

The Space Museum. The Doctor confounds the Moroks' mind-reading device by imagining a vintage bicycle and an island full of sea lions (which he describes as 'old friends').

The Doctor is present at the Indian Mutiny sometime after the chameleon circuit has ceased functioning. In the 10th or 11th Century, he encounters the Vikings, and sees them living in houses that are actually upside-down longboats. He sees King Edward laid to rest and Harold's ascension to the throne in 1066. In Earth history books, he reads that Harold went to Northumbria to meet invading Vikings prior to the Battle of Hastings. Despite an aversion to guns, he practices marksmanship.

The story about the upside-down longboats is related by the Twelfth Doctor during *Smile*. In *The Time Meddler*, the First Doctor explains his craft's former ability to change its appearance, guessing the form the TARDIS might take if it were to arrive at the Indian Mutiny in a functioning state. In episode three of the same story, he threatens the Monk with a Winchester 73 rifle (in actuality, his cane). In many stories, including *The Sensorites*, *The Dalek Invasion of Earth*, *The Savages*, *Pyramids of Mars* and *The Robots of Death*, the Doctor claims not to like weapons of any sort, but he nevertheless keeps a collection of guns in the TARDIS, according to *The Gunfighters* (in the novelization of which, he accidentally shoots down two onlookers). Earlier, during *The Web Planet*, companion Barbara is insistent that there are no weapons onboard the vessel. The Doctor uses firearms in several stories, including *Day of the Daleks*, in which his third incarnation guns down an approaching Ogron, and *Attack of the Cybermen*, where his sixth self shoots dead two of his old enemies. The Fourth Doctor steals a pistol in *The Seeds of Doom*, but companion Sarah points out that he wouldn't actually use it. He finds a laser gun in his workroom in episode six of *Shada*. In *The Visitation*, the Fifth Doctor claims he never misses when he shoots. Despite this, just a few stories later, Tegan insists in *Earthshock* that guns are not the Time Lord's style. By the time of *The Mark of the Rani*, the Sixth Doctor says he has given up guns, moments before turning the Master's Tissue Compression Eliminator on his foes. In *The Sontaran Stratagem*, the Tenth Doctor remarks that people with guns are usually the enemy.

He encounters the eight-foot-tall Visians on the planet Mira, and studies the sun in the galaxy containing the planet Tigus. The TARDIS takes him to Trafalgar Square in 1900, where he witnesses the celebrations that greet the news of the Mafeking Relief.

The Daleks' Master Plan. These events all pre-date Steven's introduction in *The Chase*. The Doctor informs him of the Tigus sun's 'unusual powers.' The planet is namechecked again in the Eighth Doctor novel *The Tomorrow Windows*. The Fourth Doctor mentions the relief of Mafeking in *The Invasion of Time*, and – in the role of teacher John Smith – lends a student the book *A Definitive Account of Mafeking*, by Aitchinson Price.

The Doctor visits Paris in 1572, and picks up several items of clothing for the TARDIS' wardrobe. He hears of the scientific theories of the apothecary Preslin, but never encounters him.

The Massacre. The Doctor has heard of Preslin, and knows all about the massacre, urging companion Steven to flee with him, once he realises the date.

He makes a brief visit to the realm of the Toymaker.

The Celestial Toymaker. The companion Steven does not know the Toymaker, so this must have occurred before his travels with the Doctor. The mischievous, cunning being does battle with the Time Lord in the audios *The Magic Mousetrap*, *Solitaire* and *The Nightmare Fair*, the Fifth Doctor novel *Divided Loyalties*, and the comic strips *Endgame* and *Relative Dimensions*.

The TARDIS takes him to a distant age of peace and prosperity. He discovers the vast scientific research accomplished by the Elders in their segment of the universe. D403 capsules find their way into the ship's emergency cabinet (worth taking whenever a person's life essence is drained, apparently).

> *The Savages.* The Doctor identifies this time period in episode one. It is prior to Steven's first appearance. In episode two, he directs his companions to the D403.

He acquires spacesuits for himself and his companions, and stores them in a chest aboard the TARDIS.

> *The Moonbase.* There are four spacesuits in the chest, clearly meant for the Doctor, Susan, Ian and Barbara, since it isn't until *The Highlanders* that the Time Lord Once again has three companions. Wherever they were used, it can't have been on Earth's moon; according to Ian, in episode six of *The Chase,* they never went there.

The Aztecs

Prior to *The Sensorites*

The Doctor and Susan discuss how much the TARDIS crew have changed since their voyages began.

> The final scene of *The Aztecs* runs into the next story, but in the opening scene of *The Sensorites,* the Doctor relates the conversation he and Susan have just been having.

Prior to *The Reign of Terror*

The Doctor dons a new coat.

> His original coat is torn to ribbons at the start of episode five of *The Sensorites.* He seems to have several, since he leaves one behind on Aridius at the end of episode two of *The Chase,* which he does not replace until episode four.

He begins to despair of the state of his granddaughter's room in the TARDIS.

> In episode six of *The Dalek Invasion of Earth,* Susan notes that her cupboard is in a muddle, and her grandfather agrees that she has become disorganised since leaving Coal Hill High School.

Planet of Giants

The Dalek Invasion of Earth

The Rescue

The Romans

The Web Planet

The Crusade

The Space Museum

Prior to *The Chase*

Two years have passed since companions Ian and Barbara entered the TARDIS ... or, at least, since the Doctor first attempted to return them to 20th Century London.

> *The Chase.* In the final episode, the Doctor says he has been trying to get them home for two years – by pure coincidence, the length of time their adventures have been running onscreen.

At some point in the late 20th or 21st Century, the Doctor and Vicki provide assistance to the military.

> *The Day of the Doctor.* There are pictures of Ian, Barbara and one of Vicki with a soldier in modern military garb on a board in UNIT's Black Archive.

The Time Meddler

Prior to *Galaxy 4*

Reading Homer's account of the Trojan Wars, the Doctor dismisses the story of the wooden horse as pure invention, little realising that he is destined one day to design it.

> *The Myth Makers.* The First Doctor somehow failed to spot the Rani during the débâcle; *The Mark of the Rani* reveals that she was conducting her experiments there at the time.

He creates a chair equipped with a powerful force-field.

> *The Daleks' Master Plan.* In episode one, the Doctor uses his 'magnetic chair' to imprison Marc Corey. There is not much of a gap between *Galaxy 4* and *The Myth Makers* (Vicki is still recovering from her twisted ankle as the latter story opens), so its construction can't occur any later than this point.

Mission to the Unknown

The Myth Makers

The Time Meddler

During *The Daleks' Master Plan*

Fleeing from the Daleks, the Doctor finds himself in his own future, aiding his third incarnation. He poses for a portrait, which later finds its way into a UNIT safe house.

> In *The Day of the Doctor,* a photograph of Steven Taylor, and another of Sara Kingdom and Mike Yates are pinned to a board in UNIT's Black Archive. That story also states that with the timelines out of synch, the earliest incarnation would retain no memory of such an encounter, and while *The Five Doctors* seems to suggest that recollections of these earlier incidents return when that same incarnation is taken out of time, the First Doctor has no memory of his next four selves during *Twice Upon a Time,* or, for that matter, the name Lethbridge-Stewart (assuming the Brig was also mixed up in this incident, and not off in Geneva or Cromer). The colour portrait of the First Doctor is seen in *The Zygon Inversion.* It could be from Steven or the Doctor that UNIT acquire the two photos of Katarina, though for what purpose, I can't imagine.

Prior to *The Massacre*

The Doctor encounters the Daleks once more, and comes away with a key to the interior sections of one of their ships. He also acquires a hand mirror.

> *The Power of the Daleks.* The newly-regenerated Second Doctor finds the key inside a trunk in the TARDIS, which he is never shown acquiring onscreen. Perhaps this relates to one of the encounters he describes to Davros during *Genesis of the Daleks.* Additionally, this may be the adventure during which the presence of his foes causes him to experience a 'prickling sensation,' which he describes to companion Dodo at the beginning of *The War Machines.* Dodo has never heard of Daleks, so that incident must be before she joins the TARDIS crew. The Second Doctor still has the hand mirror in *The Mind Robber.* In episode three of *The Face of Evil,* his fourth incarnation deflects a laser beam with a square mirror. By the

time of *The Creature from the Pit,* he has a small circular mirror.

Prior to *The Ark*

Following companion Dodo's unexpected arrival in the TARDIS, the Doctor decides that he will never again leave the ship unlocked.

> The Doctor claims, in episode one of *The Smugglers,* that he never leaves the TARDIS unlocked. He nevertheless continually forgets to secure the doors, his most extraordinarily negligent acts occurring in *The Masque of Mandragora, The Armageddon Factor, Warriors of the Deep, The Awakening, The Twin Dilemma, Attack of the Cybermen* and *Utopia.*

He plays the Trilogic Game.

> *The Celestial Toymaker.* The Doctor knows the rules, but he certainly didn't learn them in the Toymaker's domain; the dialogue in the first episode makes it clear that he wasn't in that realm long enough previously to play any games.

He watches the classic 1920 film *The Cabinet of Dr Caligari,* as well as the cowboy adventures of silent movie star Tom Mix.

> *The Gunfighters.* In episode one, the Doctor chooses to go by the alias of Dr Caligari (though he responds when he hears the phrase 'Doctor Who?'). The Doctor first hears the Caligari name in the audio *The Alchemists.* He compares companion Steven in his cowboy duds to actor Mix, who is also mentioned in the Eleventh Doctor novel *The Coming of the Terraphiles.* In *The Lie of the Land,* the Twelfth Doctor considers altering the minds of humanity in order to prevent people talking in cinemas.

To assist him in his calculations upon landing, he builds the unfortunately named 'Reacting Vibrator.'

> *The Savages.* Companions Steven and Dodo return the device to the TARDIS in episode two. The Doctor apparently fails to get any satisfaction from his Vibrator, and is never seen to use it again. As with all of the Doctor's other gadgets, the RV is either built or grown according to requirements by the ship's architectural reconfiguration system, seen in *Journey to the Centre of the TARDIS.*

The Celestial Toymaker

The Gunfighters

Prior to *The Savages*

Having arrived upon a world he suspects to be the home planet of the Elders, the Doctor instructs his companions, Steven and Dodo, to remain in the TARDIS for five minutes while he investigates.

> *The Savages.* The time limit the Doctor has imposed upon himself is not mentioned in the final scenes of *The Gunfighters.*

Prior to *The War Machines*

On more than one occasion, the TARDIS materialises at the Det Sen Monastery in Tibet, which always seems to be under some sort of threat.

> *The Abominable Snowmen*

While in Tibet, the Doctor learns the local customs and picks up the books *Everest in Easy Stages* (published in Tibetan) and *Teach Yourself Tibetan* (in English). In preparation for his assault on Mount Everest, he purchases several items of mountaineering paraphernalia.

> *Planet of the Spiders* and *The Creature From the Pit.* The Tenth Doctor recalls Sir Edmund Hillary's ascent of Everest in *The Idiot's Lantern.* In the radio play *Exploration Earth: The Time Machine,* the Fourth Doctor brands the mountain a 'slagheap.' In the Fifth Doctor audio *Circular Time: Spring,* he has the rucksack of George Mallory, who died while attempting to conquer Everest in 1924. The Third Doctor converses in Tibetan in episode five of *Planet of the Spiders,* and may have purchased the language book in order to fit in at Det Sen. Not that he should need to, given that the TARDIS should provide a translation (but see the 'Language' section of 'Musings' on page 269 for more on this, the most contradictory element of the series' continuity). The Fifth Doctor returns to Tibet in the audio *The Roof of the World.*

He is taught the skill of hypnotism by the High Lama, Padmasambhava.

> In episode two of *Terror of the Zygons,* the Fourth Doctor explains to Benton that he learned his ability from 'a Tibetan monk,' although the novels *The Roundheads* and *White Darkness* both claim that his tutor was actually the Master. In *The War Machines,* the First Doctor realises that Dodo has been hypnotised, and is able to de-program her. His second incarnation does the same for Victoria in *The Abominable Snowmen* and for Vana in *The Krotons,* his third for Jo in *Terror*

of the Autons, and his fourth for Leela in *The Face of Evil* and Henry Gordon Jago in *The Talons of Weng-Chiang.* Jo is accidentally placed in a trance by the Third Doctor in episode three of *The Curse of Peladon* (as is Leela in the final part of *The Sun Makers,* in which the Fourth Doctor describes his ability as 'a knack'). He places fellow Gallifreyan Rodan in a trance with ease in the final episode of *The Invasion of Time,* and does the same to a guard in episode two of *The Ribos Operation.* The Fifth Doctor uses gadgetry to regress Tegan in the first episode of *Snakedance.* The Sixth Doctor puts Jamie in a trance in *The Two Doctors,* but by the time of *Revelation of the Daleks,* he seems to have lost the skill (in *The Power of Kroll,* the Fourth Doctor says it is impossible to hypnotise anyone with narrow little eyes). He regains the ability following his regeneration, using it on non-military personnel in Carbury during *Battlefield.* In *The Caretaker,* the Twelfth Doctor intends to wipe Danny Pink's memories through hypnotism, but he's prevented from doing so by Clara, and he later decides against doing the same thing to Bill Potts in *The Pilot.* None of the kids from Coal Hill seem to recognise the Doctor when they bump into him a few episodes later, during *In the Forest of the Night,* so maybe he wiped all their memories. Further examples of his mesmeric skill occur in the novels *The Crystal Bucephalus* and *Eternity Weeps,* the audios *The Labyrinth of Buda Castle, Bloodtide, The Fires of Vulcan* and *Police and Shreeves,* and the Seventh Doctor comic strip *Invaders from Gantac!*

The Doctor rebuilds the TARDIS lock, removing the 21-hole defence mechanism (or else it simply malfunctions).

In episode two of *The Daleks*, Susan tells Ian that the TARDIS lock will melt if the key is not inserted correctly - an assertion repeated in episode four of *Marco Polo.* This safeguard must not be working at the end of *The War Machines,* since Polly uses Dodo's spare key to enter the ship before it dematerialises in episode four, without any unfortunate results. (Perhaps the Doctor alters the lock following the ease with which it is removed by the Sensorites.) In the audio *Here There Be Monsters,* Barbara opens the TARDIS up for the others, having been shown how to use the key in the novel *The Sorcerer's Apprentice.* It is presumably Steven Taylor who persuades the Doctor to provide his companions with spare keys - in episode four of *The Massacre,* Steven believes the Doctor dead, and attempts to find the Time Lord's key, without which he is stranded. It's worth noting that most of the Doctor's troubles in *Marco Polo* revolve around the fact that there is apparently only one TARDIS key – the Doctor's – although Susan is seen to have her own in episode two of *The Daleks* and the final part of *The Dalek Invasion of Earth*. She must surely have had one in *100,000 BC*, too, or how else could she have entered the ship in her grandfather's absence?

He hears the story of the legendary pirate Captain Henry Avery, and learns the skills of the fortune-teller.

The Smugglers. The Doctor uses a deck of cards (not his own) to tell fortunes. He recognises the name Avery here, but appears to have forgotten it when he meets the man himself in *The Curse of the Black Spot*.

The Doctor purchases a 500-year diary. He witnesses the arrival of the planet Mondas into Earth's solar system in 1986 and the subsequent Cyberman attack, during which he sees a Cybermat for the first time.

In *The Tenth Planet*, the Doctor tries to warn the crew at the Arctic base about the nature of the mysterious planet and the forthcoming Cyberman presence. In episode four, we're told that the Cybermen have landed in many parts of the world. The year 1986 is given for the invasion in *The Tenth Planet*, *Attack of the Cybermen* and Seventh Doctor comic strip *The Good Soldier*. (The *Tenth Planet* novelization places the story in 2000, while the *Power of the Daleks* novelization states that it occurred during the 1990s.) The Second Doctor has a drawing of a Cybermat in his diary in *The Tomb of the Cybermen*. In *The Moonbase*, companions Ben and Polly make it clear that they haven't encountered any Cybermen since *The Tenth Planet*. The Doctor might have had this adventure while travelling with Susan (as implied in the audio *The Alchemists*), but in *The Five Doctors*, she doesn't identify the Cybermen by name until after she's heard the Fifth Doctor's companion, Tegan, do so. In *The Power of the Daleks*, the Second Doctor states that he kept a diary during his first incarnation, but in *100,000 BC*, he records TARDIS key codes and details of his journeys in a notebook. The short story *The Three Paths* states that the Doctor began keeping the diary while still on Gallifrey.

He encounters the Troglodytes, an ancient cave-dwelling tribe from North Africa, and makes an entry concerning them in his diary. He experiences decompression sickness (also known as Caisson's Disease) and hears legends of the lost city of Atlantis. On Earth in the 1950s, he briefly corresponds with Professor Zaroff, 'the greatest scientific genius since Leonardo.' He once again uses the alias 'Doctor Who' in his letters. The Time Lord later witnesses the international incident caused by Zaroff's disappearance.

> *The Underwater Menace*. In episode one, the Second Doctor warns Polly about the effects of Caisson's Disease. The date of the story is approximately 1970, and the Doctor notes that Zaroff vanished twenty years prior. The Doctor is familiar with Zaroff's reputation, and the scientist comes to the Time Lord's rescue upon seeing a note signed 'Dr W.'

During his travels, he acquires a recorder, a tape measure, a magnifying glass and a dog whistle.

> All of these items are seen in *The Power of the Daleks*. The Doctor also has a magnifying glass in *The Highlanders, The Underwater Menace, Genesis of the Daleks, Four to Doomsday, The Unicorn and the Wasp, The Beast Below* and *Journey to the Centre of the TARDIS,* as well as in the comic strip *The Heralds of Destruction*. In *Four to Doomsday*, the Fifth Doctor explains that he uses it because he's short-sighted in his right eye. The lens his eighth incarnation wields in *Doctor Who – The TV Movie* belongs to his companion, Grace. The Fourth Doctor uses the dog whistle to summon K-9, to annoy the Shrivenzale in *The Ribos Operation* and to scramble Movellan brains in *Destiny of the Daleks.*

He meets King George at the time of the Jacobite rebellion. While there, he learns the details of the Aliens Act of 1730, despite the fact that it has nothing to do with actual aliens.

> *The Highlanders*. In the guise of the German Dr Von Wer (an alias also mentioned in the Sixth Doctor audio *The One Doctor*), the Second Doctor boasts that his grasp of English is stronger than that of the monarch, whom the Eighth Doctor claims to have befriended in the audio *Seasons of Fear*. He's familiar with the details of the period, plays a Jacobite dirge on the flute and invents a plot against the Duke of Cumberland.

The Doctor visits Earth in the year 2050, and observes the medical technology of that period. In 1888, he finally obtains his degree in medicine, studying under Lister in Glasgow. Or maybe not.

> *The Moonbase*. Upon hearing of the Gravitron, the Second Doctor assumes it's the year 2050 (in fact, he's 20 years out). He has to instruct companion Polly in the use of the base's sickbay

equipment, and tells her that he thinks he once took a medical degree. His haziness might account for the fact that if he's correct about Lister, he's wrong about either the year or the city. The issue is clarified, after a fashion, in *Death in Heaven*, when Clara states that he graduated in the wrong Century. In the audio *Pest Control*, the Eighth Doctor remembers taking the Hippocratic Oath in 1888, and the Fifth Doctor refers to Lister in the story *Blood and Hope*.

He is taken out of time by his fellow Time Lords and sent to assist his second and third incarnations. The power drain experienced on Gallifrey is such, however, that he finds himself trapped in a time eddy and can only act in an advisory capacity.

The Three Doctors

The First Doctor places some Alderberan brandy in the TARDIS in the event of emergencies.

The presence of brandy in the TARDIS is first mentioned onscreen in *The Ark in Space*, when Harry suggests reviving an unconscious Sarah with a drop. River Song helps herself to some and identifies it as originating on Aldeberan in *The Husbands of River Song*. It is stated in *Twice Upon a Time* that the decanter was placed there by the Doctor's first incarnation, though he turns down the drink in favour of milk during *The Smugglers*.

On another occasion, President Borusa snatches him up in a Time Scoop and sets him down in Gallifrey's Death Zone.

The Five Doctors. This certainly occurs after *The Three Doctors*; he asks his third self, 'What happened to the little fellow?' meaning that he recalls his second incarnation, something he fails to do in *Twice Upon a Time*. Exactly how much the Doctor remembers after these little jaunts into his own future is open to debate; he knows his other incarnations, but doesn't recognise the Brigadier or any of his later companions, nor does he know not to trust Borusa. *The Day of the Doctor* states that because the timestreams are out of sync, a Time Lord's recollections of encountering his later selves fade away very quickly, but return if they should meet again, which (sort of) explains how the Tenth Doctor prevents the TARDIS from exploding upon encountering his fifth incarnation in *Time Crash*.

He is approached by three of his later incarnations, who persuade him to begin the calculations required to place Gallifrey in a parallel pocket universe. He then travels forward to the final day of the Time War to assist his twelve other selves.

> *The Day of the Doctor.* Presumably, the program continues running over the centuries (without the Doctor's knowledge) until it is finally complete in the Eleventh Doctor's era, and that the earliest incarnations of the Doctor are only able to pilot their TARDISes with such accuracy through the assistance of later Doctors. The novelization of *The Day of the Doctor* states that it is the Twelfth Doctor who assembles all his previous selves, save for the Tenth, Eleventh and War Doctors, but the climax of the book bears little resemblance to what occurs onscreen.

The Smugglers

Prior to *The Tenth Planet*

The Doctor tells Ben and Polly about the Daleks.

> In episode two of *The Power of the Daleks,* Ben remarks that the First Doctor was 'always going on about' his famous enemies. There are no gaps between his new companions' first three adventures (although the writers of several novels, comic strips and audios seem to have found one), but there is perhaps just enough time for him to have said something prior to the start of this adventure.

The Second Doctor
Patrick Troughton
1966-1969

Prior to *The Power of the Daleks*

The Doctor's regeneration (or renewal, if you prefer) repairs a defect in his eyesight.

> In episode one of *Marco Polo*, the First Doctor claims he can't see a thing without his glasses. This can't be entirely true, since he doesn't often wear them (although he memorably uses them to set fire to the Emperor Nero's plans in *The Romans*), but he goes without them entirely for several incarnations until his fifth persona starts wearing spectacles again from time to time. The Tenth and Eleventh Doctors also wear glasses, though those worn by the Eleventh belonged originally to companion Amy Pond in *The Angels Take Manhattan*. Although the term 'regeneration' is not used until *Planet of the Spiders*, the First Doctor is familiar with it in *Twice Upon a Time*.

Prior to *The Highlanders*

The Doctor learns how to play whist.

> The Second Doctor is seen to be proficient at this card game during episode three of *The Highlanders*. His fifth incarnation is a skilful player in the audio *Phantasmagoria*.

In his wanderings, he acquires some conkers, a fur coat, a scimitar, a broken set of bagpipes (which he then tries, without success, to keep hidden from his Highland companion Jamie) and an item he is unable subsequently to identify, but is nevertheless glad to see again. In 1630, when Det Sen Monastery is under attack, the Doctor is present, but leaves without knowing the result, taking with him for safekeeping the holy ghanta, which he does not get around to returning until 1935.

> *The Abominable Snowmen*. The Abbot Padmasambhava recognises the Doctor's second incarnation, though Jamie has never been to Det Sen before. The fur coat and other items are stowed away in a chest and shown to Jamie and Victoria for the first time in episode one. The coat, which the Second

Doctor wears again in *The Five Doctors* and *The Name of the Doctor*, is seen in the hands of future incarnations in *The Twin Dilemma* and *Time and the Rani*. The Seventh Doctor wears it in the comic strip *A Cold Day in Hell!* In the final scene of *The Highlanders*, the Second Doctor says Jamie can join the TARDIS crew if he teaches the Time Lord to play the bagpipes. He obviously has had a change of hearts. In the short story *The Anti-Hero*, Jamie's playing has become a regular occurrence in the TARDIS. The Fourth Doctor has a string of conkers in *Revenge of the Cybermen*, while the Tenth has just the one left in the novel *The Price of Paradise*. The Third Doctor audio *Ghost in the Machine* states that he picked them up on Venus.

He gains an appreciation of the work of Robert Burns. Circa 1500, he sees Leonardo da Vinci's designs for a flying machine and submarine, but does not meet the man himself.

The Underwater Menace. The Second Doctor quotes Burns in episode one (and his fourth incarnation misquotes his famous poem *To a Mouse* ... in episode three of *The Android Invasion*). He is already familiar with Leonardo's accomplishments at this point, and recognises his designs for a flying machine in *The Seeds of Death* (though Jamie and Zoe do not). In *The Masque of Mandragora*, the Fourth Doctor laments not having met the man personally, and comments that his submarine plans were none too practical. He mentions the plans for the flying machine once again in *City of Death* - which, we learn in the final episode of *The Time Meddler*, were drawn up with the assistance of the renegade Time Lord known as the Monk. Leonardo makes appearances in the First Doctor short story *The Innocents* and the Tenth Doctor comic strip *da Vinci's Robots*, while the Eighth Doctor recalls him in the audio *Relative Dimensions*.

He is present as Alexander the Great (who apparently bears some resemblance to Brigadier Alistair Gordon Lethbridge-Stewart of UNIT) cuts the Gordian Knot.

The Moonbase. Jamie doesn't know what the Second Doctor means when he mentions the legendary knot to Zoe, so it must pre-date his time in the TARDIS. The Fourth Doctor mistakes the Brigadier for Alexander the Great in episode one of *Robot* and refers to him once again in *Genesis of the Daleks*. Had it been filmed, the First Doctor would have encountered

> the famous leader in Moris Farhi's *Farewell Great Macedon*. The First Doctor performs Alexander's autopsy in the short story *The Book of Shadows*, the Fourth claims to have chatted to him during a brief trip to the afterlife in the audio *The Ghosts of Gralstead*, and the Fifth Doctor brands him a bore in the novel *The Crystal Bucephalus*.

He witnesses the 'magnificent folly' of the Charge of the Light Brigade (and later meets Florence Nightingale in a field hospital), sees a Shaska (a Circassian sword) and observes the methods of alchemists during the Middle Ages.

> *The Evil of the Daleks*. In episode five, the Second Doctor identifies one of Maxtible's weapons as Circassian. He gives Jamie a brief history of the Crimean War, which the Third Doctor recalls in *The Sea Devils*. In *The Masque of Mandragora*, his fourth incarnation notes that Florence Nightingale would not have approved of his bandaging. She appears in the Seventh Doctor audio *The Angel of Scutari*, while in the audio *White Ghosts*, the Fourth Doctor claims to have been presented with her famous lamp as a gift. The Charge of the Light Brigade is mentioned in the audios *The Dark Planet* and *Assassin in the Limelight* and in the novels *King of Terror* and *Blood Harvest*.

He spends some time in Yucatan and its environs.

> In *The Enemy of the World*, the Second Doctor is quick to pinpoint Salamander's place of origin from his accent.

He rides the London Underground, shortly after its opening in 1863 (though he fails to note the date).

> *The Web of Fear*. The Second Doctor states incorrectly that the Underground is from a little after his companion Victoria's time, when, in fact, it opened three years before she joined the TARDIS crew. According to *The Snowmen*, it is the Eleventh Doctor who, in 1892, suggests the London Underground to the Great Intelligence as a possible site for invasion.

He and his companions enjoy a pleasant stay on the peaceful planet Dulkis, where – as on Dido – weapons are outlawed.

> *The Dominators*. The Dulkis trip certainly occurs pre-Jamie. The Doctor makes so little an impression that, upon his return, the Dulcians believe no extraterrestrials have visited their world before. He recalls that weapons have been outlawed, but doesn't know about the atomic testing. He is quite certain, however, that

his previous visit was in the planet's past.

He acquires an inflatable rubber dinghy, and places a book about Earth's myths and superstitions in the TARDIS library. Of particular interest are the accounts of 18th Century mariners who claim to have encountered a form of sentient seaweed. He also visits a gas refinery.

Fury from the Deep. The Second Doctor is fully familiar with the workings of the refinery. The dinghy is deployed after the TARDIS lands in the sea in the opening scene. Despite owning this book, which he reads in episode three, his fourth incarnation says, in *Horror of Fang Rock*, that he doesn't believe in mythical sea beasts. Some of the volumes stored in the library must suffer water damage when it collides with the TARDIS swimming pool in *The Eleventh Hour*, and a fair few are lost for good when the doors open in flight at the end of *Twice Upon a Time*. The room is seen in *Journey to the Centre of the TARDIS*, as well as appearing in the Seventh Doctor audio *The Genocide Machine*, the comic strips *The Mark of Mandragora* and *Sky Jacks*, and the Fifth Doctor novel *The Crystal Bucephalus*.

He hears the myth of Perseus and the Medusa, as well as the fairy tale of Rapunzel. In the early 20th Century, he reads the adventures of Captain Jack Harkaway in *The Ensign*.

The Mind Robber. Jamie is unfamiliar with the Medusa's traits, nor does he recognise Rapunzel - who reappears in the Tenth Doctor story *The Mystery of the Haunted Cottage* - when they meet in episode three. The Doctor's granddaughter Susan expresses some familiarity with the tale of the long-haired heroine in the novel *The Sorcerer's Apprentice*. The Fourth Doctor encounters the genuine Medusa in the appropriately-titled comic book *Gaze of the Medusa*. The Second Doctor may have drawn his knowledge of these mythological characters from the book he refers to in episode three of *Fury from the Deep*. The Fourth Doctor's companion Harry Sullivan discovers a copy of The Ensign in the novel *Scratchman*.

Encountering the Sontarans, involved in their perpetual war with the Rutans, he makes some notes regarding them in his 500-year diary. During the conflict, he sees a Rutan power base bombarded by Photonic missiles, visits their icy homeworld of Ruta 3, and travels on one of their ships, which have a crystalline infrastructure.

The Sontarans, first seen in *The Time Warrior*, are the subject of one of the Doctor's favourite nursery tales, according to *Night*

Terrors. The war with the Rutans has been raging for 50,000 years by the time of *The Poison Sky*. The 500-year diary, mentioned in *The Sontaran Experiment*, is commonly associated with the Second Doctor (although see *The Power of the Daleks*). Companion Jamie doesn't recognise the Sontarans in *The Two Doctors*, but the Second Doctor clearly knows all about them. The First Doctor audio *The Sontarans* describes his original encounter with the clone warrior race.

The Underwater Menace

The Moonbase

The Macra Terror

Prior to *The Faceless Ones*

He acquires (or builds) a magnetic electrometer.

The Tomb of the Cybermen. The Second Doctor uses it to check the levels of the electrified door barring the tomb on Telos.

The Second Doctor has another encounter with the Daleks - which, from their point of view, is their introduction to him.

This would explain how the Daleks are familiar with the Doctor's second incarnation in both televised stories. Companion Jamie isn't in the least bit fazed by meeting them in *The Evil of the Daleks*, though he certainly knows the name.

He befriends opera singer Dame Nellie Melba, and improves on her party piece of singing at a pitch capable of smashing wine glasses.

In the final episode of *The Ice Warriors*, the Second Doctor is familiar with the notion of a singer shattering glass with his or her voice. In episode three of *The Power of Kroll*, the Fourth Doctor escapes from certain death by breaking the window in his chamber with his voice alone, and mentions his friendship with Dame Nellie, who is also name-checked by the same incarnation in the audio *The Foe From the Future*.

The TARDIS crew acquire space packs, necessary for airless environments.

Four to Doomsday. The Fifth Doctor has four space packs, and this is the last time prior to *Logopolis* that he travels with three companions.

The Evil of the Daleks

The Tomb of the Cybermen

Prior to *The Abominable Snowmen*

During one of several jaunts to Venice, the Second Doctor, Jamie and Victoria bump into Napoleon Bonaparte. The Time Lord reminds the diminutive leader that an army marches on its stomach. The encounter does not end well, perhaps because the Doctor insists on addressing him as 'Boney,' but more likely because the Time Lord steals the Frenchman's uniform. Napoleon throws a bottle of wine at the Doctor, which he catches and eventually drinks at Lake Silencio in 2011.

The location for the meeting is pinpointed in *The Vampires of Venice*. In the Ninth Doctor novel *Only Human*, there's a Venetian ballgown hanging in the TARDIS wardrobe. The Third Doctor recounts his conversation with Napoleon in *Day of the Daleks*. Napoleon's uniform is the first outfit the newly-regenerated Seventh Doctor tries on in *Time and the Rani*. Teacher John Smith gives a lesson on Napoleon in *Human Nature*. The First Doctor makes mention of the famous general in the unscreened pilot, so make of that what you will - maybe there's an alternate universe in which the two met and the TARDIS doors never closed properly. Napoleon actually appears onscreen in *The Reign of Terror*, but the First Doctor doesn't encounter him. The Fourth Doctor recalls him in *Destiny of the Daleks*, and Victoria mentions him in episode one of *The Enemy of the World*. The story about the wine bottle is from *The Wedding of River Song*. The Second Doctor encounters the military leader in the novel *World Game*, and the First and Sixth Doctors in the audios *Mother Russia* and *The Curse of Davros*. The Fourth Doctor audio *The Sands of Life* states that the Doctor has a portrait of Boney. Beginning with *Doctor Who in an Exciting Adventure With the Daleks*, several novels, including *Shadowmind* featuring the Seventh Doctor, state that there is a bust of Napoleon in the TARDIS Control Room. In the Eighth Doctor comic strip *Endgame*, the Celestial Toymaker boasts about beating the Emperor at Risk.

In his spare time, the Doctor studies phonetics.

In *The Enemy of the World*, he says he has always been interested in the subject.

The Ice Warriors

Prior to *The Enemy of the World*

The Second Doctor teaches Jamie to read.

> Jamie is illiterate in *The Evil of the Daleks,* but he is able to read a map of the London Underground in episode two of *The Web of Fear,* and later the ticker-tape in *The Mind Robber.* He seems to know the Chameleon Tours sign in *The Faceless Ones,* but it is perhaps the logo he recognises. The Fourth Doctor's companion Leela is similarly disadvantaged, and is seen attempting to write her own name in episode one of *The Invisible Enemy.*

The Web of Fear

Prior to *Fury from the Deep*

During a long, boring night (and in private), the Second Doctor creates his first sonic screwdriver in order to put up a lot of shelves - and, in part, to take his mind off his lack of success with the opposite sex. He is satisfied that it 'never fails,' unless you try to use it on wood ... or turkey. He acquires a stethoscope, a telescope, a replacement Geiger counter, a bag of lemon sherbets, a beach ball, a deckchair and a butterfly net.

> Although the novelization of *The Faceless Ones* includes the sonic screwdriver, it first appears onscreen in *Fury from the Deep.* Companions Jamie and Victoria have never seen it before. The First Doctor uses an actual screwdriver in *The Chase, The War Machines* and *Galaxy 4,* and doesn't recognise the device wielded by the Twelfth Doctor in *Twice Upon a Time.* During *The Abominable Snowmen,* the Second Doctor uses an ordinary screwdriver to dismantle a robotic Yeti, a task for which he would certainly have used the sonic device, if it had existed at that point. The Ninth Doctor states his original reasons for making the sonic screwdriver in *The Doctor Dances,* and the Eleventh elaborates upon them in *A Christmas Carol.* Curiously, the earliest chronological reference to the device not working on wood occurs not onscreen but in the Third Doctor novel *Catastrophea.* The First Doctor audio *The Beginning* suggests that the screwdriver is standard in the toolkit of every Gallifreyan engineer. According to the Eighth Doctor novel *Frontier Worlds,* the gizmo is powered by self-regenerating diuturnix batteries. The Second Doctor uses a stethoscope to listen to the pipeline in

episode one of *Fury from the Deep*. It is seen again in several stories, including *The Creature from the Pit, Utopia, The Stolen Earth* and *The Tsuranga Conundrum*. This Geiger counter and the telescope are seen first in *The Dominators* (The First Doctor's original Geiger counter is destroyed during episode two of *An Unearthly Child*). The Fourth Doctor has a different design of Geiger counter in *The Android Invasion,* and the Seventh yet another in *Ghost Light*. The Fourth Doctor carries a telescope in several stories, including *Genesis of the Daleks, The Sun Makers* and *State of Decay,* as well as inthe Seventh Doctor novel *Parasite*. Romana is arrested for wielding it in episode one of *The Pirate Planet*. While on board the *Silver Carrier,* during *The Wheel in Space,* the Second Doctor offers a lemon sherbet to Jamie. The holiday gear is seen in episode one of *The Dominators.*

He reads *Gulliver's Travels* and *The Three Musketeers,* and hears the myths of the Knights of the Round Table (which come in handy during a yet-to-be-seen future incarnation) and the Minotaur. He meets Edmund Teach, better known as the pirate Blackbeard. In the year 2000, he is too busy to read the cartoon strips in the *Hourly Telepress.*

The Mind Robber. Both the Second Doctor and Zoe are familiar with *Gulliver's Travels,* but there hasn't been time for his companion to have read it since beginning her travels in the TARDIS. The Ninth Doctor novel *Only Human* implies that he knew the book's author, Jonathan Swift. It is not until he regenerates for a second time that the Doctor discovers the Minotaur actually exists. At some point during his fourth incarnation he encounters the creature again, according to *The Creature from the Pit* and *The Horns of Nimon*. The Fourth Doctor and Romana tackle a beret-wearing Minotaur in the comic strip *The Forgotten,* and the Eighth recalls the legendary monster in the audio *Caerdroia*. The Second Doctor has imaginary versions of Sir Lancelot and Blackbeard do battle in episode five of *The Mind Robber*. He doesn't recognise the comic book character the Karkus, who originates in the year 2000 - our old future. The Hourly Telepress gets a mention in the Eighth Doctor novel *Alien Bodies,* and the Third Doctor eventually familiarised himself with the adventures of the Karkus, according to the Ninth Doctor comic strip *Official Secrets*. The Eighth Doctor's companion Izzy has a Karkus comic book in the strip *Beautiful Freak,* and the physical embodiment of the character reappears in the Sixth Doctor audio *Legend of the Cybermen.*

The Doctor learns about camera maintenance and purchases a pack of Earth playing cards.

The Invasion. The Second Doctor repairs Isobel Watkins' camera (in *Invasion of the Dinosaurs*, his third incarnation describes the model used by the military as 'antiquated,' while his fourth carries a Polaroid camera in *City of Death*). The Second Doctor plays Patience in episode two of *The Invasion*, and again in the final instalment of *The War Games*, as well as in the audio *The Great Space Elevator*. The Tenth Doctor still has the deck of cards in the novel *The Price of Paradise*.

He meets Yuri Gagarin. In the 21st Century, he sees an ion jet rocket.

The Seeds of Death. The Second Doctor recognises Gagarin's spacesuit and a model of the ion rocket in Eldred's museum. The astronaut is mentioned in the audios *The Space Race* and *Thin Ice*.

He starts carrying a packet of drawing pins, because he likes them (usually).

The Space Pirates. Zoe asks the Second Doctor why he has them; Jamie does not ask, perhaps suggesting that he's seen them before.

The Wheel in Space

The Dominators

The Mind Robber

The Invasion

Prior to *The Krotons*

The Doctor purchases several umbrellas. An empty plastic bottle and a short length of chain find their way into his pockets. He learns that life on the planet Earth began in the sea, just as it did on Ruta 3 – a fact that becomes very useful during his fourth incarnation when he meets Scaroth, the last of the Jagaroth. He studies the architecture on low-gravity planets.

The Krotons. The Second Doctor likens the tank containing the hibernating aliens to Earth's primordial soup. He suggests the Gond dwellings are more typical of a low-gravity civilisation, and complains that the crystalline aliens have virtually destroyed his 'favourite umbrella,' suggesting that he has a selection. Most likely, he repairs it time and time again, until, like Trigger's broom (cv: *Only Fools and Horses*), it no longer resembles the original item – in *The Doctor's Wife*, the Eleventh Doctor recalls owning a patchwork umbrella. He is seen carrying umbrellas (all of which might be the same model in one incarnation or another) in *The Stones of Blood, The Two Doctors, The Mysterious Planet* and *Hide*. Companion Clara discovers a black umbrella in *Journey to the Centre of the TARDIS*. The Second Doctor loses another in the audio *The Uncertainty Principle*.

The Seeds of Death

Prior to *The Space Pirates*

The Doctor acquires a bag of marbles (of which the green one is his favourite) and some tweezers. After being trapped in a cell with an audio lock on the planet Vulcan, the Second Doctor starts carrying a tuning fork, should the situation ever arise again. He meets criminals in humanity's future who have taken to using miniature computers to overcome electronic locks. For once, he attempts to steer the TARDIS.

The Space Pirates. In episode one, the Second Doctor says they are not where he expected. Where that might be, however, he does not say. Metebelis 3, perhaps? Florana? The fifth moon of Cindie Colesta? Much to his Scottish companion's annoyance, he uses the tuning fork to attempt to free himself from a cell in episode five. At the story's climax, he disables a detonator unit with tweezers. The marbles play a part in his *Home Alone*-style escape plan in episode five. The Seventh Doctor still has all his marbles in episode three of *Silver Nemesis*, while the Twelfth gives them away in *The Magician's Apprentice*.

Prior to *The War Games*

Once they've all stopped laughing, the Second Doctor and his companions Jamie and Zoe take another trip in Milo Clancy's ship *LIZ 79*, in order to recover the TARDIS.

This is the Doctor's stated intention at the end of *The Space Pirates*.

The Second Doctor and Jamie encounter the Cybermen on Planet Fourteen.

The Invasion. The Cybermen claim to recognise the Second Doctor and Jamie from Planet Fourteen, which clearly has

> nothing to do with *The Moonbase*. Just because it's in the past for the Cybermen, it might be yet to come for this incarnation of the Doctor. Zoe might also have been involved - she is not mentioned because she's not present when Jamie and the Doctor are photographed at the International Electromatics building. The Sixth Doctor strip *The World Shapers* states that Planet Fourteen - also mentioned in the Seventh Doctor novel *The Hollow Men* and the Eighth Doctor audio *Sword of Orion* - is actually Marinus, but onscreen in *The Doctor Falls*, it's made clear that they are separate worlds on which humanity eventually became a cyber-nation.

The Second Doctor, Jamie and Zoe assist UNIT in preventing another alien invasion, possibly involving the Cybermen once again. It is at this time that he first works alongside a UNIT soldier named Zbrigniev.

> In *Battlefield*, Zbrigniev says that when he served under Brigadier Lethbridge-Stewart, the Doctor changed his physical appearance several times. He must, therefore, have met the Time Lord during his second incarnation. In *Spearhead from Space*, the Brigadier says that Earth has fought off alien invasions twice since UNIT was formed, both times with the Doctor's help. UNIT doesn't come into being until after *The Web of Fear*, so this seems to refer to a missing adventure. When the Brigadier is reunited with the Second Doctor in *The Three Doctors*, he mentions only the Yeti and the Cybermen, so it could be that this missing invasion story refers to a second attempt by the Cybermen (The Second Doctor audio *The Isos Network* confirms that at least one ship in the Cyber-fleet escaped destruction). Either that, or the Yeti were reactivated and finally made it to Tooting Bec. Whatever the truth, this is probably the moment at which the colour photo of Jamie on display in UNIT's Black Archive was taken.
>
> NOTE: All of the references in the Third Doctor stories prior to *The Three Doctors* must have taken place before the end of the Second Doctor's era as the Third Doctor had no ability to travel in the TARDIS independently until the knowledge is returned to him at the conclusion of *The Three Doctors*.

He visits the planet Delphon, where the natives communicate with their eyebrows, and learns a few basic phrases. In Earth's past (or possibly its future), he uses a lateral molecular rectifier, which he then stores in the TARDIS, the lock to which he has fitted with a metabolism detector.

> *Spearhead from Space.* The Third Doctor's recollection of using the lateral molecular rectifier is hazy, his memory having been partially wiped by the Time Lords. The Delphon species are mentioned in the novels *Lucifer Rising, The Bodysnatchers* and *The Taking of Planet 5*, as well as the audios *The Havoc of Empires* and … *Ish.* Insofar as a species who communicate non-verbally *can* appear in an audio story, they appear in *The Havoc of Empires*, where the Third Doctor recalls learning their language at a trattoria on Alpha Centauri 5, even though he spent a year on Delphon while a student, according to the audio *The Blame Game.*

The Doctor goes potholing. Two hundred thousand years before our time, he observes the Earth from space.

> *Doctor Who and the Silurians.* The recently regenerated Third Doctor says he hasn't been potholing in a very long time. He also recognises a globe depicting the Earth prior to the Great Continental Drift.

Coming in for a closer look, he sees living dinosaurs on prehistoric Earth, and nearly falls afoul of a *Tyrannosaurus Rex.* He does not get around to finding out the reason for their extinction until his fifth incarnation, however.

> By the time of his seventh incarnation, he has, according to *The Happiness Patrol*, met quite a few *T Rexes.* The Third Doctor informs companion Sarah Jane about the fierceness of the creature in episode two of *Invasion of the Dinosaurs.* The Second Doctor says he hopes to encounter prehistoric monsters at the start of *The Underwater Menace*, making this incident post-*Macra Terror* at the very earliest.

He becomes adept at something he calls 'transmigration of object,' which is apparently not the same as sleight-of-hand. He hears a signal broadcast by an unknown species.

> *The Ambassadors of Death.* The Third Doctor states, in episode one, that he has heard the aliens' signal before, but this point is never pursued as the story progresses. General Carrington later claims it's an emergency code used by Earth astronauts, but he's probably lying about this, as he is about everything else.

In 1883, he witnesses the eruption of Krakatoa (the Ninth Doctor was also present at this time). In Paris, he spends some time with the great-grandfather of Queen Elizabeth II.

> *Inferno*. The Third Doctor tells the Brigadier about Krakatoa (see also *Rose*).

He sees a Volatiser - a weapon with a force equal to a 15-megaton bomb - in use. He visits a circus, and learns the science of Steady-State Micro Welding from the Lamadines, a species with nine opposable digits.

> *Terror of the Autons*. The Third Doctor says he hasn't been to a circus in years, suggesting it was prior to his regeneration. In episode one, the Master sets a trap using a Volatiser. In *The Caves of Androzani*, the Fifth Doctor describes them as 'nasty little objects.'

During an adventure in China (perhaps during the Futu Dynasty, but then again, perhaps not), he encounters the Tong of the Black Scorpion for the first time. He witnesses their distinctive method of assassination (concentrated scorpion venom) and attends the funeral of one of their victims. He stays long enough to learn the various dialects ('Doctor Who and the Dialects'?). He converses with Mao Tse-Tung, either on this occasion or during a visit to a later period in China's history. He sees a psychic amplifier in operation, and learns to play three-dimensional chess - quite well, if he says so himself. He encounters a species of mind parasites which he believes can only be destroyed by a nuclear explosion, or a large jolt of electricity. Locked in the Tower of London, he has no choice but to listen to Sir Walter Raleigh talk about potatoes without being able to chip in.

> The Third Doctor speaks fluent Chinese in *The Mind of Evil*, and his fourth incarnation boasts of his linguism in *The Talons of Weng-Chiang*. In that same story, he says he hasn't been to China for 400 years, but it isn't clear whether this refers to his own age or Earth's history. The reference book *The Discontinuity Guide* suggests that this is a reference to *Marco Polo*, but his knowledge of the Tong and their methods (plus the way he corrects Litefoot regarding Chinese funerals) points to a missing adventure. The Fifth Doctor knows the Futu Dynasty in *Four to Doomsday*. The Doctor recalls meeting Mao Se Tung in the novels *Shadowmind* and *Revolution Man*. In episode three of *The Mind of Evil*, the Third Doctor identifies the psychic amplifier that the Master uses to murder the delegates at the peace conference. He seems to recognise the mind parasites, although he never identifies them by name. He certainly knows how to destroy them, but even though the creature inside the Keller machine is not vaporised by a nuclear blast, he's quite certain it's dead at the end of the story. The

Tower of London incident involving Raleigh (who appears in the Sixth Doctor audio *Voyage to the New World* and is mentioned in the Seventh Doctor novel *Theatre of War*) is not the same one described in *The Sensorites* or *The Impossible Astronaut.* The Third Doctor mentions three-dimensional chess after companion Jo beats him at draughts in *The Mind of Evil,* and his fourth self complains about the limitations of the one-dimensional game in episode one of *The Sun Makers.* In *Nightmare in Silver,* the Eleventh Doctor states that chess is a Time Lord invention, but doesn't reveal in how many dimensions it is played on Gallifrey. The Sixth Doctor claims to have invented the three-dimensional game in the strip *War-Game,* so no wonder he's so good at it that his seventh incarnation constantly triumphs over his companion Bernice Summerfield in the novel *Deceit.*

The TARDIS takes the Doctor to the sector of space in which the planet Uxarieus can be found, and to the part of the galaxy eventually known as the Crab Nebula, at a time when it is occupied by a giant sun. He is taught to perform feats of sleight-of-hand by the famous 19th Century conjurer John Nevil Maskelyne - but not, sadly, any good card tricks.

Colony in Space. The Third Doctor recognises Uxarieus by sight, but has to check the atmosphere once the TARDIS has materialised (meaning he's either never landed there before or did so when the atmosphere was quite different). He's informed by the Master that the sun's destruction was caused by the Uxarien super-race. He is seen performing magic tricks in *Colony in Space, The Three Doctors, The Monster of Peladon, The Talons of Weng-Chiang, Terror of the Vervoids* and *The Greatest Show in the Galaxy.* In *The Three Doctors,* he has a magic wand, and in *The Hand of Fear,* a magician's stick. The gift of sleight-of-hand eludes him by his fifth incarnation, and he has to be taught again by Adric in *Kinda.* The Eleventh Doctor shows himself to be very poor at card tricks in *A Christmas Carol,* while the Ninth Doctor has difficulty shuffling a deck in *Rose.* The Twelfth attempts a trick in *The Doctor's Meditation,* the prequel to *The Magician's Apprentice,* but it's none too effective.

During visits to the Neanderthal era, the Renaissance and the Industrial Revolution (where he learns of but does not meet George Stephenson, Michael Faraday, Humphrey Davey and Thomas Telford), he witnesses more examples of the Daemons' involvement in Earth's history. He comes to realise that on each visit, the aliens appear only three times.

The Daemons. The Third Doctor is familiar with the species and their role in human development. The Fifth Doctor audio *Time in Office* refers to an unseen encounter with the Daemons in Japan. The industrial pioneers are all mentioned by the Sixth Doctor in *The Mark of the Rani.* The Ninth Doctor, Rose and Jack encounter Neanderthals in the novel *Only Human.* The Seventh Doctor and Faraday cross paths in the audio *The Four Doctors.*

The Doctor meets Adolf Hitler and Genghis Khan (although not, presumably, in the same time period) and considers them both bounders. In fact, it is probably at the time of his meeting with the German leader that he sees the Naval cipher room in Berlin. The Mongol warlord's hordes attempt (but fail) to break through the TARDIS' doors.

The Daemons. In *The Curse of Fenric,* the Seventh Doctor calls Hitler 'dreadful' and identifies the replica of the cipher room. He meets the dictator again in, unsurprisingly, *Let's Kill Hitler.* The Sixth Doctor encounters him in the novels *The Shadow in the Glass* and *Timewyrm: Exodus.* The Second Doctor recalls Hitler's mysticism in the book *World Game,* and the Nazi leader is namechecked in the audios *Medicinal Purposes* and *The Rapture.* The Master falsely accuses his adversary of having actually been Genghis Khan in *Doctor Who - The TV Movie.* The Ninth Doctor mentions the hordes attacking the TARDIS in *Rose,* an incident also referred to in the Sixth Doctor audio *City of Spires.* This encounter must have occurred after *Marco Polo,* in which the First Doctor asserts that he has never met the mighty Khan, or faced his wrath. In the novel *Tragedy Day,* the Seventh Doctor claims to have delivered baby Genghis, mentioned as an adult in the books *Time and Relative, Blood Harvest* and *Borrowed Time.*

He observes the technology of 22nd Century Earth.

In episode two of *Day of the Daleks,* the Third Doctor pinpoints the date the guerillas' gun was manufactured. The Twelfth Doctor also identifies technology from that period in *Under the Lake.*

On mid-21st Century Earth, he encounters a man named Blinovitch, who has formed some interesting (and correct) theories on time paradoxes. Blinovitch is in the company of Courtney Woods who, despite her apparently British antecedents, has been elected President of the United States.

The Blinovitch Limitation Effect is first mentioned in *Day of the Daleks.* The man himself may also be a time-traveller, as the novelization of the audio story *The Ghosts of N-Space* has Third Doctor recalling their encounter in 1928 (where his forename is given as Aaron). The Seventh Doctor novel *Timewyrm: Revelation* identifies Blinovitch as the author of the seminal work *Temporal Mechanics,* while another Seventh Doctor book, *Original Sin,* states that the theorist's work was funded by Tobias Vaughn, villain of *The Invasion.* A much younger Courtney Woods appears as one of Clara Oswald's pupils in several early Twelfth Doctor stories. He reveals her political role in *Kill the Moon,* but isn't clear on the nature of her relationship with Blinovitch.

The Doctor attends the coronation of Victoria, or possibly Elizabeth I.

The Third Doctor reminisces about the coronation in *The Curse of Peladon,* as does the Seventh in the novels *Cat's Cradle: Witch Mark* and *Birthright.* The Tenth Doctor finally meets Victoria in *Tooth and Claw,* marries Elizabeth in *The Day of the Doctor* and flees from her in *The Shakespeare Code.* The Thirteenth Doctor is on her way to the coronation in *The Witchfinders.*

He is present during the historic battles at Gallipoli (where he hears about the historic football match played in No Man's Land on Christmas Day, 1914) and El Alamein, sustaining an injury at one or all of the conflicts. He becomes a good friend of Admiral Horatio Nelson.

During *The Sea Devils,* the Third Doctor claims his leg is playing him up, the result of an injury from one famous battle or another. Though he's not being honest about his wound, he obviously acquired information about both these conflicts. The Fifth Doctor again recalls El Alamein in the novel *The King of Terror,* as does the Eighth in *Autumn Mist.* The First and Tenth Doctors mention witnessing World War One in *Planet of Giants* and *Planet of the Dead,* respectively. His second incarnation is familiar with trench warfare in *The War Games,* and his sixth with mustard gas in *The Mark of the Rani.* In *The Five Doctors,* the Master also mentions having seen the first great conflict, but he may not encounter the First Doctor and his granddaughter - Susan doesn't have any idea who he is. Then again, he hasn't exactly regenerated, which might account for it. The Third and Ninth Doctors witnesses the armistice football game in the comic strips *The Amateur* and *The Forgotten.*

He sees Earth in the 30th Century, when the planet is mostly grey. He witnesses the sacking of the solar system by Earth's Empire, and hears of one of the last colonies on Solos.

> *The Mutants*. The Third Doctor has never been to Solos before, but knows of that world. His sixth incarnation returns to a seemingly more prosperous point in the 30th Century during *Terror of the Vervoids*.

The Second Doctor, Jamie and Zoe venture outside space-time again, encountering the terrifying Kronovores. During the Second World War, the Time Lord avoids being hit by a doodlebug. He learns that the Venusian word 'thrashkin' has been replaced with the word 'plinge.'

> *The Time Monster*. The Third Doctor recognises the sound of a doodlebug in episode three. The First Doctor audio *The Alchemists* states that he and Susan were in London at the time of the Blitz. The meeting with the Kronovores occurs after *The Mind Robber*, since in that story, his second persona makes it plain he has never ventured outside time-space before. Therefore, the incident described by the Third Doctor must take place after *The Invasion*.

He reads or sees a version of *Aladdin*, reads *The Invisible Man* by Herbert George Wells, and purchases a seemingly bottomless bag of jelly babies. The Time Lords take the Second Doctor out of his own timestream in order to assist his next incarnation with Omega.

> *The Three Doctors*. The Second Doctor recognises both Benton and the Brigadier, setting his removal from time after *The Invasion*. He likens the presence of antimatter in our universe to 'being punched on the nose by the invisible man' and Omega's ability to control antimatter to a magic lamp. The Thirteenth Doctor waxes enthusiastic about the harnessing of antimatter in *The Tsuranga Conundrum*. The Sixth Doctor meets author Wells during *Timelash* and the Seventh reads his novel *The Time Machine* at the start of *Doctor Who – The TV Movie*. It would seem, from *Horror of Fang Rock*, that the Doctor meets the writer at a later point in his life (his fourth and tenth selves do so in the comic strip *The Time Machination*, and the Third Doctor recalls encountering him in the radio adventure *The Ghosts of N-Space*, as does the Seventh in the novel *The Eight Doctors*). Wells' *The War of the Worlds* is mentioned in the Tenth Doctor short story *Revenge of the Judoon*. In episode two of *The Three Doctors*, the Second Doctor offers the Brigadier a jelly baby, and carries a bag of them in the audio *Little Doctors*, while the Third Doctor has some in his pocket in the audio *Ghost in the Machine*. This sugary

foodstuff becomes part of the Fourth Doctor's staple diet - he describes them as a delicacy in *The Invasion of Time*. The Seventh and Eighth Doctors are seen to eat them in *Doctor Who - the TV Movie* and the Twelfth in *Mummy on the Orient Express* and *The Doctor Falls*. The Eleventh is more of a jammy dodgers man, while the Thirteenth is a big fan of custard creams.

On Metebelis 3, the famous blue planet in the Acteon Group, he finds that the air smells like wine. Getting back there, however, proves somewhat complicated. In 1926, he hears the story of the *SS Bernice*, lost in the Indian Ocean two days out from Bombay on June 4th. He learns how to box from John L Sullivan. Some 1,000 years after the late 20th Century, he witnesses antimagnetic cohesion, and places a magnetic core extractor in the TARDIS, should he ever need it.

Carnival of Monsters. The Doctor has been to Metebelis 3 at least once before. The audio *The Beginning* implies that the visit occurred during his first incarnation, shortly after his flight from Gallifrey. On board the *SS Bernice,* the Third Doctor engages in fisticuffs with a sailor who bears a striking resemblance to UNIT's chief physician. It would seem that the Doctor's involvement with the miniscope eliminates the timeline in which the vessel is lost. His boxing lessons with John L Sullivan are also mentioned in the Third Doctor novels *Catastrophea* and *Deadly Reunion*, and the Sixth Doctor audio *The Lure of the Nomad.*

He encounters Ogrons working as mercenaries, sees the effects of a neuronic stungun and is grabbed by the Medusoids while on his way to the Third Intergalactic Peace Conference. He spends 'quite some time' on the planet Draconia, helping the inhabitants through a period of great difficulty when they are almost overwhelmed by a space plague. In return for his assistance, he is made a Noble of Draconia by the 15th Emperor. He qualifies as a Space Engineer.

Frontier in Space. The Third Doctor supposes that he's been hit by a neuronic stungun early in the story. He tells Jo about the Ogrons, and explains that they are not employed exclusively by the Daleks. The Fifth Doctor mentions the space monkey mafia again in episode three of *Castrovalva*, but they have not appeared onscreen since the Third Doctor's time. Pity. His Draconian title is High Earl of the Imperial House, according to the novel *Catastrophea*. The audio *The Havoc of Empires* implies that the encounter with the Medusoids may also have involved famed English cricketer W G Grace.

Despite being at a considerable disadvantage in terms of limbs, the Doctor becomes an honorary member of the Alpha Centaurian Table Tennis Club.

Robot. The Third Doctor is familiar with the species in *The Curse of Peladon.* His membership card turns up again in the Tenth Doctor novel *Forever Autumn.* The Second Doctor teaches his companion Jamie the human equivalent of the game in the audio *Helicon Prime.*

He meets Cleopatra, whom he affectionately refers to as 'Cleo.'

The Girl in the Fireplace. The Tenth Doctor novel *Ghosts of India* confirms that he did indeed carry on with Cleo. In *The Husbands of River Song,* it's implied that she and the Doctor may even have been married.

He considers Cleo a pushover.

The Wedding of River Song. Winston Churchill states that Cleopatra is a dreadful woman, but an excellent dancer. River Song meets her also, having impersonated her in *The Pandorica Opens.* In the audio drama *Loups-Garoux,* the Fifth Doctor has a very low opinion of the Egyptian Queen. She appears in the Sixth Doctor novel *State of Change* and the Tenth Doctor short story *The Lonely Computer.*

A captain in Cleopatra's bodyguard teaches him how to handle a sword.

The Masque of Mandragora. This incident is also recalled in the Fourth Doctor novel *The Shadow of Weng-Chiang.* In the novel *Scratchman,* the same incarnation of the Time Lord states that he also picked up a few fencing tips from the Musketeers, The Doctor displays his sword-fighting skills in several other stories, including *The Sea Devils* (meaning that his education occurred prior to his third incarnation), *The Monster of Peladon, The Androids of Tara, The King's Demon, The Christmas Invasion, The Next Doctor, Robot of Sherwood* (after a fashion), the Sixth Doctor comic strip *Once Upon a Time-Lord* and the Eighth Doctor audios *Seasons of Fear* and *Grand Theft Cosmos.* Evidently, more than one incarnation of his right hand is a fightin' hand.

The Second Doctor spends some time in the TARDIS' Secondary Control Room.

The Masque of Mandragora. Companion Sarah Jane finds the

Second Doctor's recorder. It later turns up in the pocket of the Eleventh Doctor in the novel *Shroud of Sorrow.*

Exploring the TARDIS, the Second Doctor and companion Jamie venture close to the main TARDIS drive.

The Fifth Doctor channels his second persona in episode one of *Castrovalva.*

The Second Doctor tracks a portion of the living metal Validium, created as Gallifrey's ultimate defence during the Dark Times, to England in the year 1638. The evil Lady Peinforte, who favours golden arrows dipped in poison as her weapon of choice, has the metal fashioned into a statue of herself, which she names Nemesis. During a Roundhead attack, the Doctor removes the statue's bow and arrow, in order to prevent her from gaining control of the Validium. The bow he sees placed in a vault at Windsor Castle. On November 23rd of that year, he launches the Nemesis into space on an orbit that will bring it back to Earth every quarter - Century. This information he records in a computerised pocket watch, noting that the planet will face destruction on the day the statue finally lands.

Silver Nemesis. Lady Peinforte calls the Doctor a 'predictable little man,' seemingly describing his second incarnation. The Seventh Doctor evades Ace's questions about how the Validium arrived on Earth in the first place, and it is unclear as well how the Cybermen know about the statue of Lady Peinforte. Validium appears to be a different 'living metal' from that seen in *Journey to the Centre of the TARDIS.* It plays a part in the Eighth Doctor novels *Interference* Books One and Two. The Doctor has a selection of pocket watches, though the one into which he programs the details of the statue's return to Earth is seen again in *Survival.* Others feature in *Revelation of the Daleks, Doctor Who – The Movie, Human Nature,* the novels *Foreign Devils, World Game, Timewyrm: Exodus* and *The Dying Days,* as well as in the Eighth Doctor comic strip *TV Action!* The Third Doctor novel *Catastrophea* states that the watch adjusts to the local time of whatever planet he happens to be on. The Sixth Doctor carries a pocket watch on a green chain, which he hardly ever uses and is presumably unreliable – in episode two of *The Twin Dilemma,* he prefers to consult Peri's watch during a life-or-death situation. Peri steps on and destroys the watch in *Revelation of the Daleks,* but the Doctor continues to wear it nonetheless.

He sees singer Kylie Minogue perform her 1989 hit *It's Never Too Late.*

The Tenth Doctor namechecks Kylie in *The Idiot's Lantern,* but his third incarnation also mentions the old adage 'it's never too late' in episode four of *Spearhead From Space.* A significant gap between the stories might explain why he fails to notice the startling resemblance between the diminutive Antipodean songstress and a waitress on the Starship *Titanic.*

The War Doctor, along with the Tenth and Eleventh Doctors, meet up with the Second Doctor, and request that he come with them to assist in freezing their home planet in a single moment in time.

The Day of the Doctor

OK, kids, this is where it gets complicated ...

The Second Doctor's appearances in *The Five Doctors* and *The Two Doctors* do not correspond with his time at the helm of the TARDIS as seen on television between 1966 and 1969. The Second Doctor who visits Brigadier Lethbridge-Stewart in *The Five Doctors* is travelling alone, although he was never without companions during the TV series. He also appears to hail from a period after *The War Games,* since, when confronted with the images of Jamie and Zoe, he remembers the details of his trial on Gallifrey, despite the fact that he was forced to regenerate and was banished to Earth at the conclusion of that story. It is notable that his recollection of the trial is faulty, and he believes that his former companions have had all knowledge of their time with him wiped (whereas they actually retained the memory of their first meeting with him).

The Two Doctors begins with the Second Doctor travelling with Jamie, and there is talk of the absent Victoria, which seems at first to place it sometime between *The Tomb of the Cybermen* and *Fury from the Deep.* But mention of the Time Lords (about whom Jamie knew nothing until the final episode of *The War Games*) quickly dispels that notion; they are on a mission for the Gallifreyans, one for which the Doctor has somehow been briefed, although his companion has not.

Clearly, this is all at odds with the Second Doctor's established history. *The Discontinuity Guide* suggests that the Doctor's trial was a sham, and that he was thereafter reunited with former companions Jamie and Victoria, and worked for a while as a Time Lord agent – he says, in *The Two Doctors,* that it is 'the price I pay for my freedom.' If this is, indeed, the case, then all incidents supposed to have occurred prior to *The War Games* should be included in this section. This notion is expanded upon in the novels *Players* and *World Game.* The audio *Helicon Prime* also seems to confirm this theory, while another audio, *The Black Hole,* states that *The Two Doctors* occurs some time before *Fury From the Deep,* and that Jamie and Victoria's memories of the Time Lords were subsequently wiped.

Another possibility is that this is not the Second Doctor as we know him, but rather one from a point in space-time that has been affected by the ripples of the Time War, thereby creating an alternate Doctor whose path occasionally crosses that of his other selves. This *Second* Second Doctor is located by the Time Lords at a far earlier point in his history, while still travelling with Victoria. He is placed on trial and allowed his freedom on the proviso that he will undertake certain missions for the Celestial Intervention Agency, one of which is to investigate the time-control experiments of Professors Kartz and Reimer, which have produced dangerously high ripples on the Bocca scale.

The fact that injuries sustained by one Doctor could cause suffering to a future incarnation on this occasion and no other should indicate that all is not well with time.

The Doctor either fails to pick Victoria up after she has completed her graphology lessons, or else she eventually parts company with him, as she did in the proper timestream, after which he and Jamie meet up with Zoe. Some act of disobedience results in this Doctor being tried again, at which point his companions are returned to their proper time periods with *all* their memories of him deleted. The Doctor either flees or cuts another deal, retaining his TARDIS and a degree of freedom. It is possible that this alternative Second Doctor eventually regenerates into the alternative Ninth Doctor seen in *Scream of the Shalka* (when he is still operating under Time Lord control).

It is perhaps during this period that he acquires some fireworks, which prove handy as well as colourful. In Earth's future (which is to say, post-20th Century), he faces off against the Terrible Zodin, 'a woman of rare guile, and devilish cunning,' and her hairy, kangaroo-like minions, also seemingly known as the Zodin.

> The Second Doctor describes Zodin to the Brigadier in *The Five Doctors.* The Sixth Doctor reminisces about her in *Attack of the Cybermen.* She is mentioned in numerous novels, including *The Colony of Lies, Verdigris, Cold Fusion, Millennial Rites, Legacy* and *Lungbarrow,* as well as in the audios *Requiem for the Rocket Men, Zaltys* and *Power Play,* and the Eighth Doctor comic strip *The Glorious Dead.* In *The Sarah Jane Adventures* episode *The Mad Woman in the Attic,* the Fourth Doctor's companion claims to have encountered the Zodin. The Second Doctor scares a Yeti with a 'galactic glitter' in *The Five Doctors.* The Fourth Doctor uses a 'little demon' during *The Brain of Morbius,* and gives Ohica a 'mighty atom' and a 'thunderflash.' The Second Doctor

uses fireworks against the Daleks in the comic strip *Bringer of Darkness*, and the Fifth spooks a Cyberhorse (yes, a Cyberhorse) with a Chinese firecracker in the audio *Spare Parts*.

On Earth, the Doctor is reading *The Times* when he spots a report of a speech given by his old friend Brigadier Lethbridge-Stewart as a guest of honour at the UNIT reunion, and decides to pop back in time a day to attend, thus bending the laws of time somewhat. He ends up being transported to Gallifrey's Death Zone by Borusa. His presence might be the reason for the disturbance that prevents the Fourth Doctor from participating.

The Five Doctors

He is drugged by a poison in the anomode group, meets the chefs Brillat-Savarin and Escoffier, and enjoys capercaillies in brandy sauce with a stuffing of black pudding, pâté de foie gras de Strasbourg en croûte, and Belon oysters at the Tour d'Argent. At some point, he repairs the TARDIS' scanner.

The Two Doctors. The Second Doctor is able to identify the drug used on him by the Sontarans (siralanimode). He recalls his experience of *haute cuisine* when transformed into an Androgum. According to *The Keys of Marinus*, a fault means that the scanner only shows monochrome pictures, but it depicts images in their full-colour glory in episode one of *The Two Doctors*. It occasionally goes on the blink during the Third Doctor's era – *Planet of the Daleks*, for instance, has companion Jo looking at a black-and-white image of the planet Spiridon.

He experiences an adventure in California, where he makes the odd decision to wear his fur coat.

The Name of the Doctor

The Third Doctor
Jon Pertwee
1970-1974

Prior to *Spearhead from Space*

As punishment for his intergalactic misbehaviour, the Time Lords remove the Doctor's reflex link, with which he is able, should he so choose, to tune into the Time Lord intelligentsia.

The Invisible Enemy. The Fourth Doctor tells companion Leela that he lost that particular faculty when he was kicked out, a reference to his exile on Earth.

The Doctor regenerates.

He is not seen to change his appearance onscreen.

Prior to *Doctor Who and the Silurians*

The Third Doctor returns the clothes and vintage roadster he 'borrowed' to Ashbridge Cottage Hospital.

Spearhead from Space. In the final scene, the Brigadier tells the Third Doctor that the items must be restored to their rightful owner. The Tenth Doctor claims, in *New Earth*, that hospitals give him the creeps, and given that no good ever comes of his stays, it is easy to see why. Very few patients wind up being shot by UNIT soldiers when attempting to discharge themselves.

The Doctor is introduced to Captain Mike Yates, who is in charge of UNIT's cleanup operation following the first Auton invasion.

Terror of the Autons. Yates is introduced to viewers in this story, though the Third Doctor already knows him. His full name, according to the novel *The Devil Goblins from Neptune*, is Michael Alexander Raymond Yates.

He persuades the Brigadier to purchase Bessie, 'a car of great character,' on which he begins modifications. He reads Arthur Conan Doyle's Sherlock Holmes stories and Lewis Carroll's Alice books.

Doctor Who and the Silurians. The Third Doctor draws an unflattering comparison between the Brigadier and Holmes. There are other references to Holmes (Sherlock, not Robert) in

The Claws of Axos, The Daemons and *The Talons of Weng-Chiang.* The Eleventh Doctor poses as the famous detective during *The Snowmen.* In the fifth episode of *The Keys of Marinus,* the First Doctor dismisses the crime of which companion Ian has been accused as 'elementary.' This may not necessarily be a sign that he's read any of the stories at this point, however. Separated from the First Doctor, companions Ben and Polly discuss Holmes in episode two of *The Smugglers.* The Seventh Doctor meets the great detective in two novels: *All-Consuming Fire* and *Happy Endings.* Other Holmes references occur in the books *Foreign Devils, Death and Diplomacy, The Eight Doctors, The Mystery of the Haunted Cottage, The Way Through the Woods* and *The Shining Man,* the Eighth Doctor comic strips *Perceptions* and *The Curious Tale of Spring-Heeled Jack,* and the audios *The Doll of Death, Iterations of I, Max Warp, The Skull of Sobek, The Beast of Orlok* and *The Time Machine.* According to the comic strip *Change of Mind,* the Doctor named his vehicle Bessie after his companion at the time, Elizabeth Shaw. *Jabberwocky* is sung by the Third Doctor in *Doctor Who and the Silurians* and by the Tenth Doctor in the novel *The Nightmare of Black Island.* Other incarnations quote from Lewis Carroll's books in *Robot, The Horror of Fang Rock, The Five Doctors* and *The Rings of Akhaten.* In episode two of *The Sun Makers,* the Fourth Doctor attempts to repeat the section regarding the three sisters and the treacle mine that he originally recounts in *The Android Invasion.* He describes himself as 'mad as a hatter' in the final episode of *The Sun Makers.* In *The Deadly Assassin,* he calls his interrogators Tweedledum and Tweedledee, and likens the Tharil Biroc to a Cheshire Cat in *Warriors' Gate.* During *Ghost Light,* the Seventh Doctor talks about going 'down the rabbit hole.' The Eighth Doctor novel *The Shadows of Avalon* has the Time Lord reminiscing about meeting Carroll. Further mentions of *Alice* appear in the audios *The Black Hole, The Foe From the Future, Night of the Stormcrow, Hornets' Nest: The Dead Shoes, Night of the Vashta Nerada, The Land of the Dead, Fallen Angels, Excelis Rising, Circular Time: Winter, A Thousand Tiny Wings, Zagreus, Foreshadowing* and *The Time Machine,* as well as the novels *Cat's Cradle: Time's Crucible, Eternity Weeps, The Eight Doctors, Revenge of the Judoon* and *Wooden Heart,* and the Sixth Doctor comic strip *Salad Daze.*

As a requirement of his unpaid position with UNIT, he is forced to sign the Official Secrets Act.

Mawdryn Undead. The amnesiac Brigadier cautions the Fifth

Doctor about mentioning UNIT in public for this reason. The novel *Millennium Shock* confirms that the Doctor did indeed sign the document, and the Sixth Doctor states in the audio *Criss-Cross* that he has done so on several occasions, a claim confirmed in the Eighth Doctor novel *Option Lock*. The Fourth Doctor confirms that he works without pay in episode one of *The Android Invasion*, but it seems from *Death in Heaven* that he received an income without realising it.

He is given the UNIT security visa 710-Apple-00.

Under the Lake.

Prior to *The Ambassadors of Death*

Somehow, the Third Doctor removes the console from the TARDIS in order to work on the Time Vector Generator. He installs a force field in Bessie.

The Ambassadors of Death. The force field seems to operate along similar lines to the First Doctor's magnetic chair, seen in *The Daleks' Master Plan*. The function of the Time Vector Generator is clarified in the Seventh Doctor novel *Birthright*.

Prior to *Inferno*

The Doctor sees *Rigoletto*, and hears the song 'Shine On, Harvest Moon', to which he adds new lyrics. He reads *Batman* comic books, or sees one of the many screen adaptations.

Inferno. He sings 'La Donna è Mobile' during the first episode, and 'Shine On, Martian Moon' in the last. He jokes about the TARDIS being entirely unlike a space-rocket piloted by Batman, and later has a toy Batmobile in *The Talons of Weng-Chiang*. The Eleventh Doctor voices a desire to be like the Caped Crusader in the comic strip *The Golden Ones*, who also gets a mention in the Seventh Doctor audio *Night Thoughts* and the Twelfth Doctor novel *The Shining Man*. The Ninth Doctor strip *Official Secrets* reveals that, during his third incarnation, he would frequent the Forever People comic book store.

Providing assistance to the British Royal Family, he receives the security designation '771.'

In *Inferno*, the Third Doctor describes the Royal Family as 'charming.' His fourth incarnation skips dinner at Buckingham Palace during the final scene of *Robot*. The Tenth Doctor uses the security code to alert Her Majesty in *Voyage of the Damned*. It is revealed at the end of *Planet of the Dead* that he has parked his TARDIS in the gardens of Buckingham Palace prior to tracking a wormhole.

He enjoys tea and scones with Queen Elizabeth II.

The Beast Below. The tea and scones have become the stuff of legend by the 29th Century. The Seventh Doctor is unable to place Her Majesty when he almost bumps into her during *Silver Nemesis*. She appears in the Fifth Doctor audio *1963: Fanfare for the Common Men* and the novel *Head Games*.

Prior to *Terror of the Autons*

The Third Doctor joins the same club as Lord 'Tubby' Rowlands. He learns Morse code, safe-cracking skills and the lyrics to the 1941 song *I Don't Want to Set the World on Fire*.

Terror of the Autons. In episode three, the Third Doctor uses his friendship with Lord Rowlands to intimidate civil servant Mr Brownrose. He signals the Brigadier using Morse code, and breaks into the safe at the plastics factory. The knack eludes him in his next regeneration, however; in episode four of *The Sun Makers*, the Fourth Doctor admits he doesn't know what he's doing while trying to unlock the Collector's safe. 'It always looks so easy,' he tells companion Leela.

He learns defences against black magic, despite not believing in it. (Better safe than sorry.)

The Daemons. In episode three, the Third Doctor scares away Bok the gargoyle using an iron trowel. The basis for this superstition is explained in the Eighth Doctor audio *Seasons of Fear*.

He appreciates the larders and cellars of several politicians.

Day of the Daleks

He experiments with turning a radio into a transmitter. In practice, however, he very quickly gets his wires crossed.

The Sea Devils. The Third Doctor explains at length to companion Jo Grant how it can be done.

Upon her departure from UNIT, the Third Doctor pockets Liz Shaw's pass card.

Battlefield. The Seventh Doctor gives the pass card to companion Ace. In *The Ambassadors of Death* and *The Sea Devils*, the Third

Doctor claims he never carries his own pass, dismissing such things as 'bureaucratic nonsense.' He displays a similar attitude when asked for his passport in episode one of *The Faceless Ones,* and for his TARDIS registration in *Colony in Space.* Companion Jo Grant carries the Doctor's pass for him in *The Mind of Evil.* The Fifth Doctor keeps it under his hat in the novel *Deep Blue.*

He pesters the Brigadier for a replacement pass for Liz, and spends three months engaged in an experiment involving Steady-State Micro Welding, probably with a view to repairing the TARDIS.

Terror of the Autons. New companion Jo ruins the Third Doctor's experiment in episode one in a fashion apparently better suited to a porcine-appendaged vendor of buns.

Prior to *The Mind of Evil*

The Third Doctor hears about the Keller Process for rehabilitating violent criminals, which causes him some concern. Before visiting Stangmoor Prison, he conducts some research into its history. He also watches the TV show *Candid Camera.*

In episode one of *The Mind of Evil,* the Doctor mis-quotes the TV prank show's famous catchphrase. He tells companion Jo that Stangmoor was once a fortress. The Keller Process is mentioned in the Eleventh Doctor novel *Apollo 23.*

The Claws of Axos

Prior to *Colony in Space*

The Third Doctor returns the TARDIS to his lab at UNIT HQ.

At the end of *The Claws of Axos,* the TARDIS materialises near the remains of Nuton Power Station.

Once there, he starts work on a new dematerialisation circuit, and learns that UNIT have detained Spain's ambassador, under the mistaken belief that he is the Master. He becomes an expert in agriculture.

Colony in Space. There is no reason the Doctor couldn't have obtained his agricultural expertise during his exile on Earth.

Prior to *The Daemons*

The Third Doctor familiarises himself with UNIT's Mark Four-A condenser unit, and develops a remote control for Bessie.

The Daemons. The Third Doctor expects to find the condenser unit in the mobile HQ.

Day of the Daleks

Prior to *The Curse of Peladon*

Following the destruction of the time-travelling Daleks, the Third Doctor and companion Jo return to the UNIT laboratory and meet earlier versions of themselves.

Day of the Daleks. In episode one, the Third Doctor and Jo see themselves in the near future.

He acquires a jeweller's glass.

The Curse of Peladon. The Third Doctor is seen using it again in *The Green Death*, and the Fourth in *Robot* and *The Ribos Operation.* The Twelfth Doctor discovers one which may very well have belonged to him in the first place while trapped within the confession dial in *Heaven Sent*, and is seen using it again in *The Pilot.*

Convinced that he has the TARDIS working again, the Third Doctor talks Jo into joining him on a test-flight.

Moments before the opening scenes of *The Curse of Peladon.*

Prior to *The Sea Devils*

The Third Doctor repairs the fault in the TARDIS' interstitial beam synthesizer (one hopes).

The Curse of Peladon. The Third Doctor identifies the problem in episode one. In the final episode, companion Jo asks him to take her to Victoria's coronation, but since he doesn't gain full control of the TARDIS until *Carnival of Monsters*, it's unlikely they arrive.

The Doctor becomes a trained diver. He requests permission to visit the Master in prison, and has a black-and-white photograph taken for his security pass. He learns about the history of the warden, Colonel Trenchard.

The Sea Devils. The Third Doctor tells the Master that Trenchard was the governor of an island that claimed independence shortly after his arrival.

Prior to *The Mutants*

The Third Doctor begins work on a minimum inertia superdrive for his roadster Bessie. He reads Gibbon's *Decline and Fall of the Roman Empire.*

The Mutants. The superdrive has been installed by *The Time Monster.*

Prior to *The Time Monster*

The Time Lords return the Third Doctor and his companion Jo to 20th Century Earth.

Following the events of *The Mutants.*

The Third Doctor does a spot of redecoration on the TARDIS, working for several nights on a Venusian device he hopes to convert into a time sensor in order to locate the Master's TARDIS. He receives a briefing into the work at the Newton Institute at Wootton, and sees the violent sport of bullfighting.

The Time Monster. The briefing must not have been very thorough, since it fails to mention Professor Thascales, whom the Third Doctor identifies as the Master the moment he hears the name in episode two. The Newton Institute is undoubtedly named after the Doctor's old friend Sir Isaac (see *The Pirate Planet, Shada*). In battling the Minotaur, he behaves like a bullfighter (and does the same again when his fourth incarnation encounters the Nimon). He defeats one of the Ogri in the same manner in episode three of *The Stones of Blood.*

Prior to *The Three Doctors*

The Doctor reads Daniel Defoe's novel *Robinson Crusoe.* He redesigns the TARDIS' Control Room interior once again.

The Three Doctors. The Third Doctor mentions Man Friday to companion Jo Grant when they are transported to the antimatter universe. In *The Sarah Jane Adventures* story *Death of the Doctor,* Jo asserts that the TARDIS interior always smells the same, regardless of its appearance. According to the Eighth Doctor audio *Orbis,* that smell is a mixture of phosphors and engine oil.

Prior to *Carnival of Monsters*

The Third Doctor builds a new force-field generator for the TARDIS.

The Three Doctors. The original force-field generator is destroyed along with Omega's antimatter universe; the Third Doctor tells companion Jo he cannot leave Earth in the TARDIS until he builds a new one.

He acquires a string file, which he keeps in his boot, should he find himself locked up and without his sonic screwdriver. He sees the famous sleight-of-hand con trick known as the 'shell game,' not dissimilar to the pastime popular among Wallarians involving three magnum pods and a yarrow seed.

Carnival of Monsters. The Third Doctor uses the string file a second time to escape from the Master's cell during *Frontier in Space.*

Prior to *Frontier in Space*

The Doctor creates a second sonic screwdriver.

Frontier in Space. A sonic screwdriver is confiscated from the Third Doctor when he is sent to the lunar prison colony. It is not the same one he wields in *Carnival of Monsters,* however; when the clairvoyant Clegg examines the device for psychic residue in episode one of *Planet of the Spiders,* he sees images of the Doctor's battle with the Drashigs.

He has occasion to use up the TARDIS' emergency oxygen supply. Tangling with the Daleks once again, he discovers that their guidance system operates by means of high-frequency radio impulses, and that opening the top section of their travel machines will often trip an automatic distress signal.

Planet of the Daleks. The Third Doctor resorts to the emergency supply of oxygen in episode one, but it runs out almost immediately. It's fortunate that companion Ian didn't trip the distress signal when entering a Dalek vehicle during the Doctor's original encounter with his mortal enemies. Could the First Doctor's decision to hide inside a Dalek in *The Space Museum* have enabled them to locate him, and thus set off the chain of events related in *The Chase*? The answer: Sure, why not?

He discovers that visiting alternate realities has become easier, so long as the Time Lords are monitoring events.

The Rise of the Cybermen. The Tenth Doctor tells companion Mickey that hopping between universes used to be easy, a fact hinted at by his fourth incarnation in *The Invasion of Time.* His knowledge of alternate realities is somewhat contradictory (see the 'Victims of the Time War' section of 'Musings' on page 266), but his unfamiliarity with them in *Inferno* certainly points to his being unaware at that point of this Time Lord legislation.

Planet of the Daleks

Prior to *The Green Death*

Following their adventure on Spiridon, the Third Doctor and his companion Jo return to Earth. The Doctor takes up hot-air ballooning.

Jo asks the Third Doctor to take her back to her home planet in the final scene. He mentions a new-found enthusiasm for ballooning in episode four of *Planet of the Daleks*.

The Doctor is impressed by Professor Jones' paper on DNA synthesis.

The Green Death. When he meets Jones in episode two, the Third Doctor praises the professor's work and says he has wanted to meet him for a very long time. There's no way of knowing, however, how much of a gap exists between *Planet of the Daleks* and this adventure.

While travelling to the planet Karfel with Jo Grant and one other companion, the Third Doctor becomes embroiled in an adventure which involves the hideous underground-dwelling Morlox, Mustakozene-80 gas and an irresponsible scientist named Megelan whom he reports to the Sanctum for his unethical experiments. Hailed as a hero, the Doctor promises to return to Karfel, but then forgets to do so for several regenerations.

Timelash. When the Sixth Doctor returns to Karfel, he explains he's 'travelling light' in terms of companions. The novel *Speed of Flight* suggests that the TARDIS' third passenger might have been Mike Yates. The Doctor recognises the unique odour of the Morlox and correctly deduces that Mustakozene-80 is responsible for transforming Megelan into the Karfelon-Morlox mutant known as the Borad. In *The Sarah Jane Adventures* story *Death of the Doctor*, Jo recalls the singing plants in Karfel's leisure gardens.

The Third Doctor realises that his failure to reach Metebelis 3 is the result of a failing Space-Time Co-ordinate Programmer.

The Green Death, immediately before the story commences.

Prior to *The Time Warrior*

Following his last journey there, the Third Doctor wires the spatial co-ordinates of Metebelis 3 into the TARDIS programmer.

> *Planet of the Spiders.* The TARDIS takes the Third Doctor further into the future than he had been during his last visit to Metebelis 3, as seen in *The Green Death.*

The Doctor obtains his Galactic Passport and his pilot's licence for the Mars-Venus rocket run. On the former world - the only one on which trisilicate is found - he witnesses the destruction of a Dalek army, caused by a virus (created by the Ice Warriors, perhaps?) that attacks the insulation on cables in their electrical systems.

> The Third Doctor mentions trisilicate in *The Curse of Peladon* (according to the Fifth Doctor audio *The Bride of Peladon,* it's a form of salt). His fourth self presents his pilot's licence in *Robot,* while the Eleventh still has it in the novel *Apollo 23.* The Mars-Venus run is also mentioned in the novels *Shakedown, Kursaal* and *The Janus Conjunction.* He describes the Dalek defeat on Mars in *Genesis of the Daleks.* If it is referred to in Martian lore as the Phobos Heresy, then this might well be the incident which led to Grand Marshal Skaldak being fêted as the Ice Warriors' greatest hero. Let's face it, it's hard to imagine a greater victory than one achieved over the Daleks. The Eleventh Doctor plans to spend a week on Mars at the start of *The Day of the Doctor.*

The Doctor reads Lavinia Smith's paper on the teleological response of the virus and considers it 'most impressive.'

> *The Time Warrior.* The paper is roughly twenty years old when the Third Doctor discusses it with Lavinia Smith's niece Sarah Jane, but there is nothing to suggest that he read it at the time of its original publication.

At an unspecified point after the late 20th Century, the Doctor meets Earth scientist Chung Sen, who completes successful experiments into time travel. Encountering the tribe known as the Vandals during the 5th Century AD, he finds them to be surprisingly decent chaps. He hears about Sir Charles Grover's Save Planet Earth Society and reads his book, *Last Chance for Man.*

> *Invasion of the Dinosaurs.* The Sixth Doctor also recalls meeting the Vandals in the audio *The Curious Incident of the Doctor in the Night-Time.*

The Third Doctor begins work on a hovercraft-style vehicle, which travels at great speeds. The vehicle can even fly, though for some reason it changes colour when doing so.

> The Whomobile (as it is never called onscreen) first appears in

episode four of *Invasion of the Dinosaurs,* though not in that serial's novelization. It flies during the lengthy chase in episode two of *Planet of the Spiders.* The Whomobile returns in the comic book *Prisoners of Time,* and is recalled with fondness by the Eighth Doctor in the audio *Army of Death.*

The Doctor learns the lyrics to the song *Oh I Do Like to Be Beside the Seaside.*

Death to the Daleks. The Third Doctor is singing this tune in the opening moments of episode one.

He experiences the effervescent waters, perfumed flowers and impossibly soft sands of Florana, one of the most beautiful planets in the universe, and comes back feeling 100 years younger. He stores an oil lamp, an extremely large torch, and a multi-coloured parasol in the TARDIS. Unable to locate the ring he used during his first incarnation to open the TARDIS following the power drain on Vortis, he installs a manual crank-handle. Following a trip to Jordan, he returns with a 5 piastre coin. He spots unusually ornate carvings on the walls of a temple in Peru, and hears a dispute between archaeologists as to the origins of such a structure. He also visits several of the 700 wonders of the universe. While tussling with the Daleks yet again, he learns of their Scorched Planet Policy, by which worlds are routinely incinerated once they have been rendered useless to the Empire.

Death to the Daleks. The Third Doctor opens the TARDIS door by hand after another power drain on Exxilon, uses the coin to demonstrate the dangerous state of the Exxilon city's flooring in the final episode, and supposes that the city must be one of the universe's 700 wonders, more of which are listed in the novels *Mission: Impractical* and *Birthright.* The Doctor first mentions Florana in the final moments of *Invasion of the Dinosaurs.* He and companion Sarah Jane finally get there in the short story *The Hungry Bomb,* as does the Fifth Doctor in the audio *The Elite* and the Seventh in the audio *Klein's Story.* The planet is mentioned in the novels *The Scales of Injustice, Legacy* and *The Dimension Riders,* as well as in the audios *The Blame Game, Pop-Up* and *The Sands of Life.*

The Doctor finds himself in a trisilicate mine.

The Monster of Peladon. In episode one, the Third Doctor spots what he calls 'a typical trisilicate vein.'

As a result of the assistance he gave the Thals during either *The Daleks* or *Planet of the Daleks,* he is given the freedom of the city of Skaro.

Robot. The city of Skaro is presumably to be found on the planet

Skaro. In Terrance Dicks' original script, it is spelled 'Scaro,' but this is presumably an error, as the correct spelling appears in the novelization, also penned by Dicks.

He hears the traditional Scottish lament *Flowers of the Forest.*

Terror of the Zygons. The Fourth Doctor recognises the piece, but companion Sarah does not.

He meets William Shakespeare, first as a rather taciturn boy, whom he advises not to speak if he hasn't anything to say, and later as a famous playwright. The Doctor is forced to write out the first draft of *Hamlet,* Shakespeare having sprained his wrist from writing sonnets. They argue over mixed metaphors, but the Bard eventually has his way.

The Fourth Doctor first mentions meeting Shakespeare in *Planet of Evil.* He quotes (and misquotes) his plays and sonnets in many stories, including *Revenge of the Cybermen, The Robots of Death, The Armageddon Factor, The Horns of Nimon, State of Decay, Warriors' Gate, Castrovalva, Kinda, The Twin Dilemma, The Mark of the Rani, The Two Doctors, The Ultimate Foe* and *Sleep No More,* as well as the Fourth Doctor short story *Ghost Ship*, the comic strips *The Star Beast, Changes, Fire and Brimstone* and *Tooth and Claw,* and the audios *The Plague of Dreams, The Paradise of Death, The Foe from the Future, The Renaissance Man, Babblesphere, The Relics of Time, Whispers of Terror, The Hollows of Time, The Sandman, We Are the Daleks, The Harvest, Dead London* and *The Red Lady*. The *Hamlet* incident is recalled in *City of Death,* and in the novels *Asylum* and *The Tomorrow Windows.* The Eighth Doctor encounters the writer as a child in an alternate timeline during the audio *The Kingmaker.* This, along with all prior encounters with Earth's greatest writer, has been erased from history (see the 'Victims of the Time War' section of 'Musings' on page 266); *The Shakespeare Code* appears to depict the first meeting between the playwright and the Doctor (specifically, the Tenth Doctor). The First Doctor watches Shakespeare on the Time-Space Visualizer in episode one of *The Chase,* but if they've already met by this point, he doesn't say so.

In 1666, the Doctor finds himself accused of starting the Great Fire of London, not realising that the accusation is entirely justified. He meets the charming Marie Antoinette, who presents him with her picklock. He sees the results of the havoc caused across half the galaxy by Sutekh (also known as Set, Satan and Sados) and believes the being destroyed by 740 of his fellow Osirans, led by Horus. While in Egypt, he learns that Sutekh was referred to as the

Typhonian Beast. He sees a cytronic particle accelerator and an Osiran war missile powered by an anti-gravity drive. He falls afoul of a parallax coil and has a close call with some sweaty gelignite.

> *Pyramids of Mars.* The Fourth Doctor tells companion Sarah about being blamed for the 1666 conflagration at the end of episode four. His fifth incarnation actually causes it while battling the Terileptils at the climax of *The Visitation.* In *The Woman Who Lived,* the Twelfth Doctor is happy to lay the entire responsibility at the scaly feet of his enemies, and the fire is recalled by the Fifth Doctor in the audios *The Gathering* and *The Demons of Red Lodge,* and by the Sixth in the audios *Point of Entry, The Marian Conspiracy* and *Doctor Who and the Pirates.* He apparently mislays the picklock (which his first incarnation uses in the comic strip *Operation Proteus* and the Sixth in the audio *Vampire of the Mind*), since he is never seen onscreen with it again - which is too bad, since the sonic screwdriver doesn't work on wood. In episode two of *Pyramids,* he does not recognise Sutekh's parallax coil trap until it's too late. He identifies a resonating tuner as being part of an anti-gravity drive, and deduces that the mummified robots are powered by cytronic induction. The Doctor advises Sarah that one good sneeze could set off the gelignite they discover in the poacher's hut. He mentions Marie Antoinette again in episode four of *The Robots of Death.* The French Queen appears in the Eighth Doctor novel *Earthworld.* Further information regarding Sutekh's imprisonment is presented in the Fifth Doctor comic strip *The Curse of the Scarab.* The Seventh Doctor novel *GodEngine* establishes that the Osirans were similarly worshipped by the Ice Warriors.

At the Battle of Malplaquet, in 1709, the Doctor meets the Duke of Marlborough. On the planet Oseidon, he encounters the android-building species known as the Kraals. He sees their handiwork, including the matter-disintegration bomb, and constructs a robot detector in order to identify the Kraals' handiwork, but later forgets all about it.

> *The Android Invasion.* The Fourth Doctor says he recognises the android containers in episode one, but that point is never pursued. He knows the Kraal home planet, and suddenly produces a robot detector in episode four, seemingly having forgotten about it for the three previous instalments, so it would seem to have occurred at least one incarnation prior. Kraals are mentioned in the Ninth Doctor novel *The Clockwise Man,* and terrorize the Fourth Doctor again in the audio *The Oseidon Adventure.*

He reads *Microsurgical Techniques Into Tissue Transplants*, by Dr Mehendri Solon, and observes the stir caused by the scientist's disappearance. He meets a member of the Birastropthe species, and observes or participates in an escape from a spaceship by using its ejection bubble.

> *The Brain of Morbius*. The Fourth Doctor recognises the ejection bubble used by the Mutt in episode one. He identifies the lungs of the Birastropthe as possessing a methane filter.

Having read Professor Thripstead's *Flora and Fauna of the Universe*, he becomes president of the Intergalactic Floral Society - quite probably based on the planet Zaakros - and sees several planets where the vegetable Krynoids have become established and devoured all animal life.

> The Doctor's position within the Society is established in *The Seeds of Doom*, and mentioned in the audio *White Ghosts*. According to K-9 in *The Leisure Hive*, Zaakros is home to the galaxy's largest floral collection, which may well be where the Twelfth Doctor is almost forcibly married to vegetation shortly before *Face the Raven*. The Sixth Doctor displays a good deal of botanical knowledge in *The Mark of the Rani*, and the Tenth recognises the taste of mistletoe in *Tooth and Claw*. In *The Seeds of Doom*, the Fourth Doctor recognises the Krynoid pods from a photograph, and is aware that they always travel in pairs, 'like policemen.' He has never seen their home planet, though, and theorises about conditions there. The Krynoids are mentioned in the audios *Brotherhood of the Daleks*, *The Day of the Troll* and *The Lost Magic*. The Fourth Doctor mentions Thripstead's book in episode four of *The Sun Makers* (it describes the Usurians' true appearance). The volume is also referenced in the Seventh Doctor book *Lungbarrow*. Thripstead's other works are listed in the novels *Unnatural History*, *Placebo Effect*, *Christmas on a Rational Planet*, *Alien Bodies* and *Interface*. By the time of *Heaven Sent*, the Twelfth Doctor has come to loathe gardening, describing it as 'dictatorship for inadequates.'

The Third Doctor visits the ship's Secondary Control Room. He sees a bigger boot cupboard than the one in his TARDIS, which is very big indeed. He has an unpleasant time in the Mediterranean during the late 15th Century. While piloting the TARDIS, he narrowly avoids the spiral of pure energy known as the Mandragora Helix.

> *The Masque of Mandragora*. Companion Sarah Jane discovers the Third Doctor's shirt and jacket in the Secondary Control Room. The Fourth Doctor is familiar with Helix energy. He sets the date and location from an examination of 'glass technology.'

Both the Seventh Doctor comic strip *The Mark of Mandragora* and the Tenth Doctor novel *Beautiful Chaos* concern the return to Earth of the Mandragora Helix, also mentioned in the Eleventh Doctor novel *Borrowed Time.*

The Doctor somehow manages to survive an encounter with a Raston Warrior Robot, 'the most perfect killing machine ever devised.'

The Five Doctors. The Raston Warrior Robots also show up in the novels *World Game* and *The Eight Doctors,* and are referenced in the Second Doctor audio *Little Doctors.*

Invasion of the Dinosaurs

Death to the Daleks

Prior to *The Monster of Peladon*

Leaving Exxilon, the Third Doctor promises to take companion Sarah to Peladon (though he neglects to tell her about the details of his previous visit). The TARDIS scanner gives him some trouble.

The Monster of Peladon. The Third Doctor doesn't realise he hasn't materialised in the citadel, due to a fault on the scanner.

Prior to *Planet of the Spiders*

The Doctor befriends the famous height-challenged escapologist Harry Houdini (who, over the course of a wet weekend, teaches him the art of muscle compression, as well as how to tie a tangle Turk's head eye-splice with a gromit). He also meets Mrs Samuel Pepys, the famous Alp-crossing military leader Hannibal, and Copernicus.

Houdini is first mentioned in *Planet of the Spiders.* In *Planet of the Ood,* Donna asks the Tenth Doctor if he's ever met the man, but he doesn't respond. The Eleventh Doctor recalls the escapologist being quite short in *The Vampires of Venice.* The knot-tying lesson is related by the Fourth Doctor in *Revenge of the Cybermen.* In the final part of *The Greatest Show in the Galaxy,* the Seventh Doctor escapes from a straightjacket for the amusement of the Gods of Ragnarok, and the Twelfth from Viking shackles in *The Girl Who Died* and a set of restraints attached to a chair in *Extremis.* That the lessons took place over the course of a weekend is established in *The Witchfinders.* In the short story *Moon Graffiti,* the Sixth Doctor discovers that he is no longer able to perform his mentor's feats. Houdini appears in the Fifth Doctor audio *Smoke and Mirrors,* the Eleventh Doctor short story *Houdini and the Space Cuckoos* and the Twelfth Doctor strip *Theatre of the Mind.* The novel *The Sorcerer's Apprentice* states that the two first met prior to *100,000 BC,* and the audio *The Destination Wars* confirms this assertion. He's mentioned in the Third Doctor short story *Prisoners of the Sun,* the novels *Eye of Heaven, Independence Day* and *The Pit,* the audios *Wrath of the Iceni, The Church and the Crown, Circular Time: Summer, The Emerald Tiger, My Brother's Keeper, The Mind's Eye, Project: Twilight, The Wrong Doctors, The Two Masters, The High Price of Parking, Masterplan* and *Nevermore,* as well as in the Sixth Doctor strip *Voyager.* The Third Doctor claims, in *Planet of the Spiders,* that Mrs Pepys made the finest cup of coffee in the world, though Sergeant Benton runs her a close second. Pepys himself appears in the Eleventh Doctor comic strip *The Broken Man,* and the Sixth Doctor recalls rescuing his diaries from a creature called the Chronosaurus in the audio *The Lure of the Nomad.* The newly-regenerated Fourth Doctor mistakes the Brigadier for Hannibal in *Robot* (though he doesn't make the same mistake about Bret Vyon). In *World War Three,* the Ninth Doctor also recalls seeing Hannibal cross the Alps, as does the First in the audio *Men of War,* and the Seventh in the novel *Shadowmind.*

The Doctor takes helicopter flying lessons, and makes a few cosmetic modifications to his trusty sonic screwdriver.

In episode five of *Fury from the Deep,* the Second Doctor nearly kills himself and his companions attempting to pilot a helicopter, but his third incarnation does so with ease in episode two of *Planet of the Spiders.* He travels by helicopter in episode one of *Enemy of the World,* but doesn't take the controls. The Third Doctor finds himself at the controls of a jet 'copter in the audio *The Sentinels of the New Dawn,* and the Sixth Doctor handles a chopper with confidence in the audio *Blue Forgotten Planet,* as does the Eleventh in the comic strip *The Golden Ones.* The Seventh Doctor is a less able pilot in the audio *Frozen Time,* and is completely incapable in the novel *Cat's Cradle: Warhead,* but he's improved in *Eternity Weeps.* Though the sonic screwdriver used in the Third Doctor's final story is different in appearance to the one he wielded in *Carnival of Monsters,* it must be the same device, or else 'Professor' Clegg wouldn't have been able to receive a psychic impression of that earlier adventure.

So impressed is the Doctor with the sonic lance used by miners on the planet Peladon that he creates a component that can be added to his screwdriver, enabling it to perform the same function. Several costumes - Pierrot, the King of Hearts, and a Viking's battle-dress - find their way into the TARDIS' wardrobe. The Doctor learns a schoolgirls' skipping-rope song. He is on the *Titanic* when it sinks, and ends up clinging to an iceberg, though it is unlikely that he has anything to do with the actual sinking of the ship. To placate the Brigadier, the Doctor provides him with a space-time telegraph, only to be used in cases of utmost emergency when the TARDIS is away.

> *Robot.* The Fourth Doctor recites the rhyme, tries on the various costumes and mentions the *Titanic* in episode one (he recalls the doomed vessel again in episode three of *The Robots of Death*). In *The Invasion of Time,* he tells Borusa he is not responsible for the *Titanic*'s sinking, and in *The End of the World,* the Ninth Doctor reveals that he wound up on the iceberg. In *Rose,* it is stated that the Ninth Doctor persuaded the Daniels family not to board the doomed vessel. The Seventh Doctor is onboard the *RMS Titanic* in the novel *The Left-Handed Hummingbird,* as well as in the comic strip *Follow That TARDIS!* The Fourth Doctor recalls multiple trips to the *Titanic* in the strip *The Forgotten.* According to the audio *Masterplan,* the Master was also travelling on the liner, and the Eleventh Doctor has a napkin from the ship in the novel *Plague of the Cybermen.* By the time of *Attack of the Cybermen,* the Sixth Doctor is using a different handheld sonic lance to perform 'repairs' around the TARDIS, and still has it in the audio *Paradise 5.* The space-time telegraph is first mentioned in *Revenge of the Cybermen.* The novel *Dancing the Code* states that the idea of the device was originally suggested by the Third Doctor's companion Jo Grant.

The Doctor learns of the Romany belief that the last thing seen by a dying person is imprinted on his or her eye. He develops a passion for the game of cricket, and enjoys visiting Lord's in the 19th Century in order to watch his favourite cricketers, Wisden, Pilch and Alfred Mynn, 'the Lion of Kent.' At some point, he plays for New South Wales, taking five wickets. He spends some time on an early 30th Century space station, and is presented with a lengthy multi-coloured scarf by witty little knitter Madame Nostradamus.

> The First Doctor does not appear to recognise the game of cricket when the TARDIS materialises at Lord's during *The Daleks' Master Plan,* though he carries a cricket ball in the comic strip *A Religious Experience.* In *The Ark in Space,* his fourth incarnation has a cricket ball in his pocket (as does the Second in the novel *Invasion of the Cat-People,* and the Tenth in *The Price*

of Paradise). He also displays his bowling prowess in episode one of *The Hand of Fear*, and tells K-9, in *The Horns of Nimon*, that he might've been a great slow bowler. The Fifth Doctor is a particularly keen cricketer (a fast-paced bowler, according to *Black Orchid*), and it is he who recalls his days with the New South Wales team in *Four to Doomsday*. By the time of *Castrovalva*, he has devoted an entire room of the TARDIS to storing cricketing gear and memorabilia, including a bat requiring a drop of linseed oil. Author Ian Potter has suggested that UNIT may have had its own cricketing eleven, of which their scientific advisor was surely a member. His favourite cricketers are name-checked in episode one of *Time-Flight*. Though one would imagine that being hit with a cricket bat by Amy Pond in *The Eleventh Hour* might have put him off the game for life, he hurls a cricket ball with some skill in the audio *Darkstar Academy* (in which the New South Wales tour is recalled once again). The Seventh Doctor recollects visiting Lord's in the novel *The Hollow Men*. In the audio *The Church and the Crown*, the Fifth Doctor claims to be a life-long member of Marylebone Cricket Club, though the novel *Happy Endings* has the Seventh Doctor claiming that he has lost whatever knowledge of the game his earlier incarnation possessed. In *The Ark in Space*, the Fourth Doctor is able to fix the date of Nerva's construction from the macro-slave drive and modified Bennett Oscillator. The Twelfth Doctor identifies an earlier model in *Kill the Moon*. The Doctor explains gypsy beliefs to Harry. Here, he seems to think it has some merit, but the Eleventh Doctor dismisses it as 'nonsense' during *The Crimson Horror*. The origins of the Doctor's scarf are revealed in the first episode of *The Ark in Space*. It's possible that the Time Lord himself made his own burgundy replacement; he asks for knitting in *The Night of the Doctor*, but seems to have forgotten the skill a few incarnations later. The divine Mrs Nostradamus is name-checked in the audios *Zygon Hunt*, *Hornets' Nest: The Dead Shoes* and *The Doomsday Quatrain*, and also in the Seventh Doctor novel *Christmas on a Rational Planet*.

The Doctor visits a galaxy where Terullian drives are common.

The Sontaran Experiment. The material Terullian is also mentioned in the novels *The Dark Path* and *Lords of the Storm*.

On a return trip to the planet Venus in the Space year 17,000, the Doctor foils a Dalek invasion with the assistance of the people of Hyperon. He acquires or builds an etheric beam locator in order to detect ion-charged emissions. He also pockets a yo-yo, a pair of handcuffs and a large yellow crystal.

> *Genesis of the Daleks*. The Venus incident is one of the Dalek defeats the Fourth Doctor describes to Davros. The various items listed are removed from his pockets during *Robot*, *Genesis of the Daleks* and *Revenge of the Cybermen*. He still has some conkers, first seen in *The Highlanders*. The Fourth Doctor has a fondness for yo-yos (he has a selection, though the yellow one seems to be his favourite), and plays with them in several stories until *The Talons of Weng-Chiang*, as well as in the comic strip *Black Destiny* and the novel *Scratchman*. Had it been made for television as originally planned, the Second Doctor would have had a yo-yo in the story *Prison in Space*.

The Third Doctor takes companion Sarah to roughly the same time period in which they will later visit Nerva Beacon. She learns of the apparent destruction of the Cybermen. The TARDIS brings the Doctor to our solar system at a time when the planet Jupiter has been studied thoroughly, but before the arrival of its 13th moon, Neo-Phobos - in actuality, the fabled planet of Gold, Voga. Centuries later, he also witnesses either the climax of the Cyberwar, in which humans plunder Voga's resources in order to create the Glitter Gun, or its results, which include the trend for using gold-plated Cybermen as hatstands. He is present (and probably takes part in) the Armageddon Convention, during which the use of the powerful but compact weapon known as a Cyberbomb is outlawed (as if the Cybermen would ever adhere to such legislation).

> *Revenge of the Cybermen*. Sarah states that she has never seen a Cyberman, but knows that they were 'wiped out ages ago.' The gap of centuries between the Cyberwar and this story is established in episode two (a deleted line from episode three specifies 427 years). Given both species' use of the Prydonian Seal (which, according to the Seventh Doctor novel *The Pit*, is supposed to ward off evil), it is probable that there are undisclosed links between the Vogans and the Gallifreyans. The Armageddon Convention is depicted in the First Doctor novel *The Empire of Glass*. The Seventh Doctor novel *Original Sin* states that the Glitter Gun was created by scientists in the employ of Tobias Vaughn (*The Invasion*).

The Doctor acquires a football rattle, meets Galileo Galilei and borrows his telescope.

> *The Masque of Mandragora*. He uses the rattle to frighten horses

in episode one, and during *The Sarah Jane Adventures* story *The Wedding of Sarah Jane Smith,* to get some attention. The Second Doctor sings a well-known football chant in the novel *World Game.* What was the Doctor's favourite team? Prydonian Rangers, perhaps? Omega Arsenal? The Fourth Doctor mentions Galileo again in Episode One of *The Sun Makers.* The astronomer appears in the First Doctor novel *The Empire of Glass* and the Eighth Doctor audio *The Galileo Trap,* and is also mentioned in the Fourth Doctor audio *The Valley of Death.*

He visits retired Time Lord Professor Chronotis (AKA Salyavin) at St Cedd's College, Cambridge.

Shada. The Doctor meets Chronotis out of sequence here, as his fourth incarnation calls at St Cedd's three years earlier. At least one of his trips to St Cedd's takes him to the physics lab - he already knows the way when Chronotis tries to direct him. The Third Doctor has a Cambridge-based adventure in the comic strip *Change of Mind,* and the Eleventh mentions St Cedd's in the audio *The Time Machine.*

Having kept a handwritten Time Log for some time, he stops when he considers himself too busy. One item relates to an incident that happened, was subsequently erased from time, and then occurred in an earlier period (the UNIT years, perhaps?). Another concerns the Union of Traken, which he probably visits, although by the time he reaches his fourth incarnation, he can no longer be certain.

The Keeper of Traken. The fact that the Fourth Doctor isn't completely sure that he ever visited Traken suggests that the logs were written during a previous incarnation. He later complains about the drop in standards of hospitality on Traken, so perhaps he's begun to remember. In the comic strip *Profits of Doom,* the Sixth Doctor has several Traken Praying Flowers stored in the TARDIS. Maybe he acquired them on this trip.

While out driving in Bessie, the Third Doctor fails to heed the warning of a mysterious young woman and is snatched up by President Borusa's Time Scoop, car and all.

The Five Doctors. The young woman - Clara - is seen attempting to get the Third Doctor's attention in *The Name of the Doctor.*

Upon returning to Earth, his memory of his adventure in the Death Zone erased, the Doctor is surprised to discover the Seal of the High Council of Time Lords in his pocket.

The Eleventh Doctor still has the Seal in *The Time of the Doctor.*

The Third Doctor is approached by several future incarnations, who convince him to travel forward in his own timeline in order to save the lives of the children of Gallifrey.

The Day of the Doctor

The Third Doctor begins conducting research into extrasensory perception (ESP) in humans. He is particularly interested in reports of the mind-reading stage act of 'Professor' Clegg, and decides to visit him. To assist him in his research, he builds an Image Reproduction Integrating System (IRIS), which translates thoughts into images.

Planet of the Spiders. Benton has never seen the IRIS machine before, so it must be a recent construction.

The Fourth Doctor
Tom Baker
1974-1981

Robot

Prior to *The Ark in Space*

The Fourth Doctor's proposed trip to Earth's moon is scuppered by Harry Sullivan's insistence on twisting the Helmic Regulator in the TARDIS.

> *The Ark in Space*. The Fourth Doctor is scolding Harry as the TARDIS materialises. His companion's clumsiness may have been more serious than it first appears, as the Helmic Regulator becomes badly damaged during *Time Crash* and is later the cause of considerable concern for the Eleventh Doctor. The unreliable component creates further problems in the Fourth Doctor novel *System Shock* and in the Fifth Doctor audio *Creatures of Beauty*. It's mentioned in a less disparaging fashion in the Tenth Doctor novel *The Pirate Loop* and the audios *The Pursuit of History*, *The Toy* and *The Star Men*.

The Sontaran Experiment

Genesis of the Daleks

Prior to *Revenge of the Cybermen*

The Fourth Doctor, Sarah and Harry make at least one other stop on their way back to Nerva.

> The Fourth Doctor's overcoat disappears somewhere between *Genesis of the Daleks* and *Revenge of the Cybermen*, despite there being no apparent gap between stories. Just such an incident is described in the novel *A Device of Death*.

In 1941, the Doctor witnesses the sinking of the German battleship *Bismarck*. Having expressed his admiration for the tam-o'-shanter in *The Highlanders*, he finally gets his hands on one. Like fezzes, they are not cool. He picks up a compass.

> *Terror of the Zygons*. The Fourth Doctor is wearing the tam-o'-shanter and using the compass when he first appears. He still

has the compass in the audio *Demon Quest: The Relics of Time,* while the First Doctor uses it in the novel *The Sorcerer's Apprentice.*

He hears the story of the sacrifice of Lawrence 'Titus' Oates during Captain Scott's ill-fated Terra Nova Expedition of 1912. In the town of Harrogate (date unknown), he purchases a tin of toffees.

Planet of Evil. The Fourth Doctor carries a tin labelled Farrah's Original Harrogate Toffee. In episode four, he repeats Oates' famous declaration, 'I'm going out now, and I may be some time.' His fifth self gives the quote in the first episode of *Earthshock,* as does the Sixth in the unrecorded story *The Hollows of Time.* In the final part of *Nightmare of Eden,* he says, 'I'm going *inside* now, and I may be rather a long time.'

Terror of the Zygons

Prior to *Planet of Evil*

The Doctor studies Vandervelt's equation of knowledge.

Planet of Evil. This story follows on from *Terror of the Zygons,* but there may have been time for the Fourth Doctor to read the equation – which he declares 'quite wrong' – between stops.

Prior to *Pyramids of Mars*

The Fourth Doctor and his companion, Sarah Jane Smith, learn that UNIT headquarters has been built on the site of a priory which was destroyed by fire. He tells her about his adventures in the city of the Exxilons. He creates a portable device (a TARDIS Tuner?) capable of picking up signals broadcast from the stars. He has a fine time in 1911, and decides that the year is one of his favourites.

Pyramids of Mars. In episode four, Sarah says that Horus' pyramid on Mars reminds her of the Exxilon city, despite not having seen it. She must know about it from the Third or Fourth Doctor.

Prior to *The Android Invasion*

The Fourth Doctor replaces the TARDIS' Time Control.

Pyramids of Mars. At the story's climax, the Fourth Doctor removes that section of the console and uses it to extend the threshold of Sutekh's time-space tunnel.

The Doctor is present when Alexander Graham Bell makes his first telephone call. The time traveller attempts to warn the scientist that wires are unreliable, but to no avail.

> The Fourth Doctor relates his conversation with Bell in episode two of *The Android Invasion*. The Ninth Doctor recognises Bell's voice when he hears it on Stuart's mobile phone in *Father's Day*.

He buys a bottle of ginger pop, which he fortunately doesn't have to share with Sarah. He develops a liking for muffins with his tea, and plays a terrific game of darts. By this point, his vessel is well overdue for its 500-year service.

> *The Android Invasion.* There is a dartboard in the TARDIS control room in the Eleventh Doctor story *The Rebel Flesh*. The Twelfth Doctor recalls that the Brothers Grimm were on his darts team in *Heaven Sent*, and in the novelization of *The Day of the Doctor*, it is noted that Ohila of the Sisterhood of Karn is also handy with a set of arrows. In the *Class* episode *For Tonight We Might Die*, he declares the game 'something worth practising for,' owing to its combination of mathematics and alcohol. In *Rise of the Cybermen*, the Tenth Doctor likens the Alternative Earth to the gingerbread house from Hansel and Gretel. He references the classic tale again during *In the Forest of the Night*.

Prior to *The Brain of Morbius*

The Doctor pockets some bolt-cutters and a torch. He hears the song *Show Me the Way to Go Home*, enjoys a dish of stewed apricots (without custard), and sees the volcanic eruptions at Cotopaxi and Popocatepetl. He hears about Vesuvius, but doesn't realise that he'll witness it for himself in a future incarnation. He sets a course for the TARDIS in order to attend 'an engagement,' but is doomed to disappointment.

> *The Brain of Morbius.* The Fourth Doctor complains that his ship has been dragged 1,000 parsecs off-course. He tells Ohica that he and companion Sarah Jane have an engagement in the final episode, where he also likens the flavour of the Sisterhood's elixir to that of stewed apricots ('no custard'). He quotes the song when regaining consciousness in the same episode. In episode two, Sarah uses the Doctor's own bolt-cutters to free him. She carries a torch for him in the first episode; the Sixth Doctor also has a torch in *The Mysterious Planet*. The Doctor has witnessed many volcanic events onscreen, but he mentions Cotopaxi, Popocatepetl and Vesuvius (which he has yet to see) in *The Brain of Morbius*, and Krakatoa in *Inferno*. The Seventh

Doctor is in Pompeii on that fateful day (somehow managing to avoid his tenth incarnation who is also present) in the audio *The Fires of Vulcan* and the novel *The Algebra of Ice*.

Prior to *The Seeds of Doom*

Meeting Wolfgang Amadeus Mozart, the Doctor finds that the composer has perfect pitch. He learns the nursery rhyme *The House That Jack Built* and reads the work of humorist Franklin Pierce Adams. Returning to companion Sarah Jane's time, the Fourth Doctor resumes his position as UNIT's scientific advisor, and becomes acquainted with Major Beresford. At the insistence of Sir Colin Thackery, he is contacted by Mr Dunbar of the World Ecology Bureau regarding a situation that has arisen in Antarctica.

The Seeds of Doom. Major Beresford already knows the Fourth Doctor, who quotes the rhyme in episode two. The Sixth Doctor encounters an alternative Mozart in the audio *My Own Private Wolfgang*, and meets the composer as a baby in the short story *Gone Too Soon*. The First Doctor expresses a poor opinion of him in the story *Time and Relative* and the Eleventh recalls the composer's hatred of cats in the comic strip *The Golden Ones*. Sir Colin Thackery and the World Ecology Bureau are mentioned again in the Eighth Doctor audio *Hothouse*.

Prior to *The Masque of Mandragora*

The Fourth Doctor and Sarah holiday on Cassiopeia. Eventually. Probably.

The Seeds of Doom. At the end of the story, the Fourth Doctor tells Sarah that it's 'a good place for a break,' but the TARDIS takes them instead to Antarctica.

The Doctor witnesses the invention of wire-drawing machines. He and Sarah Jane are present at the Battle of Agincourt, where they see a young woman posing as a male archer. He sees the film *Shane*, and develops a taste for salami.

In episode four of *The Masque of Mandragora*, the Fourth Doctor says that wire-drawing machines were developed 150 years prior. He paraphrases a famous line from *Shane*, saying 'A Time Lord has to do what a Time Lord has to do' (a phrase he repeats in the short story *Revenge of the Judoon*), and requests a salami sandwich as a reward for his services. He mentions the French at Agincourt; Sarah reminds him that they lost. In *The Talons of Weng-Chiang*, he tells companion Leela she would have enjoyed the historical fracas. The immortal Ashildr was also there, according to *The Woman Who Lived*, which would explain why the Twelfth Doctor thinks Ashildr looks familiar when he first spots her in *The Girl Who Died*.

At some point, the Doctor battles and defeats the Master's twelve other original incarnations.

Doctor Who – The TV Movie. The Master blames the Eighth Doctor for the loss of all his previous lives, as a result of which he transforms into a withered, soulless husk. Since Time Lords are usually considerate enough to meet each other chronologically – until *World Enough and Time*, anyway – this probably occurred before he's seen in his final, desiccated state in *The Deadly Assassin*.

The Fourth Doctor closes his preferred TARDIS Control Room for redecoration.

The wood-panelled control room to which he moves is first seen onscreen in *The Masque of Mandragora* (he says it was the room from which he originally piloted the ship). When the Fourth Doctor finally returns to the familiar Control Room in episode one of *The Invisible Enemy*, he still doesn't like the colour.

Prior to *The Hand of Fear*

The Doctor picks up a hookah at a Constantinople cash-and-carry, along with a Gladstone bag in which to keep it. He changes the TARDIS' lock yet again, replacing it with the original, and sees the neural inhibitor Tricophenyladehyde in use.

In episode four of *The Deadly Assassin*, the Fourth Doctor recognises the neural inhibitor used by the Master to feign death. Castellan Spandrell says the TARDIS can be opened via a cipher key. In *The Invasion of Time*, Andred notes that Type 40s are equipped with a Trimonic locking device, and later uses one of the aforementioned cipher index keys to open the doors. The shopping expedition in Constantinople does not occur at the same time as his 3rd Century battle with Fenric – the hookah would not be invented for approximately another 1,300 years. In the audio *Quinnis*, the First Doctor is said to have taken some Turkish delight from the palace of Topkapi in Constantinople.

He tells Sarah Jane all about former companion Jo Grant, and no doubt presents her with the same photos his sixth incarnation later shows to Peri.

In *The Sarah Jane Adventures* story *Death of the Doctor*, Sarah Jane has heard all about Jo and recognises her, despite the two never having met. Companion Peri states, in *Timelash*, that she has seen pictures of Jo.

The Fourth Doctor promises to take Sarah Jane to South Croydon.

The Hand of Fear. In their first scene together in episode one, Sarah berates the Fourth Doctor for failing to get the TARDIS to South Croydon. Presumably, he is taking her home, since in episode four he knows that she lives on Hillview Road (though that is not where he deposits her, of course). She originally asks to go home in the final episode of *The Android Invasion*.

The Deadly Assassin

Prior to *The Face of Evil*

The Doctor hears – and is much taken with – the *Colonel Bogey March*. In his fourth incarnation, he assists the survey team of a stricken Starfall Seven ship belonging to a species known as the Mordee. Identifying himself to the crew as a Lord of Time, he attempts to repair their faulty computer Xoanon by making a direct link with the compatible centres of his own brain, a variation on a memory-transfer process pioneered by the Sidelians. Unfortunately, despite enjoying several of Xoanon's dinner parties, he fails to realise that the computer is in the process of evolving into a new life form. He ties a knot in his handkerchief to remind himself (of what, he subsequently forgets), procures a clockwork egg-timer and supplements his jelly baby fix with a few chocolates. In Switzerland, the Doctor takes crossbow lessons from William Tell. He is amused by the construction of a time barrier as a parlour trick, but never sees it done on a large scale. Gertrude Stein entertains him with a recitation of Rudyard Kipling's *Barrack Room Ballads*.

The Fourth Doctor whistles Lieutenant F J Ricketts' famous tune in *The Face of Evil*, *The Talons of Weng-Chiang*, *The Invasion of Time* and *Destiny of the Daleks*, as does the Eighth in the novel *Grimm Reality*. As the cliffhanger to episode one of *The Face of Evil* shows, the repairs to Xoanon are evidently performed by the Fourth Doctor, long enough ago for him to have forgotten it by the time he meets Leela (it is impossible to know how much time has elapsed since he deposited former companion Sarah in not-Croydon). He uses the egg-timer to elude the invisible entities in episode one. In the final instalment, Leela is seen eating chocolates she presumably took from the pocket of the unconscious Doctor. He recognises several items from the Starfall Seven craft, including the spacesuits, low-intensity sonic disruptors, bio-analysers and ultrabeam accelerators. Though the survey team are identified as the Mordee, they are seemingly descended from our own species, as the Doctor makes clear in *The Talons of Weng-Chiang* (in which he recites Kipling's exceedingly good works again, as his sixth self later does in *Terror of the Vervoids*). The Seventh and Eighth Doctors also remember meeting William Tell in the audios *The Settling* and *Enemy Aliens*, respectively.

The Doctor sees a sandmining operation on Korlano Beta and, presumably on Earth, acquires a snorkel. He operates a Laserson probe, and also witnesses the condition referred to by the Loid species as 'Grimwade's Syndrome' (AKA Robophobia).

The Robots of Death. The Fourth Doctor uses the snorkel to escape certain death in the sandminer's hopper - proof, long before *The Runaway Bride*, that his pockets are bigger on the inside. Laserson seems to be a brand name, since the device even has its own logo. The probe pops up again in the Fifth Doctor novel *The Crystal Bucephalus*. In the Seventh Doctor novel *The Also People*, the TARDIS databank contains a treatise on Robophobia, penned by the notorious Taren Capel.

On Earth, circa the year 5,000 (during the Ice Age), the Doctor sees and disapproves of Dr Findecker's zygma energy experiments, made possible by the discovery of the double-helix particle. Findecker's Time Cabinet, with its Trionic Lattice, is just one example of what the Doctor calls the 'twisted lunacy of a scientific dark age.' Another is the Organic Distillation Plant used by the notorious Minister of Justice Magnus Greel (AKA 'the Butcher of Brisbane') in his camps to slaughter 100,000 innocents. At that time, World War Six is almost brought about by the Peking Homunculus, an android made for the Commissioner of the Icelandic Alliance. The Doctor is with the Filipino army during the final advance on Reykjavik. He acquires a toy mouse, as well as a model Batmobile. He sees music hall act Little Titch in the 19th Century. Later, in 1920, he enjoys watching music hall artiste Harry Champion performing *The Green Eye of the Yellow God* and *Any Old Iron.*

The Talons of Weng-Chiang. The Fourth Doctor removes the various items from his pocket in episode six. A comic performance of the J Milton Hayes poem (wrongly attributed to Rudyard Kipling by Henry Gordon Jago) is more closely associated with Billy Bennett. The Twelfth Doctor fondly recalls *Any Old Iron* during *Smile.* Despite averting a Sixth World War, he has witnessed the Fifth by *The Unquiet Dead* (a conflict also mentioned in the Fifth Doctor novel *The Crystal Bucephalus,* the audio *Singularity* – where it is said to have occurred during the 49th Century – and the Ninth Doctor comic strip *Art Attack*). Magnus Greel's Uber-Marshall, Run Run Hsui Leng, appears in the Eighth Doctor strip *The Keep*. The toy mouse is not the same one seen in *The Doctor's Daughter.* Findecker's full name is given as Sa Yy Findecker in the Fourth Doctor short story *Under Reykjavik* and the Fifth Doctor audio *The Butcher of Brisbane,* and as Ernst Findecker in the Fifth Doctor novel *The Crystal Bucephalus.* Turlough mentions him in the audio *The Lady of Mercia.*

At Alexandria, the Doctor sees the legendary lighthouse. He studies an early electricity generator, finds himself charged under the Malicious Damages Act of 1861, and reads the poem *Flannan Isle,* by Wilfred Gibson. He sees a Schemurly – a projectile device that fires a rocket and line.

Horror of Fang Rock. Companion Leela has not seen any sort of lighthouse before. The Fourth Doctor points out to her that the 1861 Act covers lighthouses. He recites the poem at the end of episode four, and identifies an early Schemurly when searching for a weapon to destroy the Rutan. In the short story *The Book of Shadows,* the First Doctor learns that the Pharos lighthouse at Alexandria is actually a spaceship. He returns there in his second incarnation in the story *The Anti-Hero,* but fails to do so in the Eighth Doctor strip *The Company of Thieves.*

At sea, he observes St Elmo's Fire (the weather phenomenon, not the '80s Brat Pack movie). In the year 5,000 AD, he witnesses the Great Breakout, when human pioneers spread out across the galaxy. He travels to asteroid K4067, before or after it serves as home to the Bi-Al Foundation. In addition, he follows the work of a scientist attempting to build a machine as efficient as the human brain, before realising it would have to be larger than the city of London.

The Invisible Enemy. Even in a dazed state, the Fourth Doctor knows the asteroid's co-ordinates.

The TARDIS lands near a time fissure, where the Time Lord observes instances of telepathy and precognition. He also sees what others consider ghosts, but which are actually either weaknesses in the fabric of space and time or psychic residue. He studies astral projection.

Image of the Fendahl. In *The Unquiet Dead,* the Ninth Doctor comments on weak points in time and space being the cause of ghost stories, though halfway through *Under the Lake*, the Twelfth Doctor is suddenly less cynical when considering the existence of spectres. In the audio *The Mouthless Dead*, the Second Doctor says he is unsure about such matters. In *The Pandorica Opens*, the Eleventh Doctor claims that structures have memories, which is why houses appear to be haunted. The Tenth Doctor puts telepathy down to an extra synaptic engram in *The Family of Blood*.

The Doctor sees a Liebermann Maser in action, enjoys a trip to Blackpool, hears the legends of the Flying Dutchman and Jason (of Golden Fleece fame), and measures the level of radiation in Aberdeen – as one does.

Underworld. The Fourth Doctor correctly identifies the Lieberman Maser companion Leela discovers on Jackson's ship. In the final episode, he relates to her the legend of Jason, and speculates that such myths are, in fact, prophecies of the future. (According to K-9, they are not.) The jaunt to Blackpool makes such an impression on him that during his sixth incarnation, he intends to take Peri there following the events of *Revelation of the Daleks* – probably. The Fourth Doctor recalls eating hard-boiled eggs on Blackpool Pleasure Beach in the audio *The Sands of Life*, and the resort is mentioned again in the Tenth Doctor novel *Autonomy*.

The Doctor encounters the Vardans (though not on their own planet) and learns of their plan to attack Gallifrey.

The Invasion of Time. In episode three, the Fourth Doctor tells Borusa he first met the Vardans 'a long time ago,' presumably before Leela joined him on his travels, but after he entered the Matrix in *The Deadly Assassin* (or else his intentions would have been discovered by his fellow Time Lords). He doesn't find out the location of the Vardans' planet of origin until episode four. They reappear in the Seventh Doctor novel *No Future* (where their home planet is identified as Varda), while the Seventh Doctor audio *Maker of Demons* makes mention of an adventure involving the Vardans and Nikola Tesla. The Doctor's earliest incarnation encounters the Vardans in the audios *The First Wave* and *The Locked Room*, and the Second in the audio *The British Invasion*.

Aiming for Hyde Park, the Fourth Doctor is surprised when a Nexial discontinuity causes the TARDIS to materialise on the same unnamed jungle planet where he earlier conducted the repairs on Xoanon.

Exactly what the Fourth Doctor expects to find in Hyde Park is never revealed. If he eventually arrives there, that would constitute yet another unseen story.

Prior to *The Robots of Death*

The Fourth Doctor gives new companion Leela his beloved yellow yo-yo.

The Robots of Death. Leela is playing with the yo-yo in the opening TARDIS scene.

Prior to *The Talons of Weng-Chiang*

The Doctor catches a large salmon in the River Fleet and shares it with the venerable Bede.

The Talons of Weng-Chiang. The Discontinuity Guide points out that historical fact conflicts with the Fourth Doctor's claim, but when you have a time and space machine, all things are possible. The audio *The Flames of Cadiz* suggests that it happened during the Doctor's first incarnation, prior to his arrival in 1963 London, and the Eighth Doctor recalls the piscatorially-inclined Bede in the novel *Genocide.*

Prior to *Horror of Fang Rock*

The Doctor befriends H G Wells, and is surprised to find that the author already knows him, though with a different face. The Fourth Doctor promises to take companion Leela to the opening of the Brighton Pavilion.

Horror of Fang Rock. At the start of the story, the Fourth Doctor explains to Leela that they missed Brighton. In episode one of *The Leisure Hive,* he complains that he has now missed the Pavilion's opening on two occasions, although it's actually three if you count the audio *Gallery of Ghouls.* The Doctor refers to Wells as 'Herbert' in *Horror of Fang Rock.* As a young man, the author meets the Time Lord (then in his sixth incarnation) for the first time in *Timelash.* A later encounter with either the Sixth or Seventh Doctor is mentioned in the novel *The Eight Doctors,* while the Third Doctor mentions providing assistance with his invisibility experiments in the radio drama *The Ghosts of N-Space,* and the Tenth Doctor bumps into him in the comic strip *The Time Machination.* The Eighth Doctor has stocked the TARDIS' library with Wells' works in the audio *Izzy's Story.*

Prior to *The Invisible Enemy*

The Fourth Doctor grows bored of the wood-panelled Control Room. He teaches companion Leela to program co-ordinates into the TARDIS, and also acquires a duck call whistle and a dog lead.

> *The Invisible Enemy.* The Fourth Doctor and Leela are returning to the white Control Room as the story opens. In episode two, he is in no fit state to pilot the TARDIS, but he gives Leela the co-ordinates of asteroid K4067, the implication being that she pilots the TARDIS. He uses the duck call in episode one. In episode four, he pulls K-9 along by a lead he finds in his pocket.

Prior to *Image of the Fendahl*

The Doctor learns some rather unorthodox archaeological techniques and receives a recipe for fruitcake which requires baking it for two weeks. He sees a parastatic magnetometer at work.

> *Image of the Fendahl.* The Fourth Doctor sniffs a bone and proclaims it to come from the 12th Century. He considers the parastatic magnetometer 'quaint.'

Prior to *The Sun Makers*

The Fourth Doctor and his companion Leela deposit the Fendahl skull in a supernova in the constellation of Canthares.

> This is the Fourth Doctor's stated intention at the end of *Image of the Fendahl.*

The Doctor offends the Droge of Gabrieledes to such an extent that the offer of a star system is made in return for the Time Lord's head. He takes raspberry tea for an ailment of the throat, acquires a pair of pince-nez sunglasses and adds humbugs to his diet of jelly babies.

> *The Sunmakers.* The Fourth Doctor offers a humbug to the Collector in episode two. In the audio *The Valley of Death,* he gives Leela one of the sweets. According to episode one of *Delta and the Bannermen,* there's also a bounty on the Seventh Doctor. The Droge of Gabrieledes is namechecked in the Sixth Doctor novel *Mission: Impractical,* and mention is made of other Gabrielideans in the Eighth Doctor novel *Alien Bodies.*

Prior to *Underworld*

The Doctor studies crystal cybernetics, and decides to do a spot of painting.

The Fourth Doctor and Leela meet Ulysses.

> *Underworld.* When he first appears in episode one, the Fourth Doctor is wearing a paint-stained smock and a beret. In *The Invasion of Time,* he remarks that he is not a painter and decorator.

In 1927 Buenos Aires, the Doctor watches the chess match between José Raúl Capablanca and Alexander Alekhine. The Time Lord is called away before the end, and is left with the incorrect impression that Capablanca won.

> *The Androids of Tara.* The Fourth Doctor nevertheless programs the correct result into the memory banks of K-9 Mark II. Chess plays an important part in several of his adventures, including *Battlefield, Silver Nemesis, The Curse of Fenric, The Wedding of River Song* and *Nightmare in Silver.* Companions Ian and Barbara both claim to play chess - but not all that well - in episode two of *Marco Polo,* while Turlough and Tegan play at the start of *Enlightenment.* His eighth incarnation challenges Ohila of the Sisterhood of Karn to a game in *The Night of the Doctor,* and the Twelfth Doctor claims in *Smile* that he wins by kicking over the board. In the short story *The Mystery of the Haunted Cottage,* the Tenth Doctor says he was taught to play by the great-great nephew of the Maharajah Sri Gupta. The Third and Sixth Doctors are seen playing chess in the comic strips *The Heralds of Destruction* and *War-Game,* respectively. In the audio *Night of the Whisper,* the Eighth Doctor tells his companions that Humphrey Bogart was the only person ever to beat him at chess, although the Seventh admits losing to Mel in the novel *The Also People.* The Eleventh Doctor - who defeats companion Rory Williams in the audio *Darkstar Academy* - has bad memories of playing Bobby Fischer in the novel *Dark Horizons.*

Prior to *The Invasion of Time*

Somewhat improbably, the Fourth Doctor is called 'the most insufferably arrogant, overbearing, patronising bean-tin' and 'smug' by several individuals.

> *The Invasion of Time.* K-9 has heard the Fourth Doctor referred to in these terms.

If it ever really existed, the state of temporal grace that prevents weapons from being fired within the TARDIS fails, or else is shut off by the Fourth Doctor - who, circa the year 5000, picks up a manual describing the maintenance of robots of K-9's type. He uses this book to begin work on a K-

9 Mark II, which he programs with knowledge of various forms of tennis, the results of all championship chess games since 1866, the I-Ching, an alphabetical list of leisure resorts within Earth's galaxy, and details of other worlds and cultures he has yet to visit - drawn, presumably from the TARDIS' data banks. Sadly, however, he neglects to waterproof the robot.

The TARDIS' state of temporal grace is first mentioned in *The Hand of Fear*. Andred's inability to shoot the Fourth Doctor is attributed to the fact that patrol stasers won't operate in a relative dimensional stabiliser field, but moments later, K-9 stuns Andred. Weapons are fired within the TARDIS in several later stories, including *Earthshock* and *The Parting of the Ways*. In *Let's Kill Hitler*, the Eleventh Doctor claims that his earlier claim was no more than a clever lie (unless that's a lie, too). In the Third Doctor short story *The Spear of Destiny*, not only is it real, but it also applies to throwing weapons. In *Meglos*, the Fourth Doctor keeps the TARDIS's manual under a hatstand. It may seem hard-hearted of the Doctor to have started building a second K-9 before bidding farewell to the original, but in the closing scenes of *The Invasion of Time*, he is pushing the box containing the robot into the control room while the TARDIS is still dematerialising. The new K-9's sea defences are found wanting in episode one of *The Leisure Hive*. Before exploding, he provides Romana with a list of destinations more fun than Brighton. Logically, it would have to be a very long list. In *The Creature from the Pit*, K-9 advises the Fourth Doctor on the planet Chloris and the lifespan of Tythonians, both of which the Time Lord knows nothing about. The robot dog explains the I-Ching to the Doctor's companion Adric in episode one of *Warriors' Gate*. In episode one of *The Stones of Blood*, Romana tells K-9 to forget about tennis, an instruction he takes literally.

Despite believing there to be no limit to his genius, the Doctor attempts to encourage Isaac Newton to come up with the theory of gravity, by repeatedly dropping apples on the physicist's head.

Shada and *The Pirate Planet*. The Fourth Doctor explains that his friendly encouragement was unsuccessful, and that he was forced to explain the concept over dinner. The Fifth Doctor meets up with Newton once again in the audio *Circular Time: Summer*, and refers to him in the audio *The Emerald Tiger*. K-9 quotes Newton's laws of motion in episode three of *Warriors' Gate*. Perhaps it's one of Isaac's apples that he has in his pocket in *Under the Lake*.

In the year 1913, the Doctor purchases a copy of the *Daily Mirror* relating the details of the sinking of the *Titanic*. He also acquires a Sontaran-eating plant for the TARDIS greenhouse.

The Invasion of Time. Borusa is seen reading the *Daily Mirror* in the final episode. The Fourth Doctor assures him that he was not responsible for the sinking of the *Titanic*, but comments made by the Ninth Doctor in *The End of the World* show that he was most certainly onboard when the disaster occurred. The comic strip *Follow That TARDIS!* reveals that, while in his seventh incarnation, he played a part in its sinking after all. The carnivorous plant appears again in the comic strip *Cat Litter*.

He enjoys a holiday on the resort planet Halergan 3.

The Ribos Operation. The Fourth Doctor tells K-9 Mark II that he'll like it there. In the novelization, the planet is called Occhinos, which, in the audio *Zaltys*, is the world on which a group of vampires settle while fleeing the Third Doctor.

In the company of a female companion, the Doctor travels to Tahiti and to the planet Tara, at roughly the same time as his adventure there while searching for the fourth segment of the Key to Time.

The Androids of Tara. The TARDIS wardrobe contains female clothing suitable for both Tahiti and Tara. According to both Romana and K-9, the latter is the height of fashion at the moment of their arrival.

The Fourth Doctor and Leela team up with UNIT to fight an unspecified menace.

The Day of the Doctor. There's a snap of Leela and Benton in the Black Archive. The audio *The Revisionists* has the Fourth Doctor and Leela assisting UNIT.

The Fourth Doctor makes contact with the Vardans, and materialises the TARDIS on board their spaceship, immobilising the scanner and instructing K-9 and Leela not to leave his vessel.

The Invasion of Time, moments before the beginning of episode one.

Prior to *The Ribos Operation*

During a return trip to Gallifrey, the Fourth Doctor regains some of his memories relating to the Sontaran invasion. He meets his replacement as Time Lord President, and is far from impressed. He befriends the technician

Damon, as well as the amiable Counsellor Hedin, whom he considers a man of learning. He obtains a set of Time Lord robes for the TARDIS wardrobe, and passes up the opportunity to upgrade to a Type 57 TARDIS.

> In *The Ribos Operation*, the Fourth Doctor regrets not throwing the President to the Sontarans when he had the chance. His name is not given, but Castellan Kelner seems a likely candidate both for the job and the Doctor's ire. Damon - an acquaintance of Leela's, which suggests that both K-9s met at this time - and Hedin appear for the first time in *Arc of Infinity*, but are both known to the Fifth Doctor. Unlike Borusa and Azmael, there's no suggestion that Hedin taught the Doctor at the Academy. Borusa also knows that the Doctor thinks of Hedin as a good friend, so he no doubt played a part in this missing incident prior to his regeneration. The Master dons the robes at the climax of *Doctor Who - The TV Movie*. If the Fourth Doctor had had them at the time of *The Deadly Assassin*, he would likely have worn them rather than stealing another Time Lord's clothes in order to blend in. The Fifth Doctor complains, in episode one of *Warriors of the Deep*, that he should have made the switch to a Type 57 when he had the chance. This does not seem to refer to his original flight from Gallifrey, at which time he was guided in his choice by the Eleventh Doctor's companion, Clara. In the comic book *Prisoners of Time*, the Fifth Doctor explains to his companions that he was informed he saved Gallifrey from the Sontarans, although he has no clear recollection of it.

The Doctor is disappointed by the Somerset Cricket Team's current form (whenever 'current' might be to a time traveller), and considers that they would benefit from a good leg spinner. He hears of the Key to Time, but dismisses it as a myth. Though the element is unknown to his fellow Time Lords, he sees small quantities of Jethrik. He travels to the planets of Cyrrhenis Minima and Ribos, located three light-centuries from the Megellanic Clouds. On the latter world, he manages to escape the jaws of the reptilian Shrivenzale, and discovers that they can be affected by the sound of a dog whistle. He also acquires a fur coat for the TARDIS wardrobe (fake, one hopes).

> *The Ribos Operation*. The Fourth Doctor says that the lump of Jethrik (spelled Jethryk in the serial's novelization and the novels *The Crystal Bucephalus* and *Mission: Impractical*) is the biggest he has seen, while Romana has never heard of it. He identifies Cyrrhenis Minima from its co-ordinates alone (in the novelization, the planet is called Cyrrhenis Minimis). He also recognises the co-ordinates for Ribos, but knows, too, of the

Shrivenzale. This would also explain how he is able to get out of the labyrinth after the known exits have been blocked at the story's climax. He gives Romana a fur coat to guard against the cold of Ribos.

The Doctor has a very dull time on the lifeless, icy world of Calufrax, on which the rare crystals Voolium and Madranite 1-5 occur naturally, never guessing that it is, in fact, one of the segments of the Key to Time. He travels by linear induction corridor, and pockets a two-headed Alderbaran III coin. He hears about the unexplained disappearance of Bandraginus V, one of only two planets on which Oolion can be found. He also pays a visit to the other planet, Qualactin, hears of the Mentiads of the planet Zanak, and sees Andromedan bloodstones.

The Pirate Planet. In episode one, the Fourth Doctor says he has heard of the Mentiads somewhere before, but that point is never pursued. He tells Romana how paralysingly tedious Calufrax is. He incorrectly identifies a linear induction corridor in episode two. Bandraginus V is mentioned again in the Seventh Doctor novel *First Frontier.*

He watches as an entire galaxy is destroyed by a justice machine created by a Galactic Federation to administer the law (the machine instead found the entire Federation in contempt). The TARDIS takes him to the 'repulsive' planet of Ogros, in Tau Ceti. On Earth, he sees primitive man build stone circles in order to calculate eclipses. The time traveller officiates at Albert Einstein's wedding, and attempts (without success) to explain space warping to the groom; he is impressed with the scientist's accomplishments, despite his dyslexia. In the 17th Century, he encounters philosopher and archaeologist John Aubrey, and finds that he has a great sense of humour. He acquires a barrister's wig and a sheaf of legal documents, and meets a Brownie pack.

The Stones of Blood. The Fourth Doctor leaves the wig and documents behind on the Megaran craft. He explains to Romana that Brown Owl is the term used for the leader of a Brownie pack. He suggests that Aubrey founded Druidism as a joke. His fifth incarnation comments upon 17th Century craftsmanship in *The Awakening*. The Eleventh Doctor mentions Einstein's dyslexia during *The Hungry Earth,* and parties with the scientist, as well as singer Frank Sinatra and Santa Claus (AKA Jeff), in *A Christmas Carol.* According to the mini-episode *Death is the Only Answer,* the Eleventh Doctor took a toothbrush and a fez belonging to Einstein, who retaliated by trying to steal the TARDIS. Einstein first appears onscreen in *Time and the Rani.* The Thirteenth Doctor recalls his parents not approving of his marriage in *Demons of the*

Punjab. The First Doctor manages to miss him in 1930s Berlin during the audio *The Alchemists*, and the Sixth uses his name as an alias in the audio *Bloodtide*.

He goes fishing with Izaak Walton, author of *The Compleat Angler*.

The Androids of Tara. The Fourth Doctor recalls another angling experience in *The Talons of Weng-Chiang*. His sixth incarnation is seen fishing in *The Two Doctors*, after which he seems to lose interest in the pastime, as confirmed in the audio *The Wormery*. In the novel *The Death of Art*, the Seventh Doctor recalls once penning a book on the subject of fly-fishing.

On the planet Binaca-Ananda, the Doctor sees hundreds of Methane catalysing refineries. He spends some time on one of the moons of Delta Magna, grows fond of the music of Johann Sebastian Bach, visits Samoa, witnesses a spectacular electrical storm on a planetary satellite, and reads the short story *The Lumber Room* by Hector Hugh Munro (AKA Saki).

The Power of Kroll. The Fourth Doctor recognises an early Samoan influence in the design of the Swampie's temple (though what qualifies as early to a Time Lord is, as usual, anyone's guess). He identifies the third moon from its gravity, and quotes from the Saki story in episode one. He plays *Badinere* from *Orchestral Suite No. 2* on a reed pipe. In *Attack of the Cybermen*, the Sixth Doctor plays Bach's *Toccata and Fugue in D Minor* on the pipe organ into which the TARDIS exterior has briefly changed. The composer's works are mentioned in the Fourth Doctor audio *Babblesphere*.

He learns the skills of the fire walkers of Bali, meets Christopher Columbus, and obtains a sample of Chronodyne, large enough to fashion into a replica of the final piece of the Key to Time (but only 74 percent compatible).

The Armageddon Factor. The Sixth Doctor mentions Columbus in *The Two Doctors*, and meets the explorer in the audio *Trouble in Paradise*. The Fourth Doctor recalls travelling with him in the novel *Eye of Heaven*, and in the audio *Cobwebs*, the Fifth relates the advice he gave to Columbus.

No doubt as a result of his regeneration-inducing experience on Metebelis 3, the Doctor begins carrying anti-radiation pills, as well as a bleeper to remind him when to take each dose. He encounters zombies, and sees the result of high-impact phason drilling.

Destiny of the Daleks. The Fourth Doctor tells Romana that a real zombie is cold to the touch. The Eighth Doctor still has the anti-radiation pills in the audio *Seasons of Fear*, as does the Tenth in the novel *The Eyeless* and the Eleventh in the novel *Plague of the Cybermen.*

Despite voicing a desire to study under painter Rembrandt Harmenszoon van Rijn, he settles for Leonardo da Vinci, and watches as the latter produces a sketch while suffering from a terrible cold. He is also around when the artist designs the helicopter and paints the Mona Lisa – the Doctor remembers her as a dreadful woman with no eyebrows who refuses to sit still. He's all the more impressed by the fact that Leonardo, like Albert Einstein, has achieved so much despite being dyslexic. Before departing, he makes a note of Leonardo's contact details (time-space co-ordinates?).

Rembrandt is mentioned in *The Time Warrior.* The Fourth Doctor's recollection of the painting of the Mona Lisa is from *City of Death.* In *Doctor Who – The TV Movie,* the Eighth Doctor identifies the print on Grace's wall as the one Leonardo drew with a cold (and probably with charcoal, too). The Second Doctor recognises one of Leonardo's designs in episode one of *The Seeds of Death,* while his fourth incarnation mentions his submarine in *The Masque of Mandragora* (in which he makes it clear that he and Leonardo have yet to meet). The artist's name is in the Sixth Doctor's wallet in episode one of *The Two Doctors.* The Eleventh Doctor recalls Leonardo's dyslexia in *The Hungry Earth.* In *The Sarah Jane Adventures* story *Death of the Doctor,* he tells Jo Grant that her 13th grandchild will be also be dyslexic. In the novel *The Final Sanction,* the Second Doctor has already met Leonardo. The Eighth Doctor describes another meeting with him in the audio *The Stones of Venice.* In *Fear Her,* the Tenth Doctor states that he can only draw stick figures, but judging by his artwork in *The Deadly Assassin, Human Nature, The Bells of Saint John* and *Heaven Sent,* he's just being modest.

The Doctor visits Paris in 1979 (a table wine of a year), where he visits the Louvre Museum and enjoys an excellent bouillabaisse at a café.

City of Death. He describes Paris to Romana, introduces her to the Louvre, with which he is already familiar, and recommends a restaurant where they can get bouillabaisse. By the time of *Tooth and Claw,* the Doctor has revised his opinion of 1979.

He stores a lot of junk in the No 4 hold of the TARDIS, including a ball of string, the jawbone of an ass (the same one with which the Biblical Samson slew 1,000 men, perhaps?) and the disconnected Mark 3 emergency transceiver. Encountering the Minotaur once more, the Fourth Doctor uses a ball of string to help Theseus and Ariadne out of the creature's famous maze (it was either that or his scarf). He neglects to remind Theseus to change the colour of his vessel's sails for the journey home.

The contents of No 4 hold, including the ball of string, are listed in *The Creature from the Pit*. The string is seen again in *Cold War*, as well as in the comic strips *City of the Damned* and *Funhouse*, the Tenth Doctor novel *The Eyeless*, and the audios *Phantasmagoria* and *Question Marks*. Further details of the Fourth Doctor's adventure with Theseus are provided in the final episode of *The Horns of Nimon*. In *The Mind Robber*, the Second Doctor insists that the Minotaur is entirely mythical, before his third self, in *The Time Monster*, discovers that it isn't.

While attending a seminar at which Professor Stein explains his notion of the Continuous Event Transmuter, the Doctor disapproves of the CET machine, as much as he did the very similar Miniscope. He finally achieves his childhood ambition of driving a steam train.

Nightmare of Eden. The Fourth Doctor makes it clear that he did not actually meet Stein. He tells Romana he can 'start anything from a steam engine to a TARDIS.' The Doctor expresses his enthusiasm for the workings of the 19th Century railway system in the audios *The Mouthless Dead*, *Orbis* and *The Runaway Train*.

At some point after the period in which *The Horns of Nimon* occurs, he materialises on the charming planet Aneth. The Fourth Doctor, perhaps accompanied by K-9, is also around at the time of the Skonnon Empire, though they do not actually visit it.

The Horns of Nimon. The Doctor says he has been to Aneth, but 'not yet.' K-9 knows about the history of the Skonnon Empire.

The Fourth Doctor calls upon Professor Chronotis at St Cedd's College, Cambridge, in 1955, 1960 (when he takes an honorary degree) and 1964. The 1955 encounter marks Chronotis' first verifiable meeting with the Doctor, but not vice-versa. Chronotis may also be in his company when he encounters Wordsworth, Rutherford, Christopher Smart, Andrew Marvell, Judge Jeffreys and Owen Chadwick. The Doctor is taught how to enter the space-time vortex without the aid of a TARDIS, by an ancient time mystic in the Qualactin Zones (or possibly the Quantocks).

Shada. It is very likely that, when receiving his degree, the Doctor wears the cap and gown his recently-regenerated seventh incarnation models in *Time and the Rani*. The short story *Cambridge Previsited* concerns the First Doctor visiting Chronotis. The Sixth Doctor quotes Wordsworth's poem *Resolution and Independence* in the comic strip *Profits of Doom*. The Eighth recalls meeting Judge George Jeffreys and Wordsworth in the audios *Dead London* and *The Zygon Who Fell to Earth*, respectively.

The Doctor has some dealings with the Foamasi government. He experiences the atavistic therapy on the asteroid Yegros Alpha, and the historical re-enactment world of Zeen-4.

The Leisure Hive. The Fourth Doctor confirms the authenticity of the seal of the ambassador. The planets are mentioned by K-9.

Arriving on the planet Tigella, the Fourth Doctor befriends Zastor - who, despite religious objections, shows him the power source known as the Dodecahedron. Or maybe not.

Meglos. The Fourth Doctor tells Romana he was on Tigella 'a long time ago.' He is initially sure he wasn't allowed to see the Dodecahedron, but is later able to describe it.

He meets the Brothers Grimm, who join his darts team. He travels on an *Arrow*-class scoutship, and observes that vampire legends occur on many of the inhabited planets he has visited.

State of Decay. The Fourth Doctor identifies the ship disguised as a tower by the Vampire Lords. His claim about 'virtually every inhabited planet' having vampire legends reduces to just 17 planets by the next episode. The Twelfth Doctor states that the story-telling brothers joined him for a bit of bully during *Heaven Sent*.

Prior to *The Pirate Planet*

Five hundred twenty-three years have apparently elapsed since the Doctor stole the TARDIS from Gallifrey.

The Pirate Planet. It is claimed that the Doctor has been piloting the TARDIS for this length of time, which would mean - if Romana is correct about him being 759 in episode one of *The Ribos Operation* - that he was 236 when he stole the contraption. Compare this with a statement made in *The Doctor's Wife* that the ship took the form of a Police Box 700 years earlier.

The Stones of Blood

Prior to *The Androids of Tara*

The Doctor reads *The Prisoner of Zenda*, by Anthony Hope.

The Androids of Tara. The Fourth Doctor says, of Prince

Reynard's plan to confound his enemies prior to his coronation by using a double, 'It has been done before,' an obvious reference to *The Prisoner of Zenda*, this story's inspiration. It is unlikely that there are any significant gaps between the acquisition of the segments of the Key to Time, but as episode one begins, the Doctor is complaining that he deserves a rest, and throws himself into several pastimes, including fishing and chess, so it's not impossible that he might find time to read a book, especially if he can get through one as quickly as he is seen to do in *City of Death* and *Rose*.

The Power of Kroll

Prior to *The Armageddon Factor*

Portions of the Fourth Doctor and Romana's memories are erased. He builds a handheld gun-shaped device for tracking distress signals.

The Armageddon Factor. In episode four, the Fourth Doctor says he has never seen K-9 spin around on the spot before, despite having seen that very thing during *The Pirate Planet*. In episode six, Romana forgets the Doctor telling her, in *The Stones of Blood*, that she was sent on her mission not by the Lord President of Gallifrey, but by the White Guardian. The Sixth Doctor builds a second tracker of different design, which he uses in episode one of *Attack of the Cybermen*.

Prior to *Destiny of the Daleks*

Following the installation of the Randomiser, the TARDIS takes the Fourth Doctor and Romana to the tropical paradise of Kantra. He purchases copies of *Jane's Spacecraft of the Universe* and *The Origins of the Universe*, by Oolon Coluphid. Something happens to Romana during her travels with the Doctor that causes her to regenerate. After K-9 develops a fault, the Fourth Doctor is forced to remove the robot dog's brain in order to diagnose the cause of the malfunction - which, bizarrely, turns out to be laryngitis. He encounters the Magla, an amoeba measuring 8,000 miles across that has developed a crusty shell and is frequently mistaken for a planet. He attends the Galactic Olympic Games, in which Arcturus is the victor, Betelgeuse coming in second.

Destiny of the Daleks. Romana recognises the name Kantra when the Fourth Doctor refers to it. He mentions *Jane's Spacecraft* and flips through Oolon Coluphid's inaccurate volume when trapped. Note the minor difference between the name of this

> author and that of the character featured in *The Hitchhiker's Guide to the Galaxy*, written by *Destiny of the Daleks'* script editor Douglas Adams. The Fifth Doctor has a copy of *Jane's Book of Gallifreyan Vessels* in the audio *Omega,* and the Eighth Doctor has a copy of *Jane's Alien Artefacts* in the comic strip *Endgame.* No reason is provided onscreen for Romana's regeneration, but audio *Lies* suggests that it occurs as a result of the torture she undergoes in *The Armageddon Factor* at the hands of the Shadow. The Doctor's attendance at several of Earth's Olympic Games is described in *Fear Her.*

The Fourth Doctor and Romana meet the Jagaroth, 'a vicious, callous, warlike race' and imagine them wiped out by war.

> *City of Death*

Prior to *City of Death*

In search of culture, the Fourth Doctor and Romana examine the fine art on display at the Academia Stellaris on Sirius V, in addition to the Solarian Pinaquoteche at Strikian and the Braxiatel Collection. He sees a micromeson scanner in operation, appreciates a Second Dynasty Ming vase, acquires a Polaroid camera, meets the Borgias (including Gioffre, whom he's too afraid to tell what he thinks of the leaning tower of Pisa) and enjoys a nice sit-down in a beautiful Louis Quinze chair. The Fourth Doctor parks the TARDIS in a small Parisian art gallery, circa 1979.

> *City of Death.* Romana lists all these galleries as being potentially preferable to the Louvre. She identifies Countess Scarlioni's bracelet as a micromeson scanner. The Fourth Doctor recognises the artefacts in Count Scarlioni's château. He is disturbed upon learning that Captain Tancredi's guard (whom he photographs with the Polaroid camera) was formerly employed by the Borgias. The Twelfth Doctor recalls his encounter with Gioffre Borgia in *Time Heist.* The Seventh Doctor recalls tangling with the notorious family in the audio *The Doomsday Quatrain.* Irving Braxiatel, founder of the Braxiatel Collection, appears in many Bernice Summerfield novels and audios, and in several of Virgin's New Adventures. The Fifth Doctor is on his way to the Braxiatel Collection in the audios *The Eye of the Scorpion* and *The Church and the Crown.* The Academia Stellaris is mentioned in the Fourth Doctor audio *Babblesphere,* and the Tenth Doctor comic strip *The Arts in Space.*

Prior to *The Creature from the Pit*

Having lost his last box of matches on prehistoric Earth, the Doctor finally gets his hands on a replacement. He also acquires a circular mirror and a copy of *Peter Rabbit*, by Beatrix Potter. He visits a world on which time is measured in ninods.

> *The Creature from the Pit*. The Fourth Doctor uses matches to navigate around the titular pit. He is reading *Peter Rabbit* to K-9 in the opening scene. There are, presumably, other Potter books in the TARDIS library as well, as Romana is familiar with the entire oeuvre. The Doctor uses the mirror to deflect K-9's laser blast. He translates ninods - the system used by Erato - into minutes and seconds in episode four. Wherever he learned about ninods, it was not on the Tythonian homeworld, which he has never visited.

Prior to *Nightmare of Eden*

Sometime after 2068, but prior to 2096, the Doctor becomes aware of Galactic Salvage and Insurance. He pays a visit to M37, a small system made up of three planets near the Cygnus Gap. The Fourth Doctor takes Romana to the cinema (to see *The Muppet Movie*, as he recalls doing in *Tooth and Claw*?), and also shows her a Russian doll. He sees whole communities and planets destroyed by the apathetic influence of the drug XYP, also known as Vraxoin, while the dealers make their fortunes. He and Romana watch the incineration of the planet which is the only known source of Vraxoin. The Fourth Doctor and Romana receive a distress signal from the stricken space liner *Empress* and decide to respond.

> *Nightmare of Eden*. The Fourth Doctor poses as a representative of Galactic Salvage and Insurance (formed in London in 2068), not realising that that the company - also mentioned in the Eighth Doctor audio *Max Warp* - went into liquidation in 2096. The Eleventh Doctor adopts the same identity in the comic strip *Planet Bollywood*. Romana observes that the CET machine is not unlike a cinematograph, and states that Russian dolls (known on Gallifrey as onion dolls, according to the novel *Cat's Cradle: Time's Crucible*) are, in her opinion, a model of the universe. The Seventh Doctor expands upon this notion in the audio *The Shadow of the Scourge*, and the Ninth likens a Slitheen dressing up in a slightly larger Slitheen suit to a Russian doll in the comic strip *Doctormania*.

Prior to *The Horns of Nimon*

The Fourth Doctor and Romana use the equipment in the TARDIS to return the creatures trapped by the CET machine to their homeworlds.

Their stated intention at the end of *Nightmare of Eden*. The Sixth Doctor has an entire zoo within the TARDIS in the comic strip *Changes*, so perhaps he wasn't able to return them after all.

Romana and the Fourth Doctor study the properties of the rich energy source known as Hymetusite, and also finds out about the Sargasso Sea. He wins first prize in some contest or other, acquires some star-shaped stickers and a large red hankie, and sees several different models of Neutrino Converters. The Time Lord decides to make some modifications to the TARDIS' Conceptual Geometer (which necessitates the dismantling of the dematerialisation circuits), and digs out his Type 40 Handbook for further instructions.

The Horns of Nimon. The Fourth Doctor begins his repair work immediately before episode one starts. He and Romana both recognise Hymetusite, but the Time Lady is the only one who remembers that it is highly radioactive. The substance is mentioned again in the Seventh Doctor novels *Lucifer Rising* and *Infinite Requiem*. The Doctor likens the area of space into which they are being dragged to the Sargasso Sea. In episode two, he affixes a 'First Prize' rosette to K-9's ear. He uses the stickers to find his way around the Nimon's maze, and the hankie to distract the creature, matador-style, in episode three. The Conceptual Geometer is mentioned in the Fifth Doctor audio *Time Reef*.

Prior to *Shada*

The Fourth Doctor completes his current round of repairs in the TARDIS, including re-setting the defence shields.

The Horns of Nimon

The Doctor reads the complete works of Charles Dickens and considers *The Signalman* the best short story ever written, but has issues with the American section in *Martin Chuzzlewit*. He also studies the life of the author.

In *The Unquiet Dead*, the Ninth Doctor knows the date of Dickens' death, along with certain personal details. The Fourth Doctor reads from *The Old Curiosity Shop* in *Shada*, the Sixth quotes *A Tale of Two Cities* in *The Ultimate Foe* and the Eleventh mentions *A Christmas Carol* in, well, *A Christmas Carol*. Dickens' works are mentioned in the novels *Ghost Ship*, *All-Consuming Fire*, *The Death of Art* and *Longest Day*, and the audios

Babblesphere, Legend of the Cybermen, The Crimes of Thomas Brewster, A Most Excellent Match, The Genocide Machine, The Chimes of Midnight and *Living Legend,* while the Eighth Doctor recalls arguing with the writer himself in the audio *The Man Who Wasn't There.*

The Time Lord changes the location of the TARDIS' medical kit, and tinkers with the front door lock yet again. The Fourth Doctor and companion Romana both read *The Victim,* by Saul Bellow. He introduces her to his old friend Isaac Newton. He is presented with a medal, which he eventually passes on to Romana. Thirty years prior to his final journey to Cambridge, he buys a bottle of milk and places it in stasis. He hears of the accomplishments of neurologist Dr A St John D Caldera, psychologist A S T Thira, parametricist Professor G V Santori, biologist Dr L D Ia, and Professor R F Akrotiri (field unknown). The TARDIS picks up a message from Professor Chronotis, asking the Fourth Doctor to visit him at St Cedd's at his earliest convenience. He sets the co-ordinates for May Week (which occurs in June) but forgets to take axial tilt, diurnal rotation and orbital parabola into account, and arrives in Chronotis' study four months late.

Shada. The Fourth Doctor and Romana explain to the Professor (who has already forgotten) about the message. Bellow's novel is among the volumes they search through in Chronotis' study. K-9 declares the milk from the TARDIS kitchen perfectly fresh. The stasis device presumably breaks down, as, according to *The Empty Child,* the Ninth Doctor and Rose make several stops on Earth to procure more milk. The Doctor has never met the scientists at the Think Tank Space Station, but declares them 'some of the greatest minds in existence.' Caldera is mentioned in the Seventh Doctor audio *Order of Simplicity.* Romana knows of Newton and his theories, although the Doctor first meets the scientist prior to the search for the Key to Time. In the original script for *Shada,* the medal is a badge reading 'I am a genius.' The TARDIS' medical kit is within easy reach in *The Web Planet,* but in *Shada,* Chris Parsons has to make quite a journey to recover it. In the Eighth Doctor novel *Genocide,* the medical kit can be found under a harpsichord, because of course it can. Skagra is able to use the TARDIS key without any difficulty in episode three.

Prior to *The Leisure Hive*

The Fourth Doctor confesses to Romana that he never got around to waterproofing K-9 Mark II. They observe the manipulation of solid objects by Unreal Transfer.

The Leisure Hive. Both the Fourth Doctor and Romana know about Unreal Transfer, but the Doctor cannot seem to remember the galaxy in which he saw it. Romana attempts to warn K-9 not to go into the water at Brighton (which is good advice for anyone, man or machine).

The Doctor reads the Bible.

In *Full Circle,* the Fourth Doctor likens the TARDIS to Noah's Ark and, in *The Mysterious Planet,* his sixth incarnation mentions the risk of being turned into a pillar of salt, like Lot's Wife, and refers to Ananias in *The Ultimate Foe.* In *The Night of the Doctor,* the dying Eighth Doctor quotes Luke's gospel, while the Twelfth compares a human colony to the Garden of Eden in *Smile,* and quotes from Corinthians in *Oxygen. The Horns of Nimon* implies that he may have met the mighty Samson. The Thirteenth Doctor talks about the New Testament in *The Witchfinders.* The Fifth Doctor refers to The Bible in the audio *Iterations of I.*

The Fourth Doctor and Romana meet psychiatrist Carl Jung.

Warriors' Gate. Romana make a disparaging comment about 'Astral Jung.'

He hears the TARDIS cloister bell rung. During his fourth incarnation, the time traveller visits the planet Logopolis, where the Logopolitan Monitor offers to perform the much-needed chameleon conversion on the TARDIS using block transfer computation. For reasons unknown, the Doctor declines. He is too embarrassed to ask why the Logopolitans don't use computers. On Earth, he visits the Pharos computer room. In another time period, he befriends Thomas Huxley.

Logopolis. The Fourth Doctor tells companion Adric to ring the bell in the event of an emergency. Despite never having sounded onscreen before *Logopolis,* it is heard again in many later stories, including *Resurrection of the Daleks, Doctor Who – The TV Movie, The Sound of Drums, Turn Left, The Waters of Mars, The Eleventh Hour, The Doctor's Wife, Hide, Journey to the Centre of the TARDIS, The Name of the Doctor, Deep Breath, Listen, Flatline, Dark Water, Under the Lake/Before the Flood, The Girl Who Died, The Husbands of River Song, The Doctor Falls* and *Twice Upon a Time,* as well as being mentioned in the novels *The Crystal Bucephalus, Timewyrm: Revelation Cat's Cradle: Witch Mark, The Dimension Riders, Genocide, Revolution Man* and *Engines of War,* the short stories *Under Reykjavik* and *Natural Regression,* the audios *The Abandoned, Absolute Power, Flip-Flop, The Architects of History, Protect and Survive, World Apart, The Other Side, No More Lies, Eyes of the Master* and *Backtrack,* as well as in the comic strips *Profits of Doom, The Last Word, Ground Zero, Terror in the TARDIS, Four Dimensions, Supremacy of the Cybermen* and *The Lost Dimension.* The bells on Gallifrey itself ring furiously in *Hell Bent.* The Doctor identifies the Logopolitan recreation of the Pharos project, and is recognised by the Monitor, meaning that his earlier visit occurred during his present incarnation, although the novel *Bunker Soldiers* states that it was the First Doctor, in the company of Steven Taylor and Dodo Chaplet, who first journeyed there. That same incarnation of the Doctor meets Huxley in the comic strip *Unnatural Selection.*

The Fourth Doctor's companion Romana tells him more than once that he could do with a holiday. On Earth, they assist UNIT and the Brigadier to avert an invasion by the Ice Warriors. The TARDIS' auto systems play up, and the Doctor considers returning to Logopolis to have them fixed. He places a motorised wheelchair in the TARDIS, witnesses fast particle projection and discovers that silver acts as a protection against recursive occlusion.

Castrovalva. The newly regenerated Fifth Doctor suggests that the tapestry in the town of Castrovalva operates by fast particle projection, and recalls his conversations with Romana and the Brigadier. It is impossible to know whether he is channelling his third or fourth incarnation when discussing the Ice Warriors. This is not a delusion, but an actual memory, as confirmed by *The Christmas Invasion,* in which UNIT are aware of the existence of Martians. The Eighth Doctor novel *The Dying Days* also features a tussle between UNIT and the Ice Warriors, but those events are rather at odds with *The Christmas Invasion* (blame the Time War). There are photos of both Romanas pinned to a board in the Black Archive in *The Day of the Doctor.* The wheelchair is still in the TARDIS in the Eighth Doctor novel *The Adventuress of Henrietta Street.*

The Doctor is at Heathrow Airport when some very strange things are occurring at Terminal 3. He places *Principia Mathematica,* by Alfred North Whitehead, in the TARDIS library, along with a volume by Bertrand Russell. Visiting the Inoshki solar system in Galaxy 1489, he sees the floating devices known as Monopticons. He travels on the Piccadilly Line, and plays bowls with Sir Francis Drake prior to the arrival of the Spanish Armada.

Four to Doomsday. Nyssa reads the Whitehead book in episode one. Adric recommends 'Bert' Russell's work to Tegan. The Fifth Doctor recognises the Monopticons, and knows the Inoshki system from which Monarch and his machines originate. The reference to the Piccadilly Line does not relate to the opening of the London Underground in *The Web of Fear,* nor is the Heathrow Terminal 3 incident a reference to *The Faceless Ones,* which takes place at Gatwick. The bowls incident is recalled by the Sixth Doctor audios *The Marian Conspiracy* and *Voyage to the New World,* and the Seventh Doctor novel *Birthright.* Francis Drake appears in the Tenth Doctor short story *The Lonely Computer.* The audios *Quinnis* and *Maker of Demons* state that the First Doctor travelled on Drake's vessel *The Golden Hind* on two separate occasions, first in the company of Susan, and later with Dodo. He narrowly misses meeting Drake in the audio *The Flames of Cadiz,* but Ian Chesterton's opinion that the man was little more than a pirate is one repeated by the Fourth Doctor in the audio *The Devil's Armada.* The Twelfth Doctor eventually encounters him in the audio *The Lost Magic.*

He is told the legend of the Mara, and learns that the creature cannot bear its own reflection.

Kinda

The Time Lord visits a world (possibly Raaga) where Soliton gas is present, and where he sees the suffering of the prisoners controlled by bracelets made from Polygrite as they toil in the Tinclavic mines for the psychic people of Hakol. He meets the Terileptils, whose love of art and beauty he shares, while abhorring their equal enthusiasm for war and remaining wary of their skills in android construction. He travels on spaceships lit by Vintaric Crystals.

The Visitation. Both Polygrite and Soliton are recognised by Nyssa, but not by Adric, who joined the TARDIS crew before her. The Fifth Doctor complains that the Terileptils - who are mentioned in the audios *The Lure of the Nomad, Dust Breeding* and *Technophobia,* as well as in the Eleventh Doctor novel *Hunter's Moon* - are too good at making androids before setting eyes upon a member of that species, and recognizes the scarring typical to prisoners on Raaga. Tinclavic is seen in *The Awakening,* in which it is established that the substance is mined for use by Hakol's inhabitants. It's also mentioned in the novel *Seeing I* and the audio

Neverland, both featuring the Eighth Doctor. Vintaric Crystal lighting is, apparently, very common - in fact, it is entirely possibly that almost every ship seen in the series uses it (either that, or alpha meson phosphor, which lights the Cybermen's tombs on Telos). In the audios *Prisoners of the Lake* and *Come Die With Me*, the Doctor sees structures lit by the same means.

The Doctor enjoys himself at the Great Exhibition in 1851 (despite finding the year quite dull otherwise), and decides to go back again. He encounters Plasmatons, random particles assembled from the atmosphere in the shape of primitive life forms. He visits the devastated planet Xeriphas long after its apparent destruction during the Vardon Kosnax war. In India, he sees the famous rope trick performed.

Time-Flight. The Fifth Doctor's description of the Plasmatons might match that of the guards in Omega's black hole domain, save that he dismisses them as harmless, which the gel creatures are certainly not. He suggests the Great Exhibition as a cure for the blues following Adric's death (while the Tenth Doctor declares 1851 boring in *The Next Doctor*). The Seventh Doctor heads there in the comic strip *Claws of the Klathi!*, as does the Eighth in the audio *Other Lives*, and the Eleventh in the strip *Hypothetical Gentleman*. Nyssa doesn't know what the Indian Rope Trick is.

On 21st-Century Earth (possibly in the years 2084), the Doctor is involved in a crisis on an undersea military colony commonly known as a Sea Base. It may be at this time that he concludes that very little has changed politically since the late 20th Century. Visiting Earth at a slightly earlier point in time, he sees the effects of Hexachromite gas on marine and reptile life, and fully expects it to be banned.

Warriors of the Deep. The Fifth Doctor suggests it is the year 2084. He is familiar with the layout of the Sea Base - he knows that the Command Centre is at the top of the structure - and recognises the all-clear when it is sounded. He is surprised to find that Hexachromite has not been outlawed. This all occurs pre-Tegan.

The Doctor discovers another revived clan of Silurians, possessed of a sting gland that takes 24 hours to recharge.

The Hungry Earth. The Eleventh Doctor knows about the sting gland's properties despite never having witnessed it onscreen.

Among this clan, he befriends Icthar of the noble Silurian Triad. He and the other Silurians wish for peaceful co-existence with humanity, but are attacked. Despite defending themselves with the Myrka and battle cruiser armed with a particle suppressor, they are unsuccessful. When the Doctor leaves, he believes Icthar to be dead.

> *Warriors of the Deep*. The Fifth Doctor knows of the Myrka and the battle cruiser without ever seeing them onscreen. He and Icthar have met before, and the Silurian states that his people twice offered the hand of friendship to Earth's ape-descended primitives, which certainly does not describe the plot of *The Sea Devils*. The Seventh Doctor novel *Blood Heat* confirms that Icthar did not play a part in the events of *The Silurians*. The Doctor states that this all happened during 'an earlier regeneration.' Icthar appears in the Third Doctor novel *The Scales of Injustice*, and the Myrka in the Sixth Doctor audio *Bloodtide*, Mike Tucker's Eleventh Doctor story *The Silurian Gift*, and the comic strip *The Lost Dimension*.

The TARDIS materialises on the London Docklands during the late 19th Century.

> *Resurrection of the Daleks*. The Fifth Doctor tells Tegan that the Docklands would have been bustling with activity 100 years prior, so this pre-dates the time she joined Adric and Nyssa in the TARDIS. Adric's first visit to Earth is recorded in *Logopolis*, so this is before his time, too.

He assists UNIT when the Cybermen launch another invasion attempt. The Fourth Doctor makes further modifications to Bessie in order to increase the roadster's speed, and also gives the vehicle a new licence plate.

> *Battlefield*. The Seventh Doctor is informed by the Brigadier that UNIT are now equipped with gold-tipped bullets (obviously for dealing with Cybermen). Since their allergy to gold never comes up in *The Invasion*, it must be in a later story - later, even, than the proposed 'missing' Second Doctor/UNIT adventure, since this initiative is fairly recent. In the audio *Old Soldiers*, it's stated that UNIT had occasion to requisition silver bullets, suggesting an encounter with werewolves, which sounds awesome. The Brigadier says he had Bessie put into mothballs, and in *Mawdryn Undead*, he has no memory of the Doctor after his fourth incarnation.

The Time Lord is introduced to Sir John Sudbury, head of Department C19, which has authority over UNIT.

> *Time-Flight*. The Fifth Doctor mentions Sir John in episode one. He is never seen onscreen, and they might have met at any time from *Spearhead from Space* onwards. Sir John appears in the novels *The Eye of the Giant, The Scales of Injustice, Business Unusual* and *Instruments of Darkness*. Department C19 is mentioned in the Seventh Doctor audio *The Fearmonger*.

He sees zero-balanced dwarf star alloy, and develops a fondness for pickles.

> In episode three of *Warriors' Gate*, Romana tells Adric that the hull of Rorvick's ship is constructed from dwarf star alloy. In *Day of the Moon*, the Eleventh Doctor supplies blocks of the material from which his prison/fortress is built. The 'zero-balanced' nature of the blocks presumably explains how it is that it can be lifted by hand. Very likely, it was the Doctor himself who located a supply for Canton. The Tenth Doctor traps the leader of the Family of Blood in chains forged in the heart of a dwarf star. In *The Return of Doctor Mysterio*, the Twelfth Doctor carries a gem stabilized in dwarf star crystal.

Visited by three of his future incarnations, the Fourth Doctor agrees to position his TARDIS in Gallifrey's atmosphere as part of a plan to freeze the planet in a single moment of time.

> *The Day of the Doctor*. The Fourth Doctor seen on the Time Lords' projection screens lacks the question mark collars he favours from *The Leisure Hive* onwards.

The Fourth Doctor performs some repairs on K-9, returning his voice to the factory setting. He makes a significant alteration to his wardrobe, favouring a burgundy ensemble. Having missed the opening of the Brighton Pavilion once before, he is determined to see it at last, but while the TARDIS gets the location right, it arrives in the wrong season and Century. This is what happens when you're too stubborn to stop and ask for directions.

> Immediately prior to the beginning of *The Leisure Hive*. The Fourth Doctor plans to take Leela there at the start of *Horror of Fang Rock*. The Sixth Doctor revisits Brighton in the audio *Pier Pressure* and the Fourth Doctor is on his way there in the comic strip *Party Animals*, while in the strip *The Futurists*, Rose expects the Tenth Doctor to take her to Brighton Pier. The Twelfth Doctor proposes visiting there with Clara in the opening scene of *Time Heist*.

Prior to *Meglos*

As he prepares to perform yet more repairs on K-9, Romana informs the Fourth Doctor that the TARDIS has entered the Priam planetary system.

Immediately prior to the opening of *Meglos*.

Prior to *Full Circle*

Romana and the Fourth Doctor return a kidnapped Earthman to his proper place and time.

Full Circle. The Earthman appears in the previous story, *Meglos*. He is never named onscreen, but is christened George Morris in the novelization of the serial.

State of Decay

Prior to *Warriors' Gate*

The Doctor dabbles in bioelectronics.

The Keeper of Traken. He makes this claim to Tremas.

In an attempt to escape E-Space, the Fourth Doctor suggests Romana try a little friendly persuasion with the TARDIS, with emphasis on 'little.'

Warriors' Gate

The Keeper of Traken

Prior to *Logopolis*

The Fourth Doctor tells Alzarean companion Adric about the planet Earth, and its numbering system, and a little about the TARDIS Zero Room.

Logopolis. Adric, new to this universe, knows that Earth has many oceans. He tells the Logopolitan Monitor that the Fourth Doctor has taught him how to read Earth numbers. He seems aware of the existence of the Zero Room in episode one of *Castrovalva*, though he suffers a lecture on its properties, so maybe he doesn't know too much. The short story *The Rag and Bone Man's Story* has the First Doctor making use of the Zero Room, as do the Third in the novel *The Suns of Caresh*, the Fourth in the audio *The Invasion of E-Space* and the Sixth in the audio *Patient Zero*. Although jettisoned in the Fifth Doctor's début story, the TARDIS has apparently regrown its Zero Room in the Sixth Doctor strip *Funhouse*, only to jettison it again in the Seventh Doctor novel *Deceit*. There's yet another one in the novel *Infinite Requiem*, also featuring the Seventh Doctor, though the Eighth is without one in the audio *Day of the Vashta Nerada*.

The Fourth Doctor and Adric spend many hours discussing and debating endless topics.

Earthshock. In episode one, the Fifth Doctor makes this claim in response to Adric's complaint that, with Nyssa and Tegan on board the TARDIS, such discussions have become a thing of the past.

The Doctor observes a collapsed Q-Star, the only force in the universe known to shield antimatter. He encounters the life forms known as Ergons, created by psychosynthesis.

Arc of Infinity. The TARDIS data banks state that a Q-Star can be found in the region of space known as Rondel, but it is by no means certain that this is the one he witnessed. The Fifth Doctor knows the name Ergon without having heard it in this story. The creature looks nothing like the gel guards in *The Three Doctors*, so Omega is evidently not the only being in two universes practising this science.

The Doctor becomes aware of the restorative powers of Numismaton Gas.

Planet of Fire. In episode three, the Fifth Doctor notes that Numismaton Gas is useful for Time Lords suffering regeneration difficulties; Turlough has never heard of it. Had Nyssa and Tegan known of it when they met Mawdryn posing as the Doctor in *Mawdryn Undead*, they would surely have at least mentioned it. The Seventh Doctor begins involuntarily emitting numismaton gas in the comic strip *Metamorphosis*. Any other unexpected gas emissions are, mercifully, never discussed.

On the planet Hakol, in the star system Rifta, the Time Lord discovers that the inhabitants have harnessed psychic energy as other species have harnessed electricity.

The Awakening. Hakol is the sole recipient of tinclavic from the mines on the planet Raaga, first mentioned in *The Visitation*, and later in the Sixth Doctor short story *CHAOS*, and the Seventh Doctor novel *The Hollow Men*.

He learns from an Earth history book about King John taking the Crusader's oath in London on March 4, 1215, and of the signing of the Magna Carta.

> *The King's Demons*. This is one of the very rare occasions on which the Doctor does not claim firsthand knowledge of events. Tegan, however, has next to no understanding of this portion of her planet's history. The Eleventh Doctor has his own personal copy of the Magna Carta in *The Doctor, the Widow and the Wardrobe*.

He sees a hydrazine steam generator, and visits the uninhabited rocky world of Kolkokron.

> *Frontios*. Neither Turlough nor Tegan recognize the machine that the Fifth Doctor identifies in episode one. He drops the Tractator Gravis off on Kolkokron – presumably not a world he simply picked at random - at the end of the story. It is eventually rescued and brought to Earth by an individual who may or may not be the Master in the Sixth Doctor audio *The Hollows of Time*. The planet is also mentioned in the Fifth Doctor audio *Time in Office*.

The Doctor visits the planets Androzani Major and Minor, at various points in their history, and suffers an allergic reaction to gases in the praxis range of the spectrum.

> In *The Caves of Androzani*, the Fifth Doctor tells Peri there has not been water on Androzani Minor for a billion years, but he also says that Androzani Major was becoming quite developed the last time he was there. As he cannot remember when that was, it seems likely it was during a previous incarnation. In *The Doctor, the Widow and the Wardrobe*, the Eleventh Doctor identifies an Androzani Harvester, and Androzani Major is mentioned again in the Twelfth Doctor novel *Diamond Dogs*. The Fifth Doctor reveals his reasons for wearing a stick of celery in *The Caves of Androzani* (it turns purple in the presence of gas, which is perhaps why he declares purple 'the colour of death' in *The Woman Who Lived*). Since he began to sport it in *Castrovalva*, he probably saw the importance of doing so prior to his regeneration. Why he ceased to wear it after regenerating once again is nobody's business but the Doctor's, though he asks for a stick in order to recuperate in *Cold Blood*.

While visiting Jaconda, the Fourth Doctor is reunited with his old friend and mentor Azmael, now master of that world. He is shown a beautiful forest grove, as well as an underground bolt-hole containing ancient drawings depicting the legend of the Gastropods. On their final meeting, the Doctor is forced to push Azmael into a fountain in order to sober him up.

The Twin Dilemma. The Sixth Doctor states that his most recent encounter with Azmael occurred during his fourth incarnation.

The Doctor enjoys the moonset on the Eye of Orion.

The Sixth Doctor recalls the moonset in *Timelash.* His companion for much of his fifth incarnation, Tegan, has never heard of the Eye of Orion before he mentions it at the end of *The King's Demons.* The Sixth Doctor likens it to the South Downs in the audio *Arrangements for War.* He has forgotten the co-ordinates by episode one of *The Twin Dilemma.* The Fifth Doctor promises to take Nyssa there in the audio *Psychodrome,* while the Sixth Doctor and Mel pay it a visit in the short story *A Tourist Invasion,* as does the Ninth in the comic strip *Hacked.* The Fifth and Eighth Doctors join forces to battle Sontarans on the Eye of Orion in the novel *The Eight Doctors,* and mention is made of it in the Seventh Doctor novel *Theatre of War* and the audios *Last of the Colophon, Arrangements for War, The Man Who Wasn't There, The Twilight Kingdom* and *Eye of Darkness.*

The Fifth Doctor
Peter Davison
1981-1984

Castrovalva

Prior to *Four to Doomsday*

The Fifth Doctor assigns rooms in the TARDIS to his latest companions, giving Nyssa the one closest to the Control Room.

> In *Arc of Infinity*'s second episode, we learn the location of Nyssa's room. Given that Tegan was the companion most keen to return home, you'd think the Doctor might have given her the one nearest the exit.

He places a pad and pencil in his jacket pocket, and tells companion Adric about legendary Time Lord and winner of Gallifreyan 'Moustache-wearer of the Year' four centuries in a row, Rassilon.

> *Four to Doomsday.* The Fifth Doctor gives the writing materials to companion Tegan in episode one. Adric mentions Rassilon to Monarch in episode three.

The Lateral Balance Cones on the TARDIS console give the Doctor some trouble.

> *The Visitation.* The Fifth Doctor complains that they are playing up 'again.' He takes them offline in the audio *Cuddlesome.*

The Fifth Doctor teaches Adric and Nyssa how to play draughts.

> *Kinda.* His alien companions are seen playing this Earth game in episode one. The Third Doctor plays draughts in *The Mind of Evil* and the Fourth in *The Talons of Weng-Chiang.*

He reads *The Time Machine* by Herbert George Wells (not the same copy owned by Professor Chronotis in *Shada*) and watches the plays *Charley's Aunt* and *No, No, Nanette.*

> *Black Orchid.* The Fifth Doctor alludes to this book, which his seventh self is re-reading at the start of *Doctor Who – The TV Movie.* The Fifth Doctor has a copy of the book in the novel *Warmonger.* (the Master reads *The War of the Worlds* during *Frontier in Space* – not relevant to this entry, but worth noting,

don't you think?). He also quotes from *Charley's Aunt* and sings *I Want to be Happy* from *No, No, Nanette.*

The Fifth Doctor gives Adric the co-ordinates for Heathrow Airport, with the intention of returning companion Tegan Jovanka to her place of work.

Immediately prior to *Four to Doomsday.*

Prior to *Kinda*

After companion Nyssa faints for a second time, the Fifth Doctor materialises the TARDIS on the planet Deva Loka and begins constructing a Delta Wave Augmenter.

Immediately prior to the beginning of *Kinda.*

The Visitation

Prior to *Black Orchid*

Following the Fifth Doctor's failed attempts to return her to Heathrow, stewardess Tegan Jovanka tells him she has decided to remain part of the TARDIS crew for a while.

Black Orchid. Tegan reminds the Doctor of her decision early on in episode one.

Prior to *Earthshock*

The Fifth Doctor promises to make more time for companion Adric, who feels left out now that Nyssa and Tegan are travelling in the TARDIS.

Earthshock. Adric says the Fifth Doctor has made this promise more than once.

He reads *Dr Jekyll and Mr Hyde* and a limerick by Catholic theologian Ronald Knox.

Time-Flight. The Fifth Doctor quotes the limerick to Captain Stapley. He draws comparisons with Jekyll and Hyde here and again in *Ghost Light.*

The Doctor tells his companions about the TARDIS' state of temporal grace, apparently oblivious to the fact that it has either ceased to function or never really existed in the first place.

Arc of Infinity. Companion Nyssa questions the Fifth Doctor about this, referencing the attack of the Cyberman. He replies 'Nobody's perfect,' which isn't particularly helpful.

The Fifth Doctor and his companions work alongside UNIT in the post-Lethbridge-Stewart era.

In episode two of *Mawdryn Undead,* Tegan tells Nyssa that her new friend is 'Brigadier Lethbridge-Stewart, of course,' implying some knowledge of him. There's a picture of Nyssa and Tegan (in air stewardess outfit) standing between a couple of squaddies in UNIT's Black Archive in *The Day of the Doctor.*

Prior to *Time-Flight*

Following companion Adric's death, a traumatised Fifth Doctor returns the surviving freighter crew to their own time.

Time-Flight

Prior to *Arc of Infinity*

The Doctor begins to make some repairs to the TARDIS, beginning with the audio link-up on the scanner. He leaves his ident kit on the workbench.

Arc of Infinity. The Fifth Doctor wants to use the kit to trip a handprint-activated lock at the end of episode one. It is unclear precisely when the audio link-up fails; it certainly works as late as *The Armageddon Factor.* In the Big Finish story *The Land of the Dead,* the Fifth Doctor complains about the scanner's unreliable audio circuits.

Prior to *Snakedance*

The Fifth Doctor teaches companions Nyssa and Tegan to read the TARDIS' star charts, with the intention of reaching a pre-programmed destination (apparently Earth).

Snakedance. As the story begins, the Fifth Doctor says the TARDIS hasn't materialised where it was supposed to, and companion Tegan is later surprised to find that they aren't on Earth.

Prior to *Mawdryn Undead*

The Doctor and companion Tegan are horrified by the results of a poorly maintained Transmat on organic life.

Mawdryn Undead. The Fifth Doctor lectures new companion Turlough on this subject in episode one. Tegan says that she hates Transmats, although she has not been seen encountering one at this point.

Prior to *Terminus*

In order to combat the effects of psychotropic waves, the Doctor creates four neural balancers, one for him and each of his companions.

The Battle of Ranskoor Av Kolos. The Thirteenth Doctor has the neural balancers to hand the moment she receives the distress calls from Ranskoor Av Kolos, and this is arguably the last point at which the Doctor has three permanent companions before *The Woman Who Fell to Earth.*

Prior to *Enlightenment*

The Doctor is in Seville during the 17th Century, and hears the ringing of the 25 bells in the cathedral.

The Sixth Doctor recalls Seville in *The Two Doctors.* The audio story *The Flames of Cadiz* has the First Doctor visiting there. In *Enlightenment,* his fifth incarnation recognises a gem as originating in 17th Century Spain.

The TARDIS begins to lose power, and the Fifth Doctor suspects a leak.

The opening scene of *Enlightenment.*

Prior to *The King's Demons*

The Fifth Doctor sets the co-ordinates of the TARDIS for companion Turlough's home planet, Trion. As events transpire, they never reach it.

Enlightenment. Turlough asks to be returned home at the conclusion of the story, and reminds the Fifth Doctor of his promise during the final part of *The King's Demons.*

Prior to *The Five Doctors*

During the journey to the Eye of Orion, the Fifth Doctor redesigns the TARDIS console.

The Five Doctors. Companion Tegan asks to be taken to the famously peaceful world at the end of *The King's Demons.* The reason for the console redesign is given in the novel *The Crystal Bucephalus.*

Prior to *Warriors of the Deep*

As the only incarnation not to be taken out of his timestream, the Fifth Doctor finally recalls how he came by the Seal of the High Council of Time Lords, but - despite his third self's promise - he never gets around to returning it.

> The Master gives the Third Doctor the Seal in *The Five Doctors* and his eighth self shows it off in the comic strip *The Final Chapter*. Said Seal finally performs in *The Time of the Doctor.*

The Fifth Doctor promises to show companion Tegan a glimpse of her home planet's future.

> *Warriors of the Deep.* The Doctor relates his conversation to Turlough in episode one.

Prior to *The Awakening*

In the grim surroundings of the Sea Base, the Fifth Doctor recovers his soggy clothing and conducts repairs on the TARDIS.

> *Warriors of the Deep.* In episode one, he says that repairs to the TARDIS will take some time. He changes his clothes in episode two after almost drowning.

After promising to take companion Tegan to a reunion with her grandfather in 1984, the Fifth Doctor is troubled when the TARDIS hits a time distortion.

> As *The Awakening* begins, companion Turlough and the Doctor are attempting to repair the ship.

Prior to *Frontios*

After spending some time in 1984 as guests of Tegan's Uncle Andrew, the Doctor and his companions return displaced youth Will Chandler to Little Hodcombe in 1643, after which the Time Lord checks the TARDIS computer for any information regarding why the people of Hakol failed to invade Earth, having first sent the Malus to prepare the way.

> The Fifth Doctor's stated intention in the final scene of *The Awakening,* although he doesn't actually get around to it until his seventh incarnation, according to the novel *The Hollow Men.*

He places a portable μ (mu)-field activator and five argon discharge globes inside the TARDIS.

> *Frontios.* The Fifth Doctor sends Turlough to collect them in episode one.

The Doctor and at least one female companion attend a funeral on the planet Necros, where he also takes the time to observe the fauna (mainly voltroxes and spielsnapes) and flora (*herbabaculum vitae*), all of which are, no doubt, described by Professor Thripstead in his invaluable volume.

> *Revelation of the Daleks*. The Sixth Doctor provides Peri with the traditional Necros mourning attire for females. He's also familiar with the history, geography and fauna of Necros.

Resurrection of the Daleks

Prior to *Planet of Fire*

The Fifth Doctor and his companions, Turlough and Kamelion, notify Earth authorities about the presence of Dalek duplicates in positions of influence. Quite likely, it is during this affair that the Doctor finally meets the mercenary Lytton, from Riften 5, and discovers his first name, which he knows in *Attack of the Cybermen*, despite never having heard it onscreen. UNIT are involved in some capacity.

> *Resurrection of the Daleks*. Turlough reminds the Fifth Doctor that they should do something about the duplicates during the closing scenes. In episode two of *Attack of the Cybermen*, Lytton reminds the Sixth Doctor about the 'last time we met,' though they are not seen to do so in *Resurrection*. A photo of Kamelion is pinned up at UNIT HQ in *The Day of the Doctor*. Riften 5 is mentioned in the Seventh Doctor novel *Christmas on a Rational Planet*.

During yet another battle with his arch-enemy, the Master removes the Temporal Stabiliser from the Doctor's TARDIS.

> *Planet of Fire*. In episode three, the Fifth Doctor notes that the theft of the Temporal Stabiliser is one of the Master's old tricks.

He studies Persian mythology, and has a marvellous holiday on the planet Vesta 95, and a considerably less marvellous one on the craggy knob that is asteroid Titan 3. He reads the poems *Paradise and the Peri*, by Thomas Moore, and *Excelsior*, by Henry Wadsworth Longfellow.

> *The Twin Dilemma*. The newly regenerated Sixth Doctor proposes a break on Vesta 95. He quotes from both poems, and informs companion Peri of the meaning of her name in Persian mythology, a fact she repeats in the audio *The Hollows of Time*. There's something about having someone's hands around your throat at the time that really helps information to sink in, educators take note.

The Doctor is on the planet Telos when the Cryons are in residence, and has time to admire their refrigerated cities before witnessing their apparent destruction at the hands of the Cybermen.

> *Attack of the Cybermen.* In episode two, believing the Cryons extinct, the Sixth Doctor says his companion Peri would have liked them. Though the Fourth Doctor audio *Return to Telos* doesn't feature any Cryons, the story makes it plain that the Time Lord has been back to the planet on one other occasion.

Having given up on reading it, he uses the TARDIS Manual to prop open a vent in the workshop.

> *Vengeance on Varos.* Peri discovers the abandoned volume. In *The Pirate Planet,* the Fourth Doctor declares it 'absolute rubbish.' It is seen again in the Eighth Doctor strip *The Final Chapter.* The audio story *Orbis* states that there's actually a whole library in the TARDIS devoted to it. We learn the Manual's ultimate fate in *Amy's Choice.* This is not the same volume as the TARDIS Handbook examined by companion Tegan in the final episode of *Four to Doomsday.*

His Venusian time distortion tracker having ceased to function, the Doctor puts a great deal of effort into making a new one. He hears about the primitive conditions in the outer reaches of the universe.

> *The Mark of the Rani.* The Venusian model of the tracker is seen in *The Time Monster.*

He deactivates a colour-coded Type 49 central control computer, evades the Berberese Noose (a booby trap designed to leave its victim minus their head) and encounters Vorum Gas.

> *The Two Doctors*

The Doctor visits the planet Salostopus, in the constellation of Andromeda, and builds a time-break device using Kontron crystals.

> The constellation of Andromeda is first mentioned in *The Pirate Planet.* The Sixth Doctor refers to Salostopus (home to Glitz) in *The Mysterious Planet.* In *Timelash,* he says he has not been there recently (certainly before he met Peri in *Planet of Fire*), and thus confuses its features with those of the Eye of Orion. He says he hasn't built a time-break device 'in a very long time.' The Fourth Doctor and Adric are briefly imprisoned on Salostopus in the short story *Planet of the Elves.* The planet is also mentioned in the novels *Mission: Impractical,*

Alien Bodies and *Placebo Effect.*

He befriends Professor Arthur Stengos, one of the galaxy's finest agronomists, and witnesses the combat skills of the knights of the Grand Order of Oberon.

Revelation of the Daleks. In episode two, the Sixth Doctor berates himself for attacking Orcini, not realising that he belongs to the order.

On a fishing expedition to an unnamed world, the Doctor catches four gumblejack in less than ten minutes. On the Great Lakes of Pandatorea, he sees a conga eel longer than some of the Earth trains he used to fantasize about driving.

The Two Doctors. The Fourth Doctor is seen fishing in *The Androids of Tara,* and the Sixth again goes angling in the novel *Time of Your Life* and the comic strip *Time & Time Again.* The Eighth Doctor enjoys Gumblejack fritters in the novel *The Bodysnatchers.*

He is on Earth when fossil fuels run out, and laments the fact that humanity never extracted energy from the sea.

Mindwarp. In *Dinosaurs on a Spaceship,* the Eleventh Doctor discovers that the Silurians have successfully harnessed tidal power.

Prior to *The Caves of Androzani*

The Doctor acquires a deep healing beam for the TARDIS' medical kit.

The Twin Dilemma. The Sixth Doctor remarks that this item is an improvement over the laser scalpel. Said scalpel is put to use in the Fifth Doctor audios *The Land of the Dead* and *The Mutant Phase.*

He briefly redecorates the TARDIS' interior, experimenting with a regrettable leopardskin theme, and has a run-in with the London Investigative 'N' Detective Agency (LINDA). In the vortex, the Fifth Doctor's TARDIS collides with that of one of his future incarnations.

Time Crash, the 2007 *Children in Need Special.*

The Fifth Doctor travels forward in time to his home planet on the last day of the Time War, having been summoned by the War Doctor and the Tenth and Eleventh Doctors.

The Day of the Doctor

The Sixth Doctor
Colin Baker
1984-1986

The Twin Dilemma

Prior to *Attack of the Cybermen*

The recently regenerated Sixth Doctor returns the twins Romulus and Remus to Earth.

> This is the Sixth Doctor's stated intention at the end of *The Twin Dilemma.*

In the absence of his trusty sonic screwdriver, he builds a small sonic lance, as well as another portable device capable of tracking distress signals. The Sixth Doctor undertakes a lot of repair work in the TARDIS, despite Peri's insistence that he rest. In his distracted state, he addresses his companion as Tegan, Zoe, Susan and Jamie. He even reminisces about the Terrible Zodin for the first time in years.

> *Attack of the Cybermen.* The tracking device used by the Sixth Doctor to locate Lytton's signal is not the same one wielded by his fourth incarnation in episode five of *The Armageddon Factor.* In episode three of *Robot,* the Fourth Doctor uses an attachment to turn his screwdriver into a sonic lance.

Prior to *Vengeance on Varos*

The Sixth Doctor has a fractious relationship with the TARDIS - he causes three electrical fires and a total power failure (an early indication of the Zeiton-7 shortage, perhaps?), almost collides with an asteroid storm, accidentally wipes the flight computer memory and jettisons three-quarters of the storage hold. He also gets lost in the corridors - twice. The night before the ship lands on Varos, he somehow manages to burn companion Peri's cold supper.

> *Vengeance on Varos.* Peri says that all these disasters occurred since she and the Sixth Doctor departed from Telos. Zeiton-7 is mentioned in the Seventh Doctor novel *Lucifer Rising* (where it is spelled Zyton-7), the Third Doctor audio *The Blame Game,* the Eighth Doctor audio *The Creed of the Kromon,* and the Eleventh Doctor comic strip *Buying Time.*

Prior to *The Mark of the Rani*

The Doctor gains an appreciation of the work of the artist Turner, and reads the poem *The Battle of the Baltic,* by Thomas Campbell. He promises to take companion Peri to Kew Gardens (at some point in the 19th Century, judging by her clothing), but the TARDIS is dragged off-course.

> *The Mark of the Rani.* The Sixth Doctor quotes from Campbell's poem in episode one. He sets off a trap hidden, bizarrely, in a Turner painting. In the audio *Mary's Story,* the Eighth Doctor recalls a disagreement with the artist. The Tenth Doctor visits Kew in the comic strip *The Garden Rebellion.*

Prior to *The Two Doctors*

In the 51st Century, the Doctor causes the main reactor at the weapons factory on Villengard – a planet situated at the dead centre of the universe – to go critical. He stays long enough to see a banana grove planted in its place.

> *The Doctor Dances.* The Ninth Doctor stresses to companion Jack Harkness that he went to Villengard only once. His sixth self is carrying a banana in *The Two Doctors,* and still has some bananas from the grove about his person during *The Girl in the Fireplace.* That's right, this time-placement is based on the fact that the Sixth Doctor has a banana in his pocket. Deal with it. The War Doctor is depicted as the incarnation responsible for the carnage on Villengard in the strip *The Whole Thing's Bananas.* The Seventh Doctor novel *Return of the Living Dad* states that the TARDIS contains a banana-filled room. Yes, we have too many bananas. The First Doctor notes that Villengard is to be found at the centre of the universe in *Twice Upon a Time.*

He meets Archimedes, Isambard Kingdom Brunel and Dante. The Sixth Doctor tells Peri about former companion Jamie before taking her to an unnamed planet for a spot of fishing. In a matter of hours, she grows bored.

> *The Two Doctors.* The Sixth Doctor keeps contact details for these famous individuals in his wallet. It is impossible to say whether or not Peri was with him at the time, but she knows who Jamie is without having to be told. Perhaps it's also at this point that, in reminiscent mood, he shows her a picture of Jo Grant (see *Timelash*). The First Doctor calls Archimedes 'the great man' in the audio *The Destination Wars,* while other mentions occur in the novels *City at the World's End, Fallen Gods* and *The Blood Cell.* Brunel is name-checked again in *The Mark of the Rani,* and appears in the Sixth Doctor audio *Iron Bright* and the Eighth

Doctor novel *Reckless Engineering*. Archimedes is referenced in the First Doctor novel *City at the World's End*, the Eighth Doctor story *Fallen Gods*, and the Ninth Doctor audio *Retail Therapy*. The Sixth Doctor also does a spot of angling in the audio *Arrangements for War*. Other fishing expeditions are depicted in the comic strips *Lunar Lagoon* and *Planet of the Dead*.

Prior to *Timelash*

The Doctor shows Peri photos of former companion Jo Grant. He learns that there is an intergalactic rule forbidding stowaways.

Timelash. Very likely, the Third Doctor pocketed Jo's UNIT pass as he did Liz Shaw's. Given the number of companions who have snuck inside the TARDIS over the years, it's astonishing that he hasn't quoted this rule regarding stowaways before or since.

Prior to *Revelation of the Daleks*

The Sixth Doctor is saddened to learn of the death of old friend Professor Arthur Stengos.

Revelation of the Daleks

Prior to *The Mysterious Planet*
(*The Trial of a Time Lord* episodes one to four)

Immediately after the events on Necros, the Sixth Doctor takes companion Peri 'somewhere fun.'

Revelation of the Daleks. The Sixth Doctor is almost certainly planning a return trip to Blackpool, where *The Nightmare Fair*, the first story of the aborted 23rd season, was to have taken place. His fourth incarnation recalls an earlier visit to the seaside resort during *Underworld*.

Following his ousting as Lord President of Gallifrey (an incident of which he has no knowledge), the Doctor's TARDIS is breached by a Time Lord agent, who installs the latest surveillance technology and replaces the space-time element.

The surveillance device is mentioned in *The Mysterious Planet*. In *Arc of Infinity*, the Fifth Doctor asks Damon to ensure that his new space-time element does not contain a recall circuit, meaning that the replacement has itself been replaced, enabling the Time Lords to bring the Sixth Doctor to trial. There is no opportunity for this to have happened during *The Five Doctors*, so it must have been some time after that.

The Doctor sees a Mark Seven Postidion Life Preserver.

Glitz is wearing one in *The Mysterious Planet*, but the Sixth Doctor doesn't identify it until *The Ultimate Foe*, where he also notes its spear-retardant qualities.

The Doctor reads *Moby Dick* (wishing that the author would just get to the bit with the whale), *The Water Babies* and the various theories concerning the consequences of a black light explosion. He pockets a teddy bear, a black cat mask and an oil can. He and Peri travel on the London Underground.

The Sixth Doctor quotes *The Water Babies* in *The Mysterious Planet*. The items listed are removed from his pockets during a search. *Attack of the Cybermen* represents Peri's first visit to London, but she recalls buying a candy bar and newspaper at Marble Arch, which she doesn't have the opportunity to do onscreen. The Twelfth Doctor reveals his issues with Herman Melville's whale of a tale in *Extremis*, while his fifth incarnation refers to it in the audio *Omega*. The Fourth Doctor plays charades while held captive in the audio *The Wrath of the Iceni*, and somehow manages to mime *Moby Dick* with his hands tied behind his back.

He witnesses the trial of the so-called Witches of Enderhive, which he considers a travesty of justice, and a number of interstellar battles around the rim worlds (including the planet Tokl) during the 24th Century.

Mindwarp. The Sixth Doctor mentions this incident during his own trial, but it is unclear whether the Time Lords were the prosecutors. He tells Sil about the space battles near Tokl.

The Doctor meets the 18th Century teller of tall tales Hieronymus Carl Friedrich Baron von Münchhausen.

The Ultimate Foe. The Sixth Doctor mentions the baron as an example of a famous liar.

He is at Princetown in 1984 when strange matter is discovered.

Time and the Rani

In the early 21st Century, the Doctor learns of the architectural awards won by the resort known as Paradise Towers, as well as the spectacular swimming pool on the planet Griophos, used exclusively by the flesh-eating Gulmeri.

Paradise Towers

He hears about Nostalgia Trips, 'the most notorious travel firm in the five galaxies,' and the incident involving one of that company's cruisers and the glass eaters of Tharl. He meets some particularly interesting individuals in a 1950s holiday camp, and encounters an infant Chimeron.

> *Delta and the Bannermen*, prior to his association with Mel (she fails to identify Delta, while the Seventh Doctor is familiar with the maturity rate of the infant Chimeron). Of Shangri-La Holiday camp, he tells her 'often the most interesting people stay at these places.'

The Doctor meets Plato, visits idyllic pre-20th Century Perivale, sees a functioning Poly-Dimensional Scanning Imager, and hears of the planet Proamon and the space-trading colony on the dark side of Svartos (along with the legend of the treasure-protecting dragon that lives there).

> *Dragonfire*. The Seventh Doctor recalls that Perivale has lush green fields and a village blacksmith. He cannot recall precisely how or when he heard the name Proamon. The short story *The Brain of Socrates* describes an appropriately affectionate yet non-sexual encounter the Fourth Doctor had with Plato. The Eleventh Doctor meets the Greek Philosopher in the comic strip *The Chains of Olympus*. Proamon is mentioned in the Eleventh Doctor novel *Night of the Humans*.

The Sixth Doctor and Peri are on Thordon in the last quarter of the 24th Century (by Time Lord reckoning) when they discover that the Mentors of Thoros Beta have been supplying the Warlords with advanced CD phasers.

> *Mindwarp*, immediately prior to their arrival on Thoros Beta. The Fifth Doctor mentions the planet in the audio *Zaltys*, but stresses that he has not been there yet.

Mindwarp
(*The Trial of a Time Lord* episodes five to eight)

Terror of the Vervoids
(*The Trial of a Time Lord* episodes nine to twelve)

The Ultimate Foe
(*The Trial of a Time Lord* episodes thirteen to fourteen)

Prior to Regeneration

OK, kids, this is where it gets even more complicated …

After the events of his trial, the Sixth Doctor returns Mel to her proper place in the timestream, at some point during her travels with him prior to his regeneration (about which she makes no mention of in *The Ultimate Foe*). As with Sarah Jane, all her memories of the event are erased.

> In *School Reunion*, Sarah appears to have no recollection of the events of *The Five Doctors*. The Mel who is snatched by the Master to appear at the Doctor's trial is unfamiliar with Glitz, so for her this is obviously pre-*Dragonfire*. The novelization of *The Ultimate Foe* states that Mel is sent back to the stellar fragment Oxyveguramosa in the Apus Constellation, also mentioned in the audio *The Wrong Doctors*, the Sixth Doctor novel *Business Unusual*, and the Tenth Doctor comic strip *The Lodger*.

The Sixth Doctor has at least one well-publicised adventure in the same time period as that of his visit to Necros.

> *Revelation of the Daleks*. Davros recognises the Sixth Doctor (despite their never having met onscreen) and has had a statue of him placed in the Garden of Fond Memories. The Skaro Daleks, however, have not been monitoring the Doctor, and fail to identify him in episode two. The audio *Davros* concerns an earlier encounter between the Sixth Doctor and the creator of the Daleks.

On an unnamed planet, the Doctor is paying a visit to Miracle City when the crazed architect Kroagnon is suspected of killing anyone who dares sully his vision by residing there.

> *Paradise Towers*. The Seventh Doctor recognises the name Kroagnon and later recalls the story of the murders in Miracle City.

The Doctor arrives on the fascinating planet of Pyro Shika, and has a peaceful time on Mogar, a world on the Perseus Arm of the Milky Way, rich in Vionesium and other natural resources and rare metals. In the late 30th Century, he encounters Captain 'Tonker' Travers, whom he involves in a web of mayhem and intrigue, while also managing to save the captain's ship. In the same time period, he meets and admires maverick investigator Hallet, and travels on a Grade I Security Craft, which is always commanded by a commodore. He reads Rudyard Kipling's *Just So Stories* and the poem *The Listeners*, by Walter De La Mare, and learns to 'sing' *On With the Motley*. The Sixth Doctor and Mel eventually meet for what is for her the first time, in the Sussex village of Pease Pottage, where his new companion lives a carefree life in a house with a large garden. He finds it difficult to keep up with Mel, and envies her almost-total recall. To his regret, she brings her exercise bike on board the TARDIS.

> The Sixth Doctor suggests Pyro Shika as a possible destination during *Terror of the Vervoids.* He quotes De La Mare's poem (as does his fourth incarnation in the novel *The Eight Doctors*) and Kipling's *The Elephant's Child* during the story, and reminds Mel about the compost heap in her garden. As he does not see Hallet until he is dead, it is unclear whether they knew each other during his current incarnation, or an earlier one (it might explain why the disguised Hallet does not make himself known to the Doctor). The Second Doctor's companion Zoe also has total recall, but the Time Lord never expresses any jealousy of her gift. Whether the events on the *Hyperion III* occur as they were seen at the Doctor's trial is debatable, since they clearly depend upon the Doctor being found innocent (or perhaps he just has to remember to look surprised). An earlier meeting with Captain Travers is described in the Sixth Doctor novel *Instruments of Darkness.* The Fourth Doctor and Sarah Jane encounter Kipling in the novel *Evolution.* The writer receives another mention in the Seventh Doctor novel *The Death of Art.*

At some point, the Sixth Doctor's companion Mel sees his handwriting.

> *The Ultimate Foe.* Mel recognises the writing on the Valeyard's hit-list.

The Sixth Doctor explains the process of regeneration to Mel. When she discovers that he is an expert in the field of thermodynamics, they discuss her idol, CP Snow. Unexpectedly, the Doctor doesn't consider himself clever enough to build a radiation wave meter, but he nevertheless gets his hands on one, and stores it in the TARDIS tool room. A guardsman's bearskin finds its way into the TARDIS wardrobe. In 1956, the Doctor sees Elvis Presley perform *Hound Dog* on *The Ed Sullivan Show.* He watches Richard Brinsley Sheridan's 1775 play *The Rivals,* and is with Louis Pasteur as he creates vaccines for rabies and anthrax.

> *Time and the Rani.* The Seventh Doctor mentions Mrs Malaprop, a character from Sheridan's play. He's familiar with Pasteur, and there is no indication that Mel hasn't also met him. Mel says she knows about regeneration. The Doctor models the bearskin for the Rani. Elvis is first mentioned in this story, and again in *The Christmas Invasion, 42* and *Rosa,* as well as in the Fifth Doctor audio *The Eye of the Scorpion,* the comic strips *Children of the Revolution, Interstellar Overdrive* and *Bite of the Morphuse!,* and the novels *Original Sin, The Taint, Earthworld*

and *The Resurrection Casket.* The Ninth Doctor tells Rose about the Ed Sullivan appearance in *The Idiot's Lantern.*

The Doctor listens to Michelangelo whinge while painting the Sistine Chapel.

Vincent and the Doctor. Michelangelo is first mentioned by the Seventh Doctor in *Time and the Rani.* He appears in the short stories *The Lonely Computer and The War of Art,* and the Fifth Doctor audio *Fallen Angels.* He's name-checked in the Sixth Doctor comic strip *Changes,* the Eighth Doctor audio *The Resurrection of Mars,* and the novel *The Stone Rose,* where the Tenth Doctor claims never to have met the artist.

He joins his five former selves and seven future selves in freezing the planet Gallifrey in a single moment of time on the final day of the Time Lords' conflict with the Daleks.

The Day of the Doctor

A period of more than 53 years has elapsed since the Sixth Doctor's trial. He becomes worried about the temporal flicker in Sector 13, and plans to book the bicentennial refit of the TARDIS and to pop over to Centauri 7 for reasons unknown, after which he hopes to take a short holiday. His ship is forced off-course by the Rani's Navigational Guidance System Distorter with such violence that it triggers a regeneration.

Time and the Rani. The newly regenerated Seventh Doctor mentions all these tasks as he comes round – whether he gets around to completing them, however, is debatable. In evidence shown during the trial in *The Mysterious Planet,* the Sixth Doctor is 900 years of age, but one regeneration later, in *Time and the Rani,* he is 953. Strangely, several incarnations later, he seems to have grown younger (no doubt another side-effect of the Time War). The novels *Love and War* and *Head Games* both suggest that the abrupt regeneration was brought on by the waiting Seventh Doctor.

The Seventh Doctor
Sylvester McCoy
1987-1989 and 1996

Time and the Rani

Prior to *Paradise Towers*

The Seventh Doctor returns the scientists kidnapped by the Rani to their proper places in time and space. He explains the workings of the TARDIS to Albert Einstein.

> *Time and the Rani.* This is the Seventh Doctor's stated intention at the end of the story. The Eleventh Doctor and Einstein are seen socializing in *A Christmas Carol.*

The Seventh Doctor is forced to jettison the TARDIS swimming pool when it starts leaking. He promises companion Mel a holiday at Paradise Towers.

> *Paradise Towers.* As the episode begins, the Seventh Doctor and Mel are watching a promotional video for the resort. The TARDIS eventually grows another pool (into which the Eleventh Doctor falls shortly after regenerating), but he is forced to jettison it once more in *The Doctor's Wife.* It's back again in *Journey to the Centre of the TARDIS.* According to the Second Doctor novel *Invasion of the Cat-People,* the design of the pool is based on one built for Claudius Caesar. It's used or mentioned in the Seventh Doctor novels *The Left-Handed Hummingbird* and *Eternity Weeps* (where it's deleted once again), the audios *The Final Phase, White Ghosts, Return to Telos, The Roof of the World* and *Three's a Crowd,* and the comic strips *Cat Litter* (featuring the Seventh Doctor), *Beautiful Freak* (the Eighth) and *After Life* (the Eleventh).

Prior to *Delta and the Bannermen*

The Doctor purchases an umbrella with a question mark handle, possibly from the same retailer who provided all his other question mark-bedecked clothing. On the planet Navarro, he meets the squat, wrinkled, purple-skinned species known as the Navarinos, and discovers that they have a high metabolic rate. He acquires the only Quarb crystal this side of the Softel Nebula (whichever side that happens to be), and finds that the white flag has the same meaning throughout the civilised universe (as opposed to the red alert, apparently). During either his sixth or seventh incarnation, he and companion Mel tangle with the Bannermen.

> *Delta and the Bannermen*. This story marks the first appearance of the question mark handle umbrella. There is nothing in the dialogue to indicate whether Mel was with the Doctor when he first met the Navarinos (who are also mentioned in the novels *The Return of the Living Dad* and *The Slitheen Excursion*), but she does not need to be told who the Bannermen are - when informed that they are on their way to Shangri-La Holiday Camp, she volunteers to arrange an evacuation. The Seventh Doctor uses the Quarb crystal in his repairs of the Nostalgia Trips tour bus.

He visits Melissa Majoria, the planet of origin for many of Earth's bees, of which he is rather fond. He also learns of the Tandocca Scale, the series of wavelengths used by the bees as carrier signals.

> The Tenth Doctor casually mentions the bees' planet of origin to companion Donna in *The Stolen Earth*, but the fact that his seventh incarnation isn't remotely surprised that they are able to call to the Chimeron Queen in episode two of *Delta and the Bannermen* indicates that he has, by now, discovered that they are not actually Terran insects.

Prior to *Dragonfire*

The Doctor hears the nursery rhyme *Mary, Mary, Quite Contrary*. Perhaps believing it to be his unauthorised biography, he picks up a copy of *The Doctor's Dilemma*, by George Bernard Shaw.

> *Dragonfire*. The Seventh Doctor misquotes the rhyme in episode three, and reads Shaw's play in episode one. In episode two of *Remembrance of the Daleks*, he finds a copy of Richard Gordon's *Doctor in the House*, bringing this all-too-brief running gag to an abrupt end.

During one of his many battles with the Daleks, the Doctor witnesses their Transmat operations. Possibly it is on this occasion that he returns to Spiridon to deal with the frozen Dalek army, taking with him a device capable of interfering with Dalek control systems. He storms a Dalek shuttle, determining where its weaknesses lie.

> *Remembrance of the Daleks*. The Seventh Doctor explains all about Dalek Transmats to Ace, including the fact that they usually leave an operator on station to deal with malfunctions

(or the Doctor's acts of sabotage). He talks of using the device while on Spiridon, but he is never seen to do so onscreen, indicating a second visit, at which time the accepted pronunciation of the planet's name has changed - the Third Doctor says '*Spy*ridon,' while the Seventh Doctor here and Oswin in *Asylum of the Daleks* say '*Spi*ridon.' The Doctor's pronunciation of Metebelis 3 alters sometime after his third incarnation. His seventh incarnation returns to Spiridon in the comic strip *Emperor of the Daleks,* and the audio *Return of the Daleks* (in which the planet's name has been changed to Zaleria to avoid any further mix-ups).

In 25th Century Birmingham, the Doctor encounters a ruthless alien predator known as a Stigorax. He hears some disturbing rumours about Terra Alpha, and decides to take a look for himself when he has a spare moment.

The Happiness Patrol

He receives positive reports of the inhabitants of the planet Segonax. Encountering the beings known as the Gods of Ragnarok, he retrieves a portion of a sword possessed of unique properties from their arena (the weapon previously belonged to an unnamed Gladiator who died for the Gods' amusement) and determines to fight them throughout time.

The Greatest Show in the Galaxy. The Gods of Ragnarok never appear elsewhere onscreen, but the implication is that the Doctor has battled them on many occasions, and possibly in several different incarnations.

The Doctor meets Louis Armstrong - a man who 'really understood time' - and develops a fondness for jazz. He returns to Windsor during the 11th Century, at a time when the castle is being built.

Silver Nemesis. The Seventh Doctor mentions Armstrong in a deleted scene. He claims he previously saw the Validium bow placed in a vault at Windsor Castle. Other instances of the Doctor's jazz-mania are cited in the Second Doctor story *Foreign Devils* and the Seventh Doctor novel *The Also People*.

He learns that Brigadier Lethbridge-Stewart eventually dies in his bed (although he either forgets the exact date or never knew it in the first place).

Battlefield. The Seventh Doctor is surprised when he discovers what he imagines to be the Brigadier's body. The Eleventh Doctor is equally surprised upon learning of his old friend's death in *The Wedding of River Song*. It is likely that the information the Doctor possesses about the passing was acquired before Ace became his companion, or she would probably not have addressed one of his oldest and closest friends as 'scumbag.' Presumably, the Doctor doesn't know that, after death, his old friend will suffer the ignominy of being resurrected as the Cyber-Brig.

Sometime after 1912, he acquires a badge of the Royal Flying Corps. In Africa, he witnesses the lethal use of a Zulu Assegai spear. At some unknown point in time, he visits the Khyber Pass, where he dines at a nice restaurant. He has an unpleasant experience at a bus station.

Ghost Light. The Seventh Doctor tells Ace when the Corps was formed and promises her a badge. He recalls his loathing for bus stations. The Seventh Doctor again recalls dining up the Khyber in the audio *House of Blue Fire*, and the Eighth remembers flying on a magic carpet there in the audio *Death in Blackpool*.

In a possible future (later nullified by the events of *The Curse of Fenric*), he finds the Earth a dying world covered in chemical slime, and meets the Haemovores, the species into which humanity evolves within the space of a few thousand years. Seventeen centuries prior to the incident at Maiden's Point, he plays chess with the entity known as Fenric, using pieces carved from bone. Fenric is unable to solve the Doctor's puzzle and becomes trapped within the Shadow Dimensions.

The Curse of Fenric. The full details of the Doctor's chess contest with Fenric are disclosed in the serial's novelization, which also states that it occurred in Constantinople. There is no mention of the location in the broadcast version, and even the Special Edition does not state specifically that the match took place there.

The Doctor meets Winston Churchill on several occasions. During each encounter, the wartime Prime Minister attempts to procure the TARDIS key; the Doctor responds by learning to forge Churchill's signature (as well as that of the head of the secret service). On one such jaunt, he hears about Dr Judson's work on the Ultima Machine.

The Seventh Doctor forges his friend's signature in episode one of *The Curse of Fenric*. His companion Ace has never heard of the Ultima Machine. The Tenth Doctor mentions Churchill in *The Idiot's Lantern*. *Victory of the Daleks* makes it plain that Churchill has met at least two other incarnations of the Doctor. Such encounters are described in the Sixth Doctor novels *Players*, *The Shadow in the Glass*and *The Eight Doctors*, the Tenth

Doctor short story *The Lonely Computer*, the audios *Energy of the Daleks, The Oncoming Storm, Hounded* and *The Chartwell Metamorphosis*, as well as the Eleventh Doctor comic strip *The Eagle of the Reich*. In the audio *Men of War*, the First Doctor has a letter of authority signed by Churchill. In *Thin Ice*, the Twelfth Doctor is shown to be as adept at forgery as his seventh incarnation. Dr Judson's Ultima program is mentioned in the Twelfth Doctor novel *The Crawling Terror*.

He discovers the location of the home planet of the Cheetah People, and the gift of teleportation possessed by the Kitlings, but comforts himself with the (incorrect) knowledge that they do not venture far from their own planet.

Survival. The Seventh Doctor knows of the Cheetah People and their abilities. The Second Doctor is familiar with them in the novel *Invasion of the Cat-People*.

Mel and the Doctor lend UNIT a helping hand.

The Day of the Doctor. In UNIT's Black Archive, a picture of Mel alongside a soldier appears pinned up on a board.

The Seventh Doctor begins receiving a faint tracking signal from the trading colony on the dark side of Svartos.

Dragonfire

Prior to *Remembrance of the Daleks*

Returning to Gallifrey, the Doctor is re-elected Lord President.

Remembrance of the Daleks. In episode four, the Seventh Doctor describes himself to the Emperor Dalek (AKA Davros) as 'President-elect' – this, despite the fact that he learned in *The Mysterious Planet* that he'd been deposed in his absence. He might, of course, be bluffing, but it's not as though simply being the Doctor wouldn't hold any sway with his greatest foes. Perhaps this is the occasion on which he returns *The Ancient Law of Gallifrey* to the Panopticon archives – plainly, he doesn't do so at the end of *Shada*, since *Full Circle* makes it clear that Romana has not yet returned home, and has no desire to do so. In fact, the Seventh Doctor still has it in the novel *The Dimension Riders*. In the First Doctor short story *The Book of Shadows*, it transpires that *The Ancient Law of Gallifrey* has somehow found its way to Egypt in the year 322 BC.

Prior to *The Happiness Patrol*

The Doctor reads the paper delivered by Dr John Wallace to the Royal Society in 1677. He hears the song *As Time Goes By*.

The Happiness Patrol. The Seventh Doctor again claims to be a member of the Royal Society in the novel *The Room With No Doors*.

Prior to *Silver Nemesis*

The Seventh Doctor builds companion Ace a new tape deck (which also functions as a transmitter) to replace the one destroyed by the Daleks in 1963 London. On November 23, 1988, when England is enjoying unusually mild weather, they head for an open-air jazz concert featuring Courtney Pine.

Silver Nemesis

Prior to *The Greatest Show in the Galaxy*

In the Groz Valley of Melogophon, the Doctor samples a pleasing beverage. He procures the book *Juggling for the Complete Klutz* by John Cassidy, and watches astronaut Neil Armstrong's historic moon landing. The Seventh Doctor hides the rucksack belonging to companion Ace, which contains her cannisters of Nitro Nine.

The Greatest Show in the Galaxy. The Seventh Doctor is also seen juggling in episode one of *Survival*. He misquotes Armstrong's 'One small step' speech in the final episode, though his Sixth incarnation gets it right in the audio *Return of the Krotons*. The Tenth Doctor witnesses the moon landings on a number of occasions, according to *Blink*, and his next incarnation's plan to vanquish the Silence revolves around this incident. In the comic strip *Wormwood*, it's stated that the Eighth Doctor's enemies the Threshold are based on the moon, and also watched the arrival of Apollo 11.

Prior to *Battlefield*

The Doctor acquires a valuable piece of alien coinage, part mechanical in appearance.

Battlefield. Ace doesn't say she has never seen it before, so the Seventh Doctor may have come by it during their travels together, although the Fifth Doctor appears to have the same piece of currency in the audio *Circular Time: Summer*. The First Doctor has no money in episode two of *The Reign of Terror*. The Second Doctor flips a coin during *The Invasion* and *The Three*

Doctors, as does his fifth persona in *Enlightenment* and *The Awakening*. The Fourth Doctor uses a two-headed Alderberan III coin in episode two of *The Pirate Planet* in order to get the result he desires when flipping. The Third Doctor claims, during his first adventure, that he has no use for money, and his empty wallet in episode two of *Terror of the Autons* seems to confirm this (though why carry a wallet if you never have any money?). Strangely, he has a Jordanian five piastre coin in his waistcoat in the final episode of *Death to the Daleks*, which he uses to test a trap in the Exxilon city, just as his first incarnation does in the tomb of Rassilon during *The Five Doctors*. The Fifth Doctor pays for a drink in *The Planet of Fire* with a handful of alien coins, and he must presumably have some way of purchasing the newspaper he reads in episode one of *Time-Flight*. However, he is penniless in the final episodes of *Arc of Infinity* and *Snakedance*. The Seventh Doctor buys some truly disgusting fruit in *The Greatest Show in the Galaxy*, but leaves a corner shop without paying in episode one of *Survival*. In episode two of *The End of Time*, the Tenth Doctor says he has stopped carrying money altogether, which is probably why, in *The Bells of Saint John*, his next incarnation has to take a collection to raise enough cash for breakfast. The Twelfth Doctor has no money for coffee in *Deep Breath*.

Prior to *Ghost Light*

While visiting Earth's middle-to-late Pleistocene Era, the Doctor encounters a Neanderthal tribe, learns the sayings of their elders, and pockets the fang of a cave bear. By this time, several of his incarnations are Fellows of the Royal Geographical Society. He travels on the Flying Scotsman; reads, watches or hears Douglas Adams' *The Hitchhiker's Guide to the Galaxy*; and sees a version of *My Fair Lady*. Companion Ace tells the Seventh Doctor of her frightening experience at Gabriel Chase when aged thirteen.

Ghost Light. The Doctor quotes here from *The Hitchhiker's Guide*. The Tenth Doctor mentions Arthur Dent in *The Christmas Invasion*, sings *I Could Have Danced All Night* in *The Girl in the Fireplace* and announces 'By George, she's got it!' in *The Pyramid at the End of the World*. In addition to *The Rings of Akhaten*, the audios *The Time Museum, Hornet's Nest: A Sting in the Tail, The Auntie Matter, Babblesphere, Cobwebs, The Wormery, Storm Warning* and *Max Warp*, the Seventh Doctor novel *Birthright*, the Eighth Doctor novel *The Tomorrow Windows*, and the comic strips *The Man in the Ion Mask, Bazaar Adventures, A Life of*

Matter & Death, Interstellar Overdrive, Assimilation[2], *Sky Jacks* and *Clara Oswald and the School of Death* all contain veiled references to *Hitchhiker's*. Ace recognises Nimrod as a Neanderthal, so it's probable she was with the Doctor for this adventure. He refers to her as 'Eliza,' a reference to Eliza Doolittle, the heroine of Shaw's *Pygmalion*. The Eighth Doctor addresses his companion Lucie Miller by the same name in the audio *No More Lies*.

Prior to *The Curse of Fenric*

The Doctor becomes familiar with the 'neat algorithm' known as the Prisoner's Dilemma. He tells companion Ace that he is taking her to a top secret naval camp.

The Curse of Fenric. As the TARDIS materialises in episode one, Ace is already complaining that the Seventh Doctor has taken her to the wrong place.

Prior to *Survival*

The Doctor adds a tracking feature to his pocket watch. When his companion Ace says she wonders what her old gang are up to, the Seventh Doctor takes it as a request to return her to Perivale.

Survival. The Doctor uses the watch to somehow track Ace. Needless to say, this isn't the same pocket watch seen in *Human Nature* and *The Family of Blood*, or the one worn by the Sixth Doctor throughout his travels.

Prior to *Doctor Who – The TV Movie*

A bounty is placed on the Seventh Doctor's head.

Delta and the Bannermen. Keillor the bounty hunter notes that killing the Seventh Doctor would make him rich. Just because it is in the past for Keillor, though, doesn't necessarily mean that it's the same for the Doctor. It is difficult to imagine that there isn't a price on all 13 of his heads (or 508, if you believe *The Sarah Jane Adventures*) instead of just the Seventh and the Fourth.

The Seventh Doctor's participation in the plan to save Gallifrey on the final day of the Time War is not without its hazards, and he experiences a certain amount of time fluctuation during the operation, which, fortunately, is ultimately successful.

The Day of the Doctor. The Seventh Doctor is seen both jacketless and sporting his question mark pullover, and then as he appears in *Doctor Who – The TV Movie*. The Tenth Doctor does voice some concerns over the likelihood of the plan succeeding, and this is clearly one of the side-effects.

For the first time in several incarnations, he decides to forgo the ostentatious question marked outerwear, opting instead for question marked underpants.

The Zygon Invasion. Said decorated undies are mentioned in the novel *Seeing I*, and are sported by the Eighth Doctor in the comic strip *The Glorious Dead*.

The Eighth Doctor
Paul McGann
1996

Prior to *Doctor Who – The TV Movie*

The Seventh Doctor redesigns the TARDIS' interior and key. He changes the lock on the TARDIS to accept the key he used during his third incarnation, and places a spare in the cubbyhole above the letter P in the Police Box sign. He builds a new sonic screwdriver, acquires a record player (but apparently only one record), and begins re-reading *The Time Machine* by his old friend Herbert George ('H G') Wells. For the first time in several incarnations, he plays with yo-yos. Optimistically, he replaces his 500-year diary with a 900-year version. Anticipating further battles with the Cybermen, he stocks up on gold dust. He is with Giacomo Puccini before his death, and finds it sad when Franco Alfano completes *Turandot* based on Puccini's notes. He is intimately acquainted with Madame Curie. He learns of the great accomplishments of Dr Grace Holloway. An adventure that takes place in San Francisco during Christmas of 2000 makes it plain to him that the city should be avoided at that time. More than a decade later, he meets Gareth, head of the Seismology Unit at UCLA, who informs the Doctor that while he worked as a security guard at a New Year's Eve function in 1999, a mysterious stranger dressed as James Butler 'Wild Bill' Hickock provided him with the answers to his crucial poetry examination. He also meets Doctor Sigmund Freud, with whom he discusses transference and compensation. At some point, he parts company with his companion Ace. Immediately prior to the start of the movie, he receives word that his old enemy, the Master, has been exterminated on Skaro (presumably in retaliation for his intended betrayal of the Daleks in *Frontier in Space*). He claims the remains and intends to return them to Gallifrey.

> *Doctor Who – The TV Movie*. The original sonic screwdriver is destroyed during *The Visitation*. The Seventh Doctor novel *Lungbarrow* establishes that his replacement is the screwdriver that once belonged to Romana. The novel *The Eight Doctors* states that the Eighth Doctor is using the secondary TARDIS Control Room, used by the Fourth Doctor from *The Masque of Mandragora* to *The Talons of Weng-Chiang*. He tells Grace about Puccini (also mentioned in the Third Doctor novel *The Devil Goblins from Neptune* and the Eighth Doctor audio *Something Inside*) and Leonardo da Vinci. The Fifth Doctor originally alludes to *The Time Machine* during *Black Orchid*. The Master gives Chang Lee a

bag of the Doctor's gold dust. When the boy attempts to return it, the Time Lord advises him to avoid San Francisco the following Christmas. The phrases he uses to describe Grace - such as 'tired of life, but afraid of dying' - imply that he may have read Grace's autobiography. Grace appears in a photo in UNIT's Black Archive during *The Day of the Doctor,* but there's no indication of whether or not she was in the company of the Doctor at that time. The Eleventh Doctor mentions Freud's theory of compensation in *The Curse of the Black Spot,* and has it mentioned to him by his previous persona in *The Day of the Doctor.* Freud gets name-checked in the audios *Death Match* and *Brotherhood of the Daleks,* and the Eighth Doctor novel *The City of the Dead.* The dramatised sections of the documentary *Doctor Who: The Ultimate Guide* show that the Doctor now has a 1,200-year diary. By the time of *The Girl Who Died,* he's traded it in for a 2,000-year edition. Does he have to copy out the first 1,200 years again, or just leave them blank? According to the novel *Set Piece,* the Seventh Doctor makes a gift of the original 500-year diary to companion Ace. The Doctor goes without his favourite yellow yo-yo for several incarnations, until it is seen again in *Kill the Moon,* and later in *The Girl Who Died* and *Oxygen.* The Sixth Doctor has a yo-yo in the audio *Absolute Power,* as does the Tenth in the novels *The Price of Paradise* and *The Eyeless.* The cubbyhole where the Doctor keeps a spare TARDIS key is mentioned in the Seventh Doctor audios *The Angel of Scutari* and *Survival of the Fittest,* and in the Eighth Doctor novel *The Janus Conjunction.*

Prior to *The Night of the Doctor*

The Doctor encounters the Daleks, and discovers that in their ancient legends he is known as 'The Oncoming Storm.' He does not learn for several more regenerations, however, that he is also called 'The Predator of the Daleks.' He performs an examination of Dalek life forms and classifies their DNA type as 467-989. On Skaro itself, he discovers the sewer system containing the hate-filled remains of earlier generations of Daleks.

Though first used onscreen in *The Parting of the Ways,* the term 'The Oncoming Storm' originates in the Seventh Doctor novel *Love and War* (it's what the Draconians, not the Daleks, call the Doctor). Since there are, it is supposed, no Daleks after the Time War, he must have heard about it prior to that conflict. In the Seventh Doctor audio *The Grand Betelgeuse Hotel,* he's simply 'The Approaching Inclement Weather System.' The infostamp stolen from the Daleks by the Cybermen in *The Next Doctor* contains information about the Eighth Doctor, showing that he must have tangled with them (as he does in several novels and audios). Infostamps are also mentioned in the Eighth Doctor audio *Songs of Love*. The Predator moniker is first used in *Asylum of the Daleks*. The DNA classification is mentioned by the Tenth Doctor in *Daleks in Manhattan*. It's Missy and Clara who venture into the sewers of Skaro in *The Witch's Familiar*, but the Doctor also knows of their existence.

He witnesses the banning of the mind-swapping device known as the Psychograft.

New Earth. Given the Time Lords' reaction to such technology in *Mindwarp*, it is more than likely that they would have been responsible for the outlawing of the Psychograft, too. As there are only two Time Lords in the known universe after the Time War, the ban must come into effect before that point. In *Paradise Towers*, the Seventh Doctor describes the process of transplanting a mind into a host body as corpoelectroscopy. The Tenth Doctor sees a Psychograft in operation prior to the ban in the Tenth Doctor short story *The Body Bank*.

He hears the legend of the Cult of Skaro, a secret order formed to think as the enemy thinks. Unfortunately for the Tenth Doctor, he doesn't believe the Cult truly exists.

Doomsday

The Doctor witnesses a paradox machine in action.

The Sound of Drums and *Last of the Time Lords*. Since a paradox machine is created from a cannibalized TARDIS, this cannot have happened after his species (and their vehicles) were wiped from the universe.

He befriends the Time Lord known as the Corsair, who wears the same snake tattoo throughout each of his or her incarnations.

The Doctor's Wife. The Third Doctor also has a tattoo, which he displays in *Spearhead from Space* and *Doctor Who and the Silurians*. In *Thin Ice*, the Twelfth Doctor says he's against them.

He makes a stop in Croydon during the year 1978, and leaves K-9 Mark III with the aunt of former companion Sarah Jane Smith.

The *Doctor Who* spinoff *K-9 and Company*. This particular robot dog insists that he is the third model. As the Tenth Doctor presents Sarah with a new K-9 in *School Reunion*, one which he must have begun work on in an earlier incarnation, this is the last point at which he could have dropped off the Mark III.

The Doctor helps out UNIT once again, and is granted entry to their Black Archive. He is given access to the UNIT website (password 'Buffalo').

The Day of the Doctor. The War Doctor has apparently heard of the Black Archive, and if we're assuming he was preoccupied for that entire incarnation with the Time War, then he learned about it while sporting an earlier body. The Ninth Doctor is reluctant to assist UNIT in *Aliens of London*, so it must have occurred prior to his tenure. Kate Stewart seems to think that the Doctor doesn't know about the Black Archive (which first appears, unnamed in the spinoff video *Daemos Rising* before being positively identified in *The Sarah Jane Adventures* story *Enemy of the Bane*). It seems likely, then, that he visited them when they were located somewhere else. This is implied in the Tenth Doctor comic strip *Don't Step on the Grass*. The UNIT website access - which the Ninth Doctor employs in *World War Three* - must also have been given prior to that incarnation. The Sixth Doctor uses it in the audio *Vampire of the Mind*.

A series of adventures related in the Big Finish audios follow, in which the Eighth Doctor is joined on his travels by Charlotte 'Charley' Pollard, C'rizz, Lucie Miller, Tamsin Drew and Molly O'Sullivan. Eventually, he parts company with all of them.

The Eighth Doctor namechecks his former companions in *The Night of the Doctor*. No mention is made of his assistants from the BBC novels, though it is certainly implied that there were more than just those he lists, and the novelization of *The Day of the Doctor* adds his print companion Fitz. But as stated in the introduction, that just opens up a whole can of memory-deleting worms ...

The Doctor and his companion store a motorcycle in the TARDIS' garage. He uses it when entering the first Anti-Grav Olympics in 2074 - in which he comes in last.

The Anti-Grav Olympics are first mentioned in *Tooth and Claw*, but it is not revealed that the Doctor took part in them until *The Bells of Saint John*. The motorcycle comes with two helmets, suggesting that there was a second passenger at some point.

The Eighth Doctor plays his part in helping to save Gallifrey from the Dalek fleet on the final day of the forthcoming Time War. Tragically, his memory of the conflict in which he is soon to become involved is erased.

> *The Day of the Doctor.* The Eighth Doctor is seen sporting the same hairstyle he has in *Doctor Who – The TV Movie.* His hair is noticeably shorter in *The Night of the Doctor.*

He encounters a truth field (hopefully at a time when he is not wearing a wig).

> *The Time of the Doctor.* The Eleventh Doctor claims he hasn't seen this technology in years, but as it is coming through the crack in the universe, along with the coded Time Lord signal, it would seem that it is Gallifreyan in origin. It's a good thing it was not in operation during *The Invasion of Time,* or his plan to outwit the Vardans would have been over before it began. It seems, though, a truth field can be beaten – in *The Time of the Doctor,* the Doctor lies about having a plan during the Daleks' final assault on Trenzalore.

A group of about fifty invisible android assassins menace a lone Doctor, who teleports away at the last nanosecond, only to find himself surrounded by vampire monkeys.

> *The Witch's Familiar.* This tale is related by Missy, a far from reliable narrator. The First, Fourth and Twelfth Doctors are seen in this account, so it's unclear to which incarnation it actually happened, if any, although as Missy has knowledge of this incident, and may even have programmed the androids in an earlier incarnation, it can't have occurred after the beginning of a certain conflict.

Then comes the Time War …

Despite the fact that the Time Lords and the Daleks are the main combatants, Gallifrey remains on the furthest edge of the last great Time War.

> The Doctor refers to the conflict as 'the last great Time War' in *Gridlock,* indicating that there have been others. An earlier Time War is described in the Fifth Doctor comic strip *The Tides of Time,* and the Seventh Doctor novel *Sky Pirates!* states that the first Time Wars were fought shortly after Gallifrey mastered the ability to travel through that realm.

Millions of beings at the very centre of the war are killed and resurrected every second.

> *The End of Time*

The conflict is invisible to 'smaller' species - Earth, in particular - although its effects are felt in ways unnoticed by the population, such as the continued existence of President John F Kennedy following a botched assassination attempt in 1963.

> *The Unquiet Dead* and *Let's Kill Hitler*. See the chapter on the Ninth Doctor (page 173) for more information. The identity of Kennedy's assassin is revealed in the novel *Who Killed Kennedy*. (Spoiler: it's not the Doctor, who nevertheless complains that he was accused of the crime in the audio *Zagreus*).

Many worlds are destroyed, including Perganon, Ascinta, the planet of the Zygons, the Nestene homeworld and its protein planets.

> In *School Reunion*, Brother Lassar doesn't specifically state that Perganon and Ascinta were lost in the war, but the Krillitanes are aware of the Time Lords, so it seems likely. The fate of the Nestene planets is mentioned in *Rose* (the novelization of *Terror of the Autons* gives the name of their world as Polymos). Elizabeth I reports, in *The Day of the Doctor*, that the Zygons' home (named as Zygor in the Eighth Doctor novel *The Bodysnatchers*) was among the first planets to be destroyed in the war.

The Sontarans are enraged not to be allowed to participate in the conflict, despite possessing some degree of time-travel capability.

> *The Sontaran Stratagem*

The Eighth Doctor wants no part in the war, but determines to help wherever he can. While doing his best to avoid the conflict, he observes a spaceship piloted by the humanoid Cass on a collision course with the planet Karn.

> *The Night of the Doctor*. That Cass is aware of the Time War's effect on the Universe suggests that while she may be human in appearance, she does not hail from Earth. The Twelfth Doctor returns to Karn in the online prequel to *The Magician's Apprentice*.

The War Doctor
John Hurt
2013

The Doctor grows old in his role as a warrior.

> When seen (in reflection) at the end of *The Night of the Doctor*, the War Doctor is a relatively young man. Despite this, he actually becomes younger in his next incarnation, losing around 47 years. Apparently, this is yet another side-effect of the Time War.

During the conflict, he encounters the Skaro degradations, the Horde of Travesties, and the Could-have-been-King, who leads an army of meanwhiles and never-weres.

> *The End of Time*

The Dalek leader Davros is believed dead after the Doctor fails to rescue his command ship from the jaws of the Nightmare Child. Despite this apparent attempt at a merciful act, Davros later accuses him of butchering millions.

> *The Stolen Earth*

After one particularly bloody battle, he becomes known to some as the Butcher of Skull Moon.

> The Skull Moon incident is first mentioned in *Hell Bent*. The unflattering appellation is heard in *Twice Upon a Time*.

The Dalek Emperor gains control of the weapon known as the Cruciform, after which the resurrected Master flees.

> *The Sound of Drums*. No specific details are provided onscreen regarding the Cruciform, but it seems that there are more ultimate weapons knocking around during the Time War than there are in Professor Farnsworth's basement in *Futurama*. In the comic strip *The Forgotten*, it is said to have been destroyed. Yeah, right.

But the greatest threat to the universe is posed by the Doctor's own people. He learns of Rassilon's Final Sanction – a plan to rip the time vortex apart, destroying everything else in creation, while the Time Lords themselves become beings of pure consciousness. The Doctor determines that the Final Sanction must not be initiated, even if that means sacrificing his entire species.

> *The End of Time*

The War Doctor - who has fought for so long that he no longer considers himself the Doctor at all - learns of the existence of a device even the Time Lords fear to use, one that could put an abrupt and catastrophic end to the suffering. He returns to Gallifrey on the day that its second city, Arcadia, finally falls to the Daleks.

The fall of Arcadia is first mentioned in *Doomsday*, but it is not until the online minisode *The Last Day* that it is established that Arcadia is located on Gallifrey.

The Moment has been prepared, however, and the War Doctor steals the forbidden galaxy-devouring weapon from the Omega Arsenal, relocating it in his family's old barn.

The Day of the Doctor

The War Doctor is responsible for the destruction of the fleet of the Tenth Dalek Occupation, consisting of 10 million ships. In so doing, he believes that he has wiped out the entire species of a billion billion Daleks.

Dalek. At this point, the War Doctor doesn't know about the millions of Daleks trapped by his fellow Time Lords within the Genesis Ark, as discovered in *Doomsday*.

Sontaran legend later has it that the Doctor led the battle during the last great Time War.

The Sontaran Stratagem

After the Ninth Doctor and companion Rose Tyler witness the end of her world, the Doctor tells her that Gallifrey 'burnt like the Earth' until it was nothing more than rocks and dust. He has, at this point, forgotten (and will not recollect for another two regenerations) that the planet did not actually burn, nor was it destroyed.

The End of the World. The Eleventh Doctor is quite adamant, in *The Doctor's Wife*, that he is responsible for killing the Time Lords.

The Dalek home planet of Skaro, however, *is* destroyed, seemingly for a second time.

The Cult of Skaro confirm the destruction of their homeworld in *Daleks in Manhattan*. The Seventh Doctor also destroys it in episode four of *Remembrance of the Daleks*, but the Eleventh Doctor is summoned there at the start of *Asylum of the Daleks*. Time can be rewritten, apparently. The

Fifth Doctor sees Skaro blow up in an alternate timeline during the audio *The Mutant Phase.*

The Doctor blames Rassilon for the entire conflict.

Hell Bent

The Dalek Asylum planet, surrounded as it is by an impenetrable force-field, somehow survives the Time War - apparently because no one (including the Doctor) seriously believes it exists.

Asylum of the Daleks. This would explain why there are Daleks from *The Chase, The Daleks' Master Plan, The Planet of the Daleks, The Power of the Daleks* and *Death to the Daleks* in the Asylum's Intensive Care ward.

The entire conflict - including, the Doctor supposes, the smouldering remains of his home planet - is time-locked.

The End of Time. The Tenth Doctor is unclear on who did this, or how.

The body known as the Shadow Proclamation is formed. The Doctor refers to them as 'outer space police' (though there seem to be some quasi-religious overtones), and while he knows their location, they do not know him.

The Stolen Earth. The Architect is surprised to find that the Tenth Doctor exists. She refers to the Shadow Proclamation's laws as 'holy writ.'

He does, however, encounter their footsoldiers, the Judoon, learns their language and discovers that they are prevented by galactic law from interfering on Earth.

Smith and Jones. The law comes into force in the Tenth Doctor short story *Revenge of the Judoon.* Mention is made of the brutish space-cops in the Third Doctor novel *Harvest of Time,* the Eleventh Doctor novel *The Coming of the Terraphiles* and the Seventh Doctor audio *The Blood Furnace.* They appear in several comic strips, including *A Rare Gem, The Forgotten, Hacked, Slaver's Song, Sin-Eater, Fugitive, Assimilation², Gangland* and *A Confusion of Angels,* and also show up in the novels *Judgement of the Judoon, The Forgotten Army,* and the Sixth Doctor audio *Judoon in Chains.*

Under the ratification of the Shadow Proclamation, species must identify themselves when called upon to do so. Convention 15 guarantees audience under Peaceful Contract, while Article 57 relates to interference in fully established level-five planets, such as our own.

The Ninth Doctor invokes the Shadow Proclamation laws in *Rose,* the Tenth in *Fear Her* and *The Fires of Pompeii,* and the Eleventh in *The Eleventh Hour.* Companion Rose has a go in *The Christmas Invasion.*

Jurisdiction 2 of the Intergalactic Rules of Engagement may also have been drafted by the Shadow Proclamation.

The Tenth Doctor quotes this rule in *The Poison Sky.*

A book describing the history of the Time War and the Doctor's part in it is placed in the TARDIS' library.

Journey to the Centre of the TARDIS. Companion Clara reads the book, and apparently discovers the Doctor's real name - which she subsequently forgets.

The Ninth Doctor
Christopher Eccleston
2005

Prior to *Rose*

Following his regeneration, the Doctor loses all memory of his recent encounter with his future selves, and so is utterly certain that he pressed the big threatening red button which must never be pressed under any circumstances, thus exterminating his own people, along with the Daleks.

> How much time passes between his regeneration in *The Day of the Doctor* and the episode *Rose* is open to debate, as is the issue of whether the Ninth Doctor still has the War Doctor's beard after regenerating (I can't be the only one wondering about that). His comments in *Rose* as he looks at himself in the mirror suggest a recent change, but in the same story, Clive's files point to a series of adventures featuring a solo Ninth Doctor. The War Doctor's wish - as expressed in his final moments in *The Day of the Doctor* – that his ears might be less conspicuous in his next incarnation is doomed to go unfulfilled.

One of the Ninth Doctor's first tasks post-Time War is to visit Dallas on November 22, 1963, to ensure that John F Kennedy's assassination occurs as history intended. In April 1912, he persuades the Daniels family not to set sail for the United States on the *Titanic.* In 1883, on the night Krakatoa erupts, he washes up on the coast of Sumatra, presumably after encountering either his first or second self. He hears the song *Luck Be a Lady* from the musical *Guys and Dolls.* He also meets two much-photographed celebrities, one gay, the other an alien.

> In *Rose,* the Ninth Doctor sings *Luck Be a Lady* when he visits companion Rose's flat. While there, he sees the mismatched couple in a celebrity magazine. In *The Invasion of Time,* the Fourth Doctor is adamant that he is in no way responsible for the sinking of the *Titanic,* and in *The End of the World,* the Ninth Doctor recalls clinging to an iceberg. We see a photograph of the Ninth Doctor among the crowds in Dallas, watching the Presidential motorcade pass by. In *Let's Kill Hitler,* the crew of the Teselecta cite the Kennedy incident as proof that time can be rewritten. Kennedy most certainly died in 1963 in the pre-Time War Universe (the Seventh Doctor says so in *Silver*

Nemesis), so it would seem that following the conflict, Earth history was altered in at least this one respect. As this event is closely connected to the Nemesis statue, he has no option but to put time back on track. The Eleventh Doctor and Clara return to Dallas shortly after Kennedy's death in the novel *Shroud of Sorrow*. The Third Doctor talks about witnessing the eruption of Krakatoa in episode one of *Inferno*. His presence so close to the event is discovered by the Torchwood Institute in the Tenth Doctor comic strip *The Time Machination*.

The Doctor redesigns the TARDIS lock yet again.

The TARDIS key, as seen in several stories, but most notably in *Father's Day*, is now a standard Yale again.

He develops a 'Universal Roaming' feature for mobile phones.

Rose's phone receives the Universal Roaming feature in *The End of the World*, and later Doctors apparently do the same for their companions. An early version of this technology is used in the Fifth Doctor audio *Renaissance of the Daleks*.

He acquires a piece of psychic paper, which proves to be a big time-saver. The TARDIS takes him to the year 12005 (where he sees the new Roman Empire), and to the day the Earth's sun expands in the far future. He experiences the effects of a gravity pocket, and also meets the living trees of the Forest of Cheem.

The End of the World. The Ninth Doctor knows what to expect on the Earth's last day, so he's surprised by developments on Platform One (which are ascribed to a gravity pocket, but don't feel like one, apparently). He knows all about the Trees. Their home planet of Cheem is mentioned again in the Tenth Doctor book *The Game of Death*. The psychic paper makes its first appearance here and is used fairly frequently from this point forward. The novel *World Game* claims that it was originally given to the Second Doctor by the Celestial Intervention Agency following his sham trial. In *Frontier in Space*, the Master presents the Draconians with a 'warrant of authority,' not dissimilar to the wallet used by the Doctor, stating that he is a commissioner of interplanetary police. Might he have his own psychic paper?

He either watches the movie *Barbarella*, or reads the original comic strip. He witnesses the Fifth World War and pushes boxes at the Boston Tea Party (though in which direction is unknown).

> *The Unquiet Dead*. The Ninth Doctor calls Rose 'Barbarella.' The Fourth Doctor recalls averting the Sixth World War in *The Talons of Weng-Chiang*. WWV is mentioned in the Fifth Doctor novel *The Crystal Bucephalus*, the audio *Singularity* (also featuring the Fifth Doctor) and the Ninth Doctor comic strip *Art Attack*. The Seventh Doctor's companion Ace was also present at the Boston Tea Party, according to the novel *Set Piece*.

He spends enough time on Earth in 2005 to determine that it is a 'middling' year. During an adventure involving the British military, he sees Defence Plan Delta being carried out. On a trip to the Victorian era, he witnesses a showman displaying a mocked-up mermaid. Former British Prime Minister David Lloyd-George drinks him under the table.

> *Aliens of London*. The poster at the beginning of the episode states that Rose has been missing since March 2005. The 'Defence Plan Delta' line, uttered by the Ninth Doctor in order to gain the trust of the soldiers at Albion Hospital, does not appear in the original script.

Two thousand years before the present day, the Doctor visits the Island of Thorns, on which will later stand Number 10 Downing Street. In 1730, he meets then-owner of the land Mr Chicken, whom he considers to be 'nice.' He sees the first Cabinet Room in 1796, and is there again in 1991 when three inch-thick steel plates are added as a security measure. Post-2006, he hears of Harriet Jones, three-term Prime Minister and architect of Britain's 'Golden Age,' a future subsequently nullified by the actions of the Tenth Doctor. The TARDIS takes him to the planet Raxacoricofallapatorius, where he discovers the natives' qualities (some of them deeply unpleasant) and abilities (some of them deadly).

> The Ninth Doctor relates the history of Downing Street in *World War Three*. We learn in *Boom Town* that he is aware of female Raxacoricofallapatorians' ability to produce a poison dart from their finger and emit poison (to which he is seemingly immune) from their lungs. Despite this, he has never heard of Raxacoricofallapatorius' twin planet, Clom, and does not discover the name until *Love & Monsters*. It's possible that the Doctor sees the poison dart fired for the first time in the comic strip *Doctormania*. The short story *A Comedy of Terrors* suggests that his knowledge of this race may date back to his second incarnation.

He is present at the famous UFO crash in Roswell, New Mexico, in 1947, learns how to play an alien musical instrument, uses an alien hairdryer, and hears of plans to revive *Buffy the Vampire Slayer*.

> *Dalek*. The instrument, the hairdryer and the milometer from the Roswell crash ship are all parts of Van Statten's collection. The Ninth Doctor taunts the Dalek about everything it has learned from the Internet, including the ill-fated *Buffy* revival. In the animated story *Dreamland*, the Tenth Doctor seems to have no first hand knowledge of the Roswell incident, although the Seventh Doctor novel *First Frontier* suggests otherwise. Canon or not? You be the judge. The Eleventh Doctor also mentions Roswell in the novel *Shroud of Sorrow*.

Circa 200,000 AD, the Doctor sees the Fourth Great and Bountiful Human Empire, when the planet Earth has a population of 96 billion, vast mega-cities and five moons. This future is subsequently erased by the Emperor Dalek, working through the Mighty Jagrafess of the Holy Hadrojassic Maxarodenfoe. On a trip to Paris, he uses the wrong verbs, is charged double and kisses several strangers.

> *The Long Game*. The Ninth Doctor's recollections of Paris do not in any way match the details of *The Reign of Terror*, so this must be a different visit (perhaps his meeting with Marie Antoinette mentioned by his fourth incarnation in *Pyramids of Mars*). Why he should use the wrong verbs, when the TARDIS translates all languages for him, is another matter.

On several alien worlds, he witnesses misunderstandings relating to red alerts. He also encounters the space-faring species known as the Chula.

> *The Empty Child*. The Ninth Doctor recognises the name Chula in this episode, and identifies Jack Harkness' stolen ship as being of Chula construction in *The Doctor Dances*. He tells companion Rose that red means 'camp' on all other worlds but Earth, although in the animated Tenth Doctor story *Dreamland*, it seems to imply an emergency. Canon or not? You be the judge. Again.

The Doctor learns how to dance, 1940s-style.

> *The Doctor Dances*. For once in this episode, the Ninth Doctor doesn't mean dancing as a euphemism for sex – he actually means dancing.

The TARDIS takes him to the planet Barcelona, where the dogs have no noses.

> *The Parting of the Ways*. It is the newly regenerated Tenth Doctor's intention to take Rose there.

He witnesses the control of individual blood groups.

> *The Christmas Invasion.* The Tenth Doctor says he hasn't seen blood control in years.

Circa the year 5 billion, he is on New Earth in Galaxy M87. He appreciates the apple grass in New New York, having been to the fourteen previous New Yorks. In roughly the same time period, he has cause to pay a call at a hospital. He views the results of Marconi's disease and Pallidome Pancrosis (which, he learns, is fatal in ten minutes). A millennium later, he witnesses the development of a cure for Petrifold Regression.

> *New Earth.* The Tenth Doctor identifies a hospital by its green moon logo, and recognises the various diseases suffered by the patients.

He is present at the Battle of Trafalgar, and watches as Julius Caesar crosses the Rubicon. Having previously dismissed the year 1979 during his fourth incarnation, he is later surprisingly busy in that period. In November, he sees Ian Dury at the Top Rank, in Sheffield. He witnesses the Chinese invasion of Vietnam, Britain's election of Margaret Thatcher, and *The Muppet Movie*. He is also responsible for returning Skylab to Earth, nearly losing his thumb in the process. During the 19th Century, he meets Joseph Merrick (the famous 'Elephant Man') and Dr Joseph Bell of Edinburgh University. He studies the life of Queen Victoria.

> *Tooth and Claw.* The Tenth Doctor has never met Queen Victoria before (although during his first or second incarnation, he was at her coronation, possibly, according to *The Curse of Peladon*, and his Fifth incarnation encounters the famously-unamused monarch in the novel *Empire of Death*), but knows about the six attempts on her life, her haemophilia and the history of the Koh-i-noor diamond. Her education being what it is, his companion Rose is fairly ignorant of this era. The Fourth Doctor claims to have breakfasted with Nelson shortly before Trafalgar in the novel *Eye of Heaven*, reminisces about the battle in the audio *The Ghosts of Gralstead*, and has a signed photograph taken at Trafalgar in the audio *Hornet's Nest: The Stuff of Nightmares*. The Fifth Doctor recalls his friendship with the Admiral in the audio *The Lions of Trafalgar*. He mentions Caesar in the audios *Phantoms of the Deep* and *The Settling*, The Fifth Doctor novel *Empire of Death*, and the novelization of *The Stones of Blood*. The Third Doctor is seen taking his orders directly from Mrs Thatcher in the stage play *The Ultimate Adventure* and the Fifth Doctor shuts down a timeline in which she has been murdered in the short story *The Assassin's Story*.

> Further details of the Skylab crash are provided in the Tenth Doctor story *Bennelong Point.*

The Doctor matches wits with the Krillitanes, at the point when they appear to be long-necked humanoids.

> *School Reunion.* The Krillitanes are mentioned in the novel *The Art of Destruction,* and reappear in the novel *The Krillitane Storm.*

He is in France a couple of years before the French Revolution, and hears a good deal about the life and reputation of Madame de Pompadour. He has a rubbish time in August 1787.

> *The Girl in the Fireplace.* The Tenth Doctor is able to date the mantel on the 51st Century spaceship. He advises the young Reinette to 'stay indoors' during August.

He places a moped inside the TARDIS. 1953 is a terrific year for him, what with the coronation of his good friend Elizabeth and the conquest of Mount Everest.

> *The Idiot's Lantern.* In the novel *The Dying Days,* the Eighth Doctor claims to have been the first climber to have conquered Everest.

The TARDIS materialises on a deep-space Sanctuary base. The Doctor studies the presence of the Horned Beast in the mythology of the planets Draconia and Vel Consadine, as well as the Kaled God of War.

> *The Impossible Planet.* The Tenth Doctor recognises the Sanctuary base within moments of arriving.

He visits Club Med - easily mistaken for the First Olympiad. Speaking of which, he also attends the Olympic opening ceremony in Wembley, 1948 - twice. He befriends the torch-bearer, but later forgets his name. He attends a tea party (possibly more than one) and develops a love for crunchy ball-bearings on cakes; he searches the entire galaxy looking for something similar, but fails to find it. He also watches the 2012 Olympic Games, during which Papua New Guinea surprises everyone during the shot-put event. He meets the empathic beings known as the Isolus.

> *Fear Her.* The Tenth Doctor describes the behaviour and abilities of the Isolus to companion Rose Tyler, who doesn't know if he's kidding about Papua New Guinea. The 2012 Olympics are also mentioned in the Fifth Doctor audio *The King of the Dead* and the Seventh Doctor audio *Frozen Time.*

The Doctor hears the theory of the Void ship, a vessel capable of existing in the realm outside time and space, known to the Eternals as the Howling. He doesn't believe in it.

> *Army of Ghosts.* The Tenth Doctor finally sees a Void ship, much to his surprise.

He attempts to avert a Cyberman invasion led by the Dreadnought-Class warship known as a CyberKing.

> *The Next Doctor.* The Tenth Doctor recognises the CyberKing and explains its function to Jackson Lake. The term is first used in *Army of Ghosts.*

He begins work on another K-9 to keep him company, this new model containing omni-flexible hyperlink facilities. One of the K-9s he has created over the years possesses the ability to hover.

> In *The Power of Three*, the Eleventh Doctor remarks that he had a robot dog that could hover. None of the K-9s seen in the series have displayed that ability onscreen, though K-9 Mark I possesses a propulsion unit in the Fourth Doctor audio *Death Match.* It's doubtful that the Tenth Doctor could have built another K-9 for Sarah Jane at a moment's notice following the destruction of the previous model in *School Reunion.* In the same story, his companion Rose has never seen the dog before, so its construction must occur before the Ninth Doctor's first story.

Passing close to Earth, the Ninth Doctor detects signs of warp shunt technology and locates a relay device built by Autons on the roof of Henrik's Department Store, in London. Determined to stop the invasion, he constructs a bomb to destroy the relay and formulates a liquid capable of neutralizing the Nestene Consciousness. In the store's basement, he finds the body of chief electrician H P Wilson.

> All immediately before the beginning of *Rose.* The Ninth Doctor christens his magic potion 'Anti-Plastic.' The Seventh Doctor deploys a very similar substance when battling the Autons in the comic strip *Plastic Millenium* (sic).

The End of the World

Prior to *The Unquiet Dead*

The Ninth Doctor and companion Rose eat chips in Piccadilly Circus.

> This is their stated intention in the last scene of *The End of the World.*

Aliens of London

World War Three

Dalek

The Long Game

Father's Day

Prior to *The Empty Child*

The Ninth Doctor and companion Rose return to Earth several times to buy milk.

> *The Empty Child.* In *Shada,* the Fourth Doctor keeps a bottle of milk in stasis for thirty years.

Visiting London during the Christmas of 1998, the Ninth Doctor delivers a red bicycle to the home of the 12-year-old Rose Tyler, without telling the adult Rose what he has done.

> *The Doctor Dances.* The Ninth Doctor shocks his companion by telling her what gift she received for Christmas when she was twelve. Further context is provided in the short story *The Red Bicycle.*

On the planet Woman Wept, they walk on a thousand-mile-wide frozen beach.

> *Boom Town.* Companion Rose tells Mickey this happened 'a while back,' and makes no mention of Jack Harkness, indicating that it occurred before his first appearance in *The Empty Child.* Woman Wept is one of the worlds listed as having been taken by the Daleks during *The Stolen Earth,* and also gets a namecheck in the Ninth Doctor audio *Night of the Whisper.*

Without companion Rose's knowledge, the Ninth Doctor installs an emergency program designed to return the TARDIS (and Rose) to early 21st-century Earth in the event of his impending death.

> *The Parting of the Ways.* The Ninth Doctor's recorded message makes no mention of Jack and takes no account of his well-being, suggesting this was made before the Time Agent joined the TARDIS crew at the end of *The Doctor Dances.* The emergency program is still in effect during *Silence in the Library,*

though the Tenth Doctor has re-recorded his hologram message, since Donna would have no idea who the Ninth Doctor was, or what he was talking about.

The Doctor experiences difficulty breaching a door constructed from Hydra Combination.

Bad Wolf. The Ninth Doctor advises companion Jack that his defabricator weapon will have no effect. The DVD subtitles misidentify the phrase as 'vital combination.'

The Ninth Doctor and Rose Tyler are placed in a dicey situation in which they are forced to hop for their lives.

During the first *Children in Need Special* (sometimes referred to as *Born Again*), the newly regenerated Tenth Doctor remembers this incident - which, again, apparently pre-dates Jack Harkness' first appearance.

The Doctor Dances

Prior to *Boom Town*

The Ninth Doctor and Rose journey to Justicia and the Glass Pyramid of San Kaloon.

Boom Town. An account of the events on Justicia can be found in the novel *The Monsters Inside*, a rare early example of a tie-in product being advertised within the series, and yet one that fails to account for my large collection of plastic sonic screwdrivers.

In the early 21st Century, he watches the television series *Big Brother*. More than 198,000 years later, he enjoys the game show *Bear With Me* (especially the celebrity edition).

Bad Wolf. The Ninth Doctor is familiar with the layout of the original *Big Brother* House and the typical Z-list fate of former contestants. Companions Rose and Jack aren't around when he reminisces about *Bear With Me*, so they might have seen it, too.

He also watches *This Is Your Life* and *The Lion King*.

The Christmas Invasion. The Tenth Doctor unintentionally quotes the lyrics from Elton John's *Circle of Life*.

He hears of the Carrionites of the Rexel Planetary configuration, who apparently disappeared at the dawn of the universe.

The Shakespeare Code. The Tenth Doctor struggles to recall the name of this witch-like species, suggesting that he knew of them during a previous incarnation. The Sixth Doctor audio *The Carrionite Curse* describes an earlier encounter, as does the Fourth Doctor short story *Toil and Trouble.* They are name-checked in the Tenth Doctor novels *Forever Autumn, The Many Hands* and *The Taking of Chelsea 426.*

Singer Janis Joplin gives the Doctor a long brown overcoat, which he wears throughout his next incarnation.

Gridlock

He travels to New York, when it is still called New Amsterdam. He is in the city again at the time of the Wall Street Crash and the formation of Hooverville.

Daleks in Manhattan. The First Doctor visits New York in *The Chase,* the Eleventh in *A Christmas Carol* and *The Angels Take Manhattan,* and the Twelfth in *The Return of Doctor Mysterio.* In episode one of *The Time Meddler,* Vicki asks the First Doctor to take her back there.

He makes contact with the species to which the Family of Blood belong, discovering their abilities and their limited lifespans. They learn enough about him in return to place his life in jeopardy should their paths ever cross again.

Human Nature. The Tenth Doctor knows all about the Family, but they do not recognise his present incarnation. They reappear in the short story *Blood Will Out.*

The Ninth Doctor is no doubt elated to learn that, with the assistance of his former and future incarnations, he can save Gallifrey at the height of the Time War, having believed since his regeneration that he is responsible for its destruction. Tragically, he is destined to forget his participation in this operation, and will continue to think of himself as the man who activated the Moment, condemning all of his planet's children to death.

The Day of the Doctor. As established here, the realignment of the timelines wipes the memories of all the Doctors save for the Eleventh.

The Ninth Doctor determines that the TARDIS needs to refuel, and sets it down in early 21st Century Cardiff.

Immediately prior to *Boom Town*

Prior to *Bad Wolf*

The Ninth Doctor and his companions Jack and Rose return the egg containing the infant Blon Fel Fotch Passameer-Day Slitheen to the planet Raxacoricofallapatorius. Shortly thereafter, they find themselves in a dicey situation in 14th Century Kyoto, from which they escape, only to be waylaid by the Daleks' powerful Transmat beam.

Bad Wolf. The Ninth Doctor relates all this to Lynda with a Y.

The Parting of the Ways

The Tenth Doctor
David Tennant
2005-2010

The Christmas Invasion

Prior to *New Earth*

Following the destruction of the Sycorax spaceship, Ursula Blake takes the Tenth Doctor's photo in Trafalgar Square without his knowledge.

Love & Monsters. The Sycorax go on to menace the Doctor in the comic strips *Agent Provocateur, The Widow's Curse* and *Ghost Stories.* The Seventh Doctor audio *Harvest of the Sycorax* describes an earlier encounter. They are mentioned in the Tenth Doctor novel *Snowglobe 7.*

Via the psychic paper, the Tenth Doctor receives a message from the Face of Boe, summoning him to a hospital on New Earth.

New Earth

Prior to *Tooth and Claw*

The Doctor becomes aware of the beloved BBC children's TV programme *Balamory.*

Tooth and Claw. The Tenth Doctor introduces himself to Queen Victoria as Dr McCrimmon of the University of Balamory.

Prior to *School Reunion*

The Doctor visits the Dagmar Cluster. He acquires enough multi-grade anti-oil to fill a goblet of wine, and a pair of John Lennon-style sunglasses (from Lennon himself, perhaps?).

The Girl in the Fireplace

On an asteroid, the Doctor and companion Rose face a weird munchkin lady who breathes fire.

Rise of the Cybermen. The Tenth Doctor and Rose are relating this incident to Mickey Smith as the episode begins.

Mickey Smith contacts them regarding a number of UFO sightings and the abnormally high test results at a nearby school. The Tenth Doctor posts a winning lottery ticket through the door of one of the school's teachers, and subsequently replaces her. He begins teaching physics at the school under the name John Smith.

> *School Reunion*. The Tenth Doctor has been teaching at the school for two days as the episode begins.

The Girl in the Fireplace

Rise of the Cybermen

The Age of Steel

The Idiot's Lantern

Prior to *The Impossible Planet*

The Tenth Doctor records over the videotape on which he has trapped the entity known as the Wire. He is shocked by what he sees in Russia under Stalin's rule.

> *The Idiot's Lantern*. He compares Elizabeth's England to Stalin's Russia, visited by the Second Doctor in the novel *World Game*. The video cassette is very likely the same one seen in the TARDIS during the Twelfth Doctor's final story.

He watches a none-too-cheery Christmas episode of the BBC soap opera *EastEnders* (for those unfamiliar with the show, there are no other kind). He also studies the religions of the Arkiphets, Quoldonity, Pash Pash, Neo-Judaism, San Claar, and the Church of the Tin Vagabond.

> In *The Impossible Planet*, the Tenth Doctor jokes about phrases that precede disaster, citing *EastEnders* as an example. The episode he sees in *Army of Ghosts* is not set at Christmas, by the way. Companion Rose is not present when he lists the religions with which he's familiar, so she might know at least some of them.

The Satan Pit

Prior to *Love & Monsters*

The Tenth Doctor and Rose track an elemental shade from the Howling Halls to the home of young Elton Pope. The Doctor recaptures the shadow, but is unable to save Elton's mother. Rather callously, he leaves the distraught boy behind. Some decades later, the adult Elton witnesses the Time Lord and his companion tracking down a creature with a fondness for raw pork chops, using a not-blue bucket.

> *Love & Monsters*. Rose is not seen at Elton's home in his childhood flashbacks, but the Tenth Doctor recognises adult Elton, so she must have been with him.

Prior to *Fear Her*

The Doctor learns to play squash reasonably well. He watches *Inspector Morse* (or reads the novels by Colin Dexter, or is aware of the show), *Police 5* and *Star Trek*. He also experiments with back-combing.

> *Fear Her*. When posing as a police officer, the Tenth Doctor introduces Rose Tyler as 'Lewis,' borrowing the surname of Morse's long-suffering sergeant. He quotes the catchphrase of *Police 5* host Shaw Taylor, 'Keep 'em peeled.' He gives no indication during *The Empty Child* that he has ever heard of Mr Spock, but he makes the Vulcan salute here. The Eleventh Doctor is familiar with *Star Trek*'s transporter beams in *Closing Time*, and the Twelfth describes space as 'the final frontier' in *Oxygen*. There are *Trek* references in the audios *Cryptobiosis*, *The Crimes of Thomas Brewster*, *The Cannibalists*, *Pest Control* and *The Nemonite Invasion*, and the Eleventh Doctor encounters characters from *Star Trek: The Next Generation* in the comic strip *Assimilation²*, while the Seventh Doctor strip *Party Animals* features a cameo by the Klingon Worf. Izzy Sinclair, the comic strip Eighth Doctor's companion, is somewhat obsessed with the show, as is Bernice Summerfield in the novels *The Left-Handed Hummingbird*, *Sanctuary*, *Return of the Living Dad* and *The Dying Days*. The novels *Invasion of the Cat-People*, *The Crystal Bucephalus*, *War of the Daleks*, *Autumn Mist* and *Big Bang Generation* all contain references to *Trek*. In the Seventh Doctor strip *Cat Litter*, there is a model of the Starship Enterprise aboard the TARDIS.

Prior to *Army of Ghosts*

The Tenth Doctor and companion Rose attend the 2012 Olympic Games.

> *Fear Her*. This is the Tenth Doctor's stated intention at the end of the episode.

The duo spend time on a planet with flying manta-ray creatures, not unlike the Swarm from *Planet of the Dead*. They also visit a market on an asteroid bazaar, where Rose buys a trinket filled with bazoolium, an element capable of predicting the weather. The Doctor sees a version of the film *Ghostbusters*, acquires a pair of old-fashioned 3-D glasses, and travels on a Jathaa Sun Glider.

> *Army of Ghosts*. The unnamed planet is seen in the pre-titles sequence. Rose gives the bazoolium trinket to her mum. The Tenth Doctor finds the 3-D glasses useful for detecting 'Void stuff,' recognises the Jathaa craft at Torchwood HQ, and quotes from Ray Parker Jr's theme song for *Ghostbusters.* Clara also mentions it in the opening scene of *Hide*, as does the Twelfth Doctor in *Last Christmas*, and Rose in the Ninth Doctor comic strip *Slaver's Song*. There's yet another reference to the movie in *Under the Lake.*

The Doctor creates a bio-damper in the shape of a ring. Travelling back to the Dark Times, he battles the omnivorous Racnoss.

> *The Runaway Bride*. The Tenth Doctor uses the ring to try to hide companion Donna from the Robo-Scavengers. He recognises the Empress of the Racnoss. A previous battle with the multi-legged foes is presented in the Fifth Doctor audio *Empire of the Racnoss*; they are also mentioned in the Tenth Doctor novels *Peacemaker*, *Ghosts of India* and *The Eyeless*. When the TARDIS heads for the formation of the Earth, he says it's further back than he has travelled before, which is not strictly the case – it is, however, the furthest back into Earth's history that he has ever gone.

Doomsday

The Runaway Bride

Prior to *Smith and Jones*

Assisting Benjamin Franklin with his kite-flying, the Doctor suffers rope burns, a soaking and electrocution. He builds a laser spanner that is later stolen by famous suffragette Emmeline Pankhurst. He encounters slave drones known as slabs, who always travel in pairs, as well as the Plasmavores. Travelling to Rio de Janeiro, he meets 'Great Train Robber' Ronnie Biggs. He also develops a taste for banana milkshakes.

> *Smith and Jones*. The First Doctor's original meeting with Benjamin Franklin is described in the audio *The Founding Fathers*.

> The Eighth Doctor claims to have encountered him at a meeting of the Hellfire Club in the audio *Seasons of Fear,* while the Eleventh Doctor bumps into Franklin in the comic strip *The Long Con.* Emmeline Pankhurst is also mentioned in the Eighth Doctor novel *Casualties of War.* The Eleventh Doctor later fails to reach Rio in *The Hungry Earth.* The Fifth Doctor has an adventure there in the audio *Loups-Garoux.* The Eighth Doctor's companion Izzy references Ronnie Biggs in the comic strip *By Hook or by Crook.*

He pays a visit to London in the year 1599. He watches the 1933 Marx Brothers comedy *Duck Soup* and the 1985 sci-fi adventure *Back to the Future,* and cries after reading J K Rowling's *Harry Potter and the Deathly Hallows.*

> *The Shakespeare Code.* The Tenth Doctor identifies the location and date within moments of stepping out of the TARDIS. He tells Will that his companion Martha Jones is a native of Freedonia, a fictitious country from the Marx Brothers film, and does so again in the novel *Sting of the Zygons.* He attempts to explain alterations to the timestream in terms of *Back to the Future,* a film the Eleventh Doctor references in *The Day of the Doctor,* and which is also mentioned in the audios *The Raincloud Man* and *The Time Machine.* The Second Doctor claims to be a fan of the middle part of the movie trilogy in the novel *The Colony of Lies.* The Ninth Doctor comic strip *A Groatsworth of Wit,* which served as the inspiration for *The Shakespeare Code,* features a different Harry Potter reference. The Eighth Doctor has all the J K Rowling books in the audio *Izzy's Story* and the novel *The Gallifrey Chronicles,* while the Sixth has placed them all in the Demonology and Witchcraft section of the TARDIS library in the audio *The Carrionite Curse.*

The Doctor reads the James Bond books, or possibly watches the film series, or otherwise learns of the character. He sees a sonic micro-field manipulator in use, and discovers that all the variables cannot be accounted for. He is taught both how to play the organ and how to arm-wrestle by Ludwig van Beethoven.

> *The Lazarus Experiment.* The Tenth Doctor recognises Lazarus' device instantly, and references the famous 'up to 11' scene from *Spinal Tap* at the climax, as does the Ninth Doctor in the comic strip *A Groatsworth of Wit.* The Sixth Doctor quotes the former President in the audio *Urgent Calls.* Companion Martha likens the Doctor in his tuxedo to Bond, and he is flattered by the comparison. The comic strip *The Doctor and the Nurse* depicts a meeting between the Eleventh Doctor and Bond's creator Ian

Fleming. There are several Bondian references in the Eighth Doctor strips; in *Endgame*, the Celestial Toymaker claims in the comic strip to have defeated Le Chiffre, the villain from *Casino Royale*, at Baccarat, *Tooth and Claw* (the strip not the TV episode) references *Octopussy*'s baddie Kamal Khan, and in *The Final Chapter* there's a safe house on Gallifrey known as the Quantum of Solace. Bond is also mentioned in the Fifth Doctor audio *The Gathering* and the Eighth Doctor audio *Death in Blackpool*. The Twelfth Doctor has a bust of Beethoven and his Fifth Symphony on vinyl in *Before the Flood*. It is he who recalls the composer's fondness for arm-wrestling. The Sixth Doctor witnesses Ludwig's birth in the short story *Gone Too Soon*, while the Eighth mentions him in the audio *The Silver Turk*.

The TARDIS takes the Doctor to the Toragy System, half a universe away from Earth. He learns of the outlawing of energy scoops, and also tries ice-skating on the mineral lakes of Kur-ha.

42. The Tenth Doctor recognises the Toragy System on the SS *Pentallian*'s readouts. Later, he suggests taking Martha to Kur-ha.

His journeys in the TARDIS are tracked by a Time Agent's Vortex Manipulator.

Human Nature. The Tenth Doctor knows this is how the Family of Blood will follow him wherever he goes. He later tinkers with Captain Jack Harkness' Vortex Manipulator in *The Sound of Drums*. The Time Agents are first mentioned in *The Talons of Weng-Chiang*. One makes a brief appearance in the comic strip *Prisoners of Time*.

He sees a cloning process (the Drahvins', perhaps?) in operation, and a third-generation terraforming device.

The Doctor's Daughter. The Tenth Doctor explains how the cloning device works in detail to companions Donna and Martha. It cannot have been a Sontaran system since it does not require Clonefeed (as mentioned in *The Poison Sky*). If he has witnessed human cloning, it must have been after the year 3922, when – according to K-9, in episode two of *The Invisible Enemy* – the first successful clones were created.

In a confrontation with the Sontarans, the Doctor witnesses *their* cloning process, which requires Clonefeed, a form of amniotic fluid, made up of Caesofine concentrate (one part Bosteen, two parts Probic 5).

The Poison Sky

In our far future, he sees humanity evolve into clouds of gas, and later still, existing as downloads. He learns a little about end-time gravity mechanics. Visiting California, he sees a quake caused by the San Andreas Fault.

Utopia

He wonders at the beauty of a starfire burst over the coast of Meta Sigma Folio.

Last of the Time Lords

On 21st Century Earth, having noticed plasma coils around London's Royal Hope Hospital, the Tenth Doctor admits himself as a patient, faking abdominal pains.

Immediately before the beginning of *Smith and Jones*.

The Shakespeare Code

Prior to *Gridlock*

The Tenth Doctor tells companion Martha about the Daleks.

Daleks in Manhattan. Martha recognises the name despite never having encountered the Daleks before.

Without his companion's knowledge, he records a lengthy series of instructions for Martha, regarding what might happen should he need to use the Chameleon Arch to rewrite his biology.

Human Nature. Presumably, each incarnation of the Doctor has had to record a fresh message for each new companion. Good thing he doesn't need much sleep (unless, as he says in *Knock Knock*, he's just regenerated or had a large lunch).

Prior to *Daleks in Manhattan*

Despite his low opinion of the artificial mood states on sale in New New York, the Doctor purchases several that induce a dream-state, and possibly some that treat insomnia.

Dark Water. Clara steals a patch, assuming it will put the Twelfth Doctor to sleep. In fact, it's a dream patch, meaning he either has both or just lied about them being for the purpose of catching up on sleep, having neither regenerated or had a big lunch lately.

Evolution of the Daleks

Prior to *The Lazarus Experiment*

The Doctor reads the poem *The Hollow Man*, by T S Eliot.

The Lazarus Experiment. According to Martha, there is no gap between stories from the time she joined the Tenth Doctor on his travels, but he could conceivably have managed to read Eliot's poem.

Prior to *42*

The Doctor sees the results of endothermic vaporisation.

42. The Tenth Doctor says he has never seen such a ferocious endothermic vaporisation before, suggesting that he has at least seen something like it. There's no indication whether or not Martha was with him at the time.

Prior to *Human Nature*

The Doctor learns the skill of olfactory ventriloquism.

The Family of Blood. The Tenth Doctor uses this trick to outwit the Family.

On Earth in the year 2007, the Tenth Doctor and Martha are ambushed by the Family of Blood, but manage to enter the TARDIS before their new enemies can view their faces.

Mere moments before the beginning of *Human Nature*.

The Family of Blood

Prior to *Blink*

The Doctor learns of the species known as either the Weeping Angels or the Lonely Assassins. Their origins are apparently unknown, but he believes them to be almost as old as the universe. The Tenth Doctor and Martha attend the moon landings four times. In late 21st Century London, they take a taxi to a destination near Sally Sparrow's DVD store, where they must deal with a thing (actually, four things and a lizard). They arm themselves with a bow and arrow, and their cab pulls up 20 minutes before hatching (whatever that means). With astonishing foresight, the Doctor installs Security Protocol 712 in the TARDIS, which detects the presence of an authorised control disc (a DVD featuring the Doctor – I've got loads of those) and activates the ship's echelon circuit. Afterwards, the TARDIS takes them to the house known as Wester Drumlins a year or so before their meeting with Sally Sparrow. The Weeping Angels somehow take the TARDIS key before sending the Doctor and Martha back in time to 1969, where, acting on Sally's instructions, he writes her a message on the wall advising her to duck. Stranded without the TARDIS, Martha gets a job in a shop in order to support the Doctor while he builds a timey-wimey detector (that not only goes 'ping' but also accidentally boils eggs - often inside the chicken). Following police officer Billy Shipton's arrival in the past, the Doctor persuades him to include the footage he films based on Sally's notes on the 17 DVDs she will one day own.

> *Blink.* Sally Sparrow spots the Tenth Doctor and Martha from the window of her shop. The moon landing proves to be of tremendous significance to the Eleventh Doctor's plans to rid the world of the Silence during *Day of the Moon,* and is also mentioned in the Tenth Doctor novel *The Krillitane Storm.* By arriving prior to Neil Armstrong (on multiple occasions), the Doctor himself is technically the first man on the moon, an achievement to which he alludes in *Empress of Mars.* The Seventh Doctor makes oblique reference to Neil Armstrong in the final episode of *The Greatest Show in the Galaxy.* Sally Sparrow's DVD and others like it are still in the TARDIS during *Kill the Moon.* The echelon circuit is first mentioned in *Before the Flood.*

Prior to *Utopia*

The Tenth Doctor shows companion Martha where to find the TARDIS' medical kit.

> *Utopia.* Seemingly, the Doctor has moved it since *Shada,* since Martha seems to find it in no time at all.

The Doctor watches the Wesley Snipes action movie *Passenger 57* and the TV series *The Apprentice.* On the planet Sto, in the Casivanian Belt, he watches the game show *By the Light of the Asteroid* (if you're not sure you remember it, it's the one with the twins). For some reason, he also familiarises himself with the Sto/Earth Exchange Rate. Back on Earth, he visits New Zealand, and is present at the birth of Jesus Christ. He undertakes a study of nitrofine metal. During one intergalactic adventure, he survives death by taking refuge in an Omnistate Impact Chamber.

> *Voyage of the Damned.* On board the *Titanic,* the Tenth Doctor identifies himself as 'Passenger 57' and references *The Apprentice.* He vaguely remembers *By the Light of the Asteroid,* recommends New Zealand as a beauty spot to Astrid, informs Mr Copper of the exact value of a million pounds in Sto Credits, instantly recognises nitrofine and the make of Max Capricorn's Impact Chamber, and recollects the first Christmas,

> which, according to the Eighth Doctor audio *Relative Dimensions,* he attended alongside his old pal Leonardo da Vinci (so that's two wise men right there). *Planet of the Dead* reveals that he was also present at Christ's resurrection, while in *Thin Ice,* the Twelfth Doctor tells Bill that Jesus was considerably less Caucasian than motion pictures would have us believe.

He enjoys the work of author Agatha Christie, including *Murder on the Orient Express* and *Death in the Clouds* (a reprint of which he purchases around the year 5,000,000,000). He is fooled by her plots only once, but considers it 'a good once.' He studies the details of her famous disappearance in 1926.

> *The Unicorn and the Wasp.* The Tenth Doctor first suggests meeting Agatha Christie in the final scene of *Last of the Time Lords.* In the audio *Bang-Bang-A-Boom!,* the Seventh Doctor seems to have little knowledge of her works, while the Eighth Doctor owns a signed copy of *The Murder of Roger Ackroyd,* and later claims (in the audios *Storm Warning* and *Terror Firma,* respectively) that the author is a former companion. She is mentioned again in the Tenth Doctor novel *The Taking of Chelsea 426.* In *Flatline,* the Twelfth Doctor claims to love locked-room mysteries, and while John Dickson Carr is that acknowledged master of that particular sub-genre, Dame Agatha wrote her share. The Thirteenth Doctor mimics Hercule Poirot in *The Tsuranga Conundrum.*

The Sound of Drums

Last of the Time Lords

Voyage of the Damned

Prior to *Partners in Crime*

The Doctor meets Spartacus, witnesses the San Francisco earthquake, watches the television show *Fawlty Towers* (in which the lead actor looks staggeringly like a pompous art critic he brushed past in Paris), and acquires a water pistol.

> *The Fires of Pompeii.* The Tenth Doctor introduces himself as Spartacus to a Roman who looks staggeringly like one of his future incarnations. And so does companion Donna. Since this appears to be her first trip into Earth's past, it is unlikely she was with him then or in 1906 when the famous earthquake

occurred. He explains away her behaviour by saying 'she's from Barcelona.' He uses the water pistol to defend himself.

He sees the lightning skies of Cotter Paluni's world and the diamond coral reefs of Kataa Flo Ko.

The Sontaran Stratagem. The Tenth Doctor plans to take companion Donna to all these places. The history of Cotter Paluni's World is outlined in the *Torchwood* audio *Red Skies*.

He is present on either Earth or an Earth colony when the New Byzantine Calendar is adopted.

The Doctor's Daughter. The Tenth Doctor eventually recognises the date system used by the human colonists.

Arriving in the Silfrax Galaxy, he sees the hives of the Vespiforms, and the telepathic recorders used by the insect species.

The Unicorn and the Wasp

The Doctor has a pleasant time on the planet known as the Library, in particular the biographies section at the equator. He reads the novels of Jeffrey Archer, Helen Fielding's *Bridget Jones* series and *Monty Python's Big Red Book* (which, by the way, is blue). In the 51st-Century, he sees faces donated to Flesh Banks. He writes a message signed with a kiss. He witnesses the upsetting phenomenon of data ghosts, which he likens to a footprint on the beach when the tide is about to come in. On Earth and many other planets, he encounters small clusters of Vashta Nerada, 'the shadows that melt the flesh.'

Silence in the Library. The Doctor has been to the Library before, and mentions these particular books to companion Donna. The radio drama *Slipback* ends with the Sixth Doctor intending to seek out the largest library he can find, which might lead into his original visit. Of River's summons, which she signs with a kiss, he remarks 'We've all done that.' He's also seen Vashta Nerada, but never a large swarm. He knows that the only defence against them is simply to run. Despite being living shadows, the Vashta Nerada appear to be unconnected to either the creature captured by the Tenth Doctor in Elton Pope's home during *Love & Monsters* or the Shadow Kin from the *Class* episode *For Tonight We Might Die*. The Fourth and Eighth Doctors battle the shadows that melt the flesh in the audios *Night of the Vashta Nerada* and *Day of the Vashta Nerada*, respectively, while a tussle with the Eleventh Doctor is recounted in the comic strip *Space Oddity*. The short story *Not*

So Much a Programme, More a Way of Life reveals that the Fifth Doctor's companion Adric is an avid watcher of *Monty Python's Flying Circus*. In the audio *The Lure of the Nomad*, the Sixth Doctor attempts to introduce his new companion Mathew Sharpe to the joys of the Dead Parrot sketch, from which he quotes in *The Ratings War* and *The Shadow Heart*. The Tenth Doctor mentions *Python*-inspired musical *Spamalot* in the short story *Revenge of the Judoon*.

He enjoys the local beverage on the planet Shan Shen, and encounters a beetle-like creature, one of the Trickster's brigade, which is capable of altering an individual's life in minor ways.

Turn Left. The Trickster appears in person on *The Sarah Jane Adventures*, and the Tenth Doctor finally confronts it during *The Wedding of Sarah Jane Smith*. He says that he has fought the Trickster's shadows and changelings many times. Shan Shen is mentioned in the Third Doctor audio *The Blame Game*.

He watches mountains swaying in the breeze on the planet Felspoon.

Journey's End. Companion Donna knows about Felspoon once she becomes part-Doctor.

Passing by Earth (as he so often does), the Tenth Doctor begins investigating Adipose Industries.

Immediately prior to *Partners in Crime*.

The Fires of Pompeii

Planet of the Ood

Prior to *The Sontaran Stratagem*

The Doctor pockets a grey clockwork mouse.

The Tenth Doctor uses the mouse to cause a distraction during *The Doctor's Daughter*. It is not the one the Fourth Doctor has in his pocket at the start of episode six of *The Talons of Weng-Chiang*, which is brown in colour.

He witnesses aliens using a Cordolaine signal, which stops bullets firing from a gun by means of copper excitation. Against his better judgement, the Tenth Doctor allows companion Donna to pilot the TARDIS.

The Sontaran Stratagem. The Tenth Doctor is surprised to find that the Sontarans are using Cordolaine signals, indicating that he knows what they are. As the episode begins, Donna is getting close to putting a dent in the 1980s … another dent.

The Poison Sky

The Doctor's Daughter

Prior to *The Unicorn and the Wasp*

In the Ardennes, circa 800 AD, the Tenth Doctor discovers that King Charlemagne has been kidnapped by an insane computer.

The Unicorn and the Wasp. The flashback doesn't feature companion Donna, but that's no reason to suppose she was not around at the time. The incident is described in greater detail in the short story *The Lonely Computer*. The First Doctor recalls being trapped in Charlemagne's burning library in the audio *The Drowned World*.

Prior to *Silence in the Library*

The Doctor dines at a restaurant on the planet Darillium, with an excellent view of the fabled Singing Towers.

It's first mentioned in *The Forest of the Dead* that the Doctor eventually takes River Song up the Singing Towers, but he evidently knows about the restaurant, and invests in its construction during *The Husbands of River Song*. In the Season Six DVD extra *Last Night*, it seems that the Eleventh Doctor is on his way there with River, but he evidently changes his mind at the last minute.

The Tenth Doctor plans to take Donna to the beach, but decides against doing so after receiving a message on the psychic paper summoning him to the planet known simply as the Library.

Silence in the Library. The Doctor neglects to tell Donna his reasons for going there.

The Forest of the Dead

Prior to *Midnight*

The Doctor reads *Goblin Market*, by Christina Rosetti. He finds himself in a structure or vehicle protected by Fenito glass. He and Donna holiday on the planet Midnight.

> *Midnight*. The duo arrive on the planet prior to the start of the episode. The Doctor recognises a quotation from this poem and identifies Fenito glass.

Prior to *Turn Left*

The Tenth Doctor notifies the authorities on Midnight about the presence of a hostile life-form.

> This is the Doctor's stated intention at the end of *Midnight*.

The Doctor sees Donna's grandfather Wilfred Mott once again, and tells him all about the Time Lords.

> In *The End of Time*, Wilf recalls the Tenth Doctor talking to him about his people, though he has never done so onscreen.

The Stolen Earth

Journey's End

Prior to *The Next Doctor*

The Doctor sees an infostamp - possibly, but not necessarily, of Dalek design.

> *The Next Doctor*. The Tenth Doctor recognises an infostamp, and theorises that the one containing information about his previous incarnations was stolen from the Daleks. The Cybermen do not appear to have any shortage of infostamps, so it seems they're not exclusively Dalek property.

Prior to *Planet of the Dead*

The Doctor is present at the very first Easter, learns to drive a bus, enjoys the comedy of Arthur Askey, sees a spaceship powered by a crystal nucleus and anti-gravity clamps, and finds himself in the middle of a war between China and Japan. In the court of King Athelstan, in 924 AD, he views the coronation gift known as the Cup of Athelstan. Tracking a hole in the fabric of reality, the Doctor parks the TARDIS in the gardens of Buckingham Palace, and goes in search of Rondium particles, pausing only to purchase a chocolate egg.

> *Planet of the Dead*. The Tenth Doctor knows that buses do not require keys. He repeats Askey's famous catchphrase, 'Ay thang yew' ('I thank you,' for the uninitiated), as does the Eighth Doctor in the audio *Immortal Beloved*. He recognises both

the crystal nucleus and the anti-gravity clamps in the Tritovore ship. His experience of Easter festivities probably extends to a knowledge of the Easter Bunny, mentioned by the Twelfth Doctor during *Last Christmas.*

Prior to *The Waters of Mars*

The Tenth Doctor nudges the wormholes created by the Swarm onto uninhabited planets.

Planet of the Dead. At the end of the episode, the Doctor tells Magambo he'll do this, and he's nothing if not a Time Lord of his word.

The Doctor studies the history of the space-faring Brooke family, beginning with Adelaide Brooke's childhood encounter with a Dalek following their abduction of the planet Earth, her eventual death on Bowie Base One on November 21, 2059, and the achievements of her descendants. He learns to speak North Martian, and sees Steel Combination being manufactured in Liverpool.

The Waters of Mars. Had the Doctor known about the stolen Earth prior to ... well, *The Stolen Earth* ... he wouldn't have been so surprised when the Daleks, you know, stole the Earth. He notes that Bowie Base One is constructed of Steel Combination.

Prior to *The End of Time*

After a busy period, the Tenth Doctor keeps his appointment with the Ood, sees the phosphorous carousel of the Great Magellan Gestalt, saves an unnamed planet from the Red Carnivorous Maw, and decides to name a galaxy Allison. Seemingly only because he finds it funny, he fits the TARDIS with a car-style lock. In 1562, the Doctor suspects that his old enemies, the Zygons, are attempting to infiltrate the court of Elizabeth I. To facilitate his investigations, he invents a device that goes 'ding' (but only in the presence of shape-shifting DNA). Suspecting that Elizabeth herself might be a Zygon, he invites her on a picnic and unwisely takes a recently procured horse with him. Following his marriage to the ginger monarch, he and his former and future selves are forced to nip off and battle the Zygon menace in the 21st Century. Doctor No 10 returns to his new bride in order to consummate the union (assuming he hasn't already done so) and to pose for a portrait, but very quickly views the marriage as a mistake, and abandons the monarch in a glade.

The wedding between the Tenth Doctor and Elizabeth is

established first in *The End of Time*. In *The Shakespeare Code*, Elizabeth calls him her sworn enemy, although at that point in his personal history, he has yet to meet her. The Third Doctor says in *The Curse of Peladon* that he may have attended her coronation (or it might have been Victoria's). The Dream Lord, in *Amy's Choice*, puts it down to a weakness for redheads. In *The Beast Below*, Liz 10 says the Doctor behaved like a 'bad, bad boy' with Elizabeth. The Virgin Queen first appears onscreen in *The Chase*, but she and the First Doctor do not meet. In *The Wedding of River Song*, the Eleventh Doctor tells Dorium that Elizabeth is still in the glade, waiting to elope with him. If she wound up harbouring such hostile feelings for the Time Lord, it is anyone's guess why she didn't rescind his credentials as curator of the Under Gallery. The portrait seen in *The Day of the Doctor* shows the Tenth Doctor in full period garb, when he actually wears his usual getup (including sand shoes) for the wedding. As with all other encounters with his other selves, he forgets most of the pertinent details of the incident beyond the fact that he deflowered the Queen of England, but the Eleventh Doctor puts it down to him not paying enough attention. The Eighth Doctor claims to have met the pasty-faced monarch in the audio *Terror Firma*. The car lock is presumably destroyed during his traumatic regeneration.

The Doctor watches *He-Man and the Masters of the Universe*, or becomes aware of the lead characters. He meets several people who have been searching for him for hundreds of years, as well as an alien disguising its appearance with a cloaking device known as a Shimmer.

The End of Time. The Tenth Doctor describes the Master as 'Skeletor.'He mentions to Wilf that people have been waiting hundreds of years for him, and recognizes a Shimmer instantly. The instant disguise kit is also put to use in the comic strips *Ripper's Curse*, *Love is in the Air*, *Fooled* and *Shock Horror*, as well as in the Twelfth Doctor novel *Big Bang Generation*.

He befriends famous astronomer Sir Patrick Moore, and also sees actual cowboys in someone's bedroom. During the early 17th Century he makes the acquaintance of Pierre de Fermat, who explains to him the proof that was too big to fit into the margin of his famous theorem. Sadly, the Doctor is unable to prevent Fermat's death in a duel.

The Eleventh Hour. The Eleventh Doctor explains to Jeff that Fermat is dead because the Time Lord 'slept in.' A proof of the theorem appears in the novel *All-Consuming Fire*, and the

Seventh Doctor claims to have solved it himself in the novel *The Death of Art*. He tells young Amelia that although she hasn't had literal cowboys in her room, that *has* happened - hopefully, not in an untelevised scene from *The Gunfighters*. Rose Tyler mentions Patrick Moore in *Aliens of London*, and the Third Doctor's companion Liz Shaw recollects meeting him in the novel *The Devil Goblins from Neptune*.

In the 29th Century, the Doctor hears of Starship UK, but the TARDIS doesn't take him there. He sees a high-speed air cannon in action, and becomes a drinking buddy of Henry XII.

The Beast Below. The Eleventh Doctor calls high-speed air cannons a 'lousy way to travel.' Liz 10 knows of the Doctor's friendship with Henry XII. The Twelfth Doctor recognises 29th Century spaceship design in *Robot of Sherwood*. In the First Doctor audio *Rise and Fall*, Susan dons a dress from that period.

He purchases a packet of jammy dodgers.

Victory of the Daleks. The Eleventh Doctor pretends the biscuit is a self-destruct device (in *Journey to the Centre of the TARDIS*, he claims that the TARDIS has no self-destruct function). In this incarnation, he becomes as fond of the snack as his fourth self was of jelly babies (though the Sixth Doctor is seen to still have the bag in his pocket in *The Mysterious Planet*, and he reverts to his earlier taste in snacks during the Twelfth Doctor's era).

He pays several visits to the asteroid containing the Delirium Archive, travels on a Starliner with gravity provided by Grav-Globes and oxygen by an Eco-Pod. He sees the ship's Home Box. He joins the same bowling team as Virginia Woolf. On Alfava Metraxis, the seventh planet in the Dundra System, he dines with the very relaxed chief architect of the Aplans, and learns of recently imposed laws against self-marriage among the two-headed species. He learns how the church has progressed in the 51st Century, and begins a relationship with Tasha Lem, Mother Superious of the Papal Mainframe. If, at this time, he sees any of the species commonly known as the Silence, he understandably forgets about it.

The Time of the Angels and *Flesh and Stone*. The Home Box does not belong to the Starliner *Titanic* from *Voyage of the Damned*, or the Terradonian craft from *Full Circle*. The quasi-military religious order the Doctor encounters here is almost certainly the Church of the Papal Mainframe seen in *The Time of the Doctor*, in which Tasha Lem makes her only appearance, having been mentioned by name in *A Good Man Goes to War*. She doesn't recognise the Eleventh Doctor in the body he has been rocking for centuries. Soldiers of the Papal Mainframe appear in the Twelfth Doctor novel *Big Bang Generation*. The Delirium Archive is mentioned again in the Eleventh Doctor novel *The Forgotten Army*. It would appear that a way to counteract the memory-suppressing ability of the Silence has been discovered by the 67th Century, since a picture of one appears on the Perils of the Constant Division databank in *The Tsuranga Conundrum* (Threat Level Beetroot, no doubt). The Doctor's bowling team may include beings from other worlds; in *Demons of the Punjab*, the Thirteenth Doctor assures Ryan that several different races enjoy the game. In the novel *Scratchman*, the Fourth Doctor implies that fellow bowler Virginia Woolf may have been an alien.

The Doctor bursts out of the wrong cake. (Awkward!) He sees the founding of Venice by refugees escaping Atilla the Hun, and revisits the city at several later points in its history, where he meets Lord Byron and Giacomo Casanova (to whom he owes a chicken following a lost bet). The TARDIS takes him to Saturnyne, sometime before the planet fell to the Silence.

The Vampires of Venice. The Eleventh Doctor is able to identify the vampires' planet of origin. In the audio *The Stones of Venice*, the Eighth Doctor recalls visiting Venice at various stages of its history (including, presumably, during the First Doctor novel, *The Empire of Glass*) and claims to have known Atilla the Hun in the audio *Memory Lane*. In the novel *Managra*, the Fourth Doctor says he befriended Byron.

In a fit of pique, the Doctor throws the TARDIS Manual into a supernova. He meets the Eknodine, 'a proud, ancient race.' A trip to the Candle Meadows of Karass Don Slava results in a fragment of psychic pollen finding its way into the TARDIS' Time Rotor. In the Earth of the future, he learns of the benefits of D96 compound in treating stiff joints. He acquires a golden egg-whisk from who knows where.

Amy's Choice. The Eleventh Doctor says the psychic pollen has been 'hanging around for ages,' making the possibility that it occurred during a previous incarnation quite likely. He mentions D96 when visiting the nursing home. The egg-whisk becomes part of a makeshift generator.

The Doctor visits Earth in the year 2020 (or thereabouts). Far in the future, he witnesses bio-programming conducted on jungle planets.

The Hungry Earth. The Eleventh Doctor knows the ground does not feel as it should in that period.

He is unable to persuade artist Pablo Picasso to paint the eyes on either side of the head.

> *Vincent and the Doctor*. The Fifth Doctor mentions the artist's works in the novel *The Crystal Bucephalus*, and the Eleventh Doctor encounters him in the short story *The War of Art*. The novel *The Scarlet Empress* states that the Third Doctor also knew Picasso.

He becomes a skilful football player.

> *The Lodger*. The Eleventh Doctor says 'I'm good at football, I think,' suggesting that whatever experience of the game he has, it was acquired during a former incarnation. He does five million keepy-uppies in under an hour in *The Power of Three*, so he must be quite good. The Fourth Doctor has a football rattle in *The Masque of Mandragora*, and the Tenth in *The Sarah Jane Adventures* story *The Wedding of Sarah Jane Smith*. The Twelfth Doctor, however, declares football an 'unbelievably boring sport' in the *Class* episode *For Tonight We Might Die*. In the audio *The Next Life*, the Eighth Doctor claims to have memorised the names of all Liverpool FC strikers from 1964 to 2014, and attends a Delchester United match in the comic strip *Doctor Who and the Nightmare Game*. The Ninth and Eleventh Doctors are both present at the 1966 World Cup final, according to the strips *The Love Invasion* and *They Think It's All Over*, while the First Doctor becomes involved in the theft of the trophy in the audio *This Sporting Life*.

He is present at the fall of Rome, and witnesses the tragic result of repeated memory wipes.

> *Day of the Moon*. Given companion Amy's Roman fetish, had she been present she would surely have mentioned that fact in *The Pandorica Opens*. It pre-dates Rory's travels in the TARDIS, though his Auton duplicate was in Rome at the time, it seems.

The Doctor hears both the legend of the message written into the diamond cliffs of Planet One, and the tale of the Pandorica (which he dismisses as a fairy story). He studies the mating habits of the fruit flies on Hoppledom Six.

> *The Pandorica Opens*. The Eleventh Doctor mentions the fruit flies, but then cannot remember why.

He learns the legend of the Siren.

> *The Curse of the Black Spot*

He makes one of his very-infrequent house calls.

Night Terrors. The Eleventh Doctor tells companions Amy and Rory that he hasn't made a house call in a while. His definition of a house call is, of course, far from conventional.

Following the events of *Castrovalva*, the Doctor creates a fail-safe which prevents individuals from vanishing with deleted rooms.

The Doctor's Wife

He becomes a fan of performer Dusty Springfield.

The Rebel Flesh. The Eleventh Doctor mentions this after companion Rory recalls his mother's obsession with the singer (which would doubtless have come up before if he'd been introduced to her music more recently). All the Eleventh Doctor stories prior to *The Vampires of Venice* – when Rory joins the TARDIS crew – run into one another, so this is the latest possible date for his Dusty initiation.

During a jaunt to Earth in the 22nd Century, he hears of the invention of the Flesh.

The Rebel Flesh and *The Almost People*. The Eleventh Doctor clearly knows of the Flesh in the first episode, and confesses in the second that he deliberately took the TARDIS to Earth in the 22nd Century in order to study it. In the audio *Old Soldiers*, the Third Doctor mentions beings created by a psycho-plasma matrix, which might refer to the Flesh, or perhaps the Plasmavores.

He becomes scared on a ghost train.

Good Night, an additional scene on the Season Six DVD.

The TARDIS takes him to Ravenscala, where the life-forms are 600 feet tall, and to another planet, the name of which translates as 'Volatile Circus.' He calls in at an English pub in Majorca. He is once threatened by someone wielding a chair leg, earns a degree in cheese-making, and sees an inhabitant of the much-invaded planet Tivoli.

The God Complex. The Eleventh Doctor is planning to take Amy and Rory to Ravan-Skala at the start of this story. He mentions 'Volatile Circus' as he returns them to Earth. He must not have actually visited Tivoli, however, since he doesn't become aware of the people's sly nature until this particular adventure. Another member of the race appears in *Under the Lake*. The Doctor's cheese-making degree is mentioned again in the Eleventh Doctor novel *Shroud of Sorrow*.

Hearing of former companion Sarah Jane Smith's impending nuptials, the Tenth Doctor heads for early 21st Century Ealing, only to find that the Trickster is somehow preventing his TARDIS from materialising.

The Sarah Jane Adventures story *The Wedding of Sarah Jane Smith*

On 'one terrible night,' he calculates that there were 2.47 billion children living on Gallifrey when he activated the Moment - or, more accurately, when he *imagines* he activated the Moment.

The Day of the Doctor. The Tenth Doctor knows the figure, but the Eleventh has forgotten it.

The Doctor receives free tickets and an official summons to board the Orient Express. In space. He rejects both offers.

Mummy on the Orient Express. The Twelfth Doctor states that he did not succumb to these lures, and while *The Big Bang* apparently ends with him on his way there, he eventually scents a rat, and alters course.

During *The End of Time* ...

In addition to looking in on Rose, Martha, Donna and Captain Jack, the very gradually regenerating Tenth Doctor visits all of his other former companions, with the exception of Jo Grant - though he learns of her exploits on the Yangtze in a tea crate.

The Sarah Jane Adventures story *Death of the Doctor*

The Eleventh Doctor
Matt Smith
2010-2013

The Eleventh Hour

The Beast Below

Victory of the Daleks

Prior to *The Time of the Angels*

The Doctor reads the works of fantasy author JRR Tolkien and watches the *Star Wars* movies.

> In the Season Five DVD extra *Meanwhile in the TARDIS,* set immediately after *Flesh and Stone,* the Doctor describes himself as 'Space Gandalf' and 'the little green one in *Star Wars.*' The comic strips *Once Upon a Time-Lord* and *The Warkeeper's Crown* (featuring the Sixth and Tenth Doctors, respectively) contain references to Tolkien's works, while the Eleventh Doctor and Amy meet the man himself in the strip *The Professor, The Queen and the Bookshop. Star Wars* is also mentioned in the novels *Mission: Impractical* and *Autonomy,* and the Tenth Doctor comic strip *Agent Provocateur.*

Flesh and Stone

The Vampires of Venice

Amy's Choice

Prior to *The Hungry Earth*

The Eleventh Doctor promises to take companions Amy and Rory to Rio. He acquires a pair of sunglasses and a catapult, and tries but fails to make a decent meringue. He hears what he calls 'the Klempari Defence,' and considers it old hat.

> *The Hungry Earth.* Amy complains throughout the episode that she is dressed for Rio.

Cold Blood

Prior to *Vincent and the Doctor*

Following Rory's deletion from all of time and space, the Eleventh Doctor and his companion Amy Pond go on a galactic sightseeing tour, taking in Arcadia and the Trojan Gardens.

> *Vincent and the Doctor.* Amy mentions these destinations at the start of the story. The Tenth Doctor talks about Arcadia during *Doomsday,* in which he states he hopes one day to get over what occurred there during the Time War. Since those events are depicted in *The Day of the Doctor,* and we now know that Arcadia is to be found on Gallifrey - which only exists close to the end Universe - this is evidently a different Arcadia entirely, perhaps the one featured in the Seventh Doctor novel *Deceit.* The Sixth Doctor is heading for Arcadia in the comic strip *Profits of Doom.*

He visits a moon that appears to be made of honey, but isn't ... nor is it actually a moon.

> *A Christmas Carol.* The Eleventh Doctor tells companion Rory about the sentient carnivorous moon. It is possible Amy might have been with him.

Prior to *The Lodger*

The Doctor watches the Gerry Anderson shows *Stingray* and *Thunderbirds.* On the planet Lammasteen, he learns to copy the natives' non-technological technology. The TARDIS rectifier gives the Eleventh Doctor some difficulties when he plans to take companion Amy to the fifth moon of Cindie Colesta.

> *The Lodger.* Early on, the Eleventh Doctor states that he and Amy have failed to reach their intended destination. He complains that the rectifier is playing up 'again' and introduces himself as 'Troy Handsome of International Rescue.' In *Death in Heaven,* the Twelfth Doctor recalls dancing a sensational foxtrot with Sylvia Anderson, who, among her many other accomplishments, provided the voice of Lady Penelope in the original *Thunderbirds,* a show referenced in the Ninth Doctor novel *Winner Takes All* and the Tenth Doctor audio *Dead Air.* Gerry Anderson's *Fireball XL-5* is mentioned in the First Doctor audio *Hunters of Earth,* and in the audio *The Nemonite Invasion,* the Tenth Doctor's companion Donna addresses him as 'Joe 90.'

The Eleventh Doctor and Amy are involved in an *Androids of Tara*-style mix-up involving a King and his robot duplicate.

> *The Doctor's Wife*. The Eleventh Doctor relates this story to companion Rory.

Prior to *The Pandorica Opens*

Relations between the Doctor and the Draconians go from cordial to strained. He tangles with both the Chelonians and the Haemogoths, and learns not to underestimate the Celts.

> *The Pandorica Opens*. Along with the Chelonians and the Haemogoths, the Draconians are part of the Alliance formed to seal the Eleventh Doctor in the Pandorica. According to *Frontier in Space*, his first or second incarnation is made a Noble of Draconia by the Fifteenth Emperor. The Chelonians appear in several Seventh Doctor novels, beginning with *The Highest Science*, but have never been seen in the television series. Haemogoths are mentioned in the Eleventh Doctor novel *The Forgotten Army*.

The Eleventh Doctor takes companion Amy Pond to Space Florida (in spite of the Twelfth Doctor's insistence in *Sleep No More* that no-one uses the word 'space' as a prefix, before describing Gallifrey as 'Space Glasgow' in *Hell Bent*). He sees an Egyptian Goddess sealed into 'the Seventh Obelisk' following a prayer meeting.

> *The Big Bang*. The Doctor says that the Space Florida vacation was a week before their arrival in Roman-occupied Britain. The events of *The Lodger* were, apparently, three weeks prior. At the episode's conclusion, he receives a call claiming to be from a Royal personage, stating that the Goddess has escaped and is now running amok on the *Orient Express*. In space. There's nothing to suggest that Amy wasn't with him at the prayer meeting.

He constructs a pair of spectacles containing a microphone and camera.

> *The Girl Who Waited*. Companion Rory has never seen the spectacles before, but Amy seems to recognise them. He upgrades this technology considerably by the time of *Flatline*.

The Big Bang

Prior to *A Christmas Carol*

Remembering the fishy attempts to lure him there before, the Eleventh Doctor decides against visiting the *Orient Express*. In space.

> *The Big Bang*. At the end of the episode, the Doctor and his companions are apparently headed for the *Orient Express*. In space. The Twelfth Doctor makes it clear that they never got there.

The Doctor sees *Mary Poppins*, and has a ball at Frank Sinatra's hunting lodge in 1952, in the company of Albert Einstein and Santa Claus (AKA Jeff). He acquires two Santa hats, possibly from Jeff himself, as well as replacements for the fez destroyed by River Song in *The Big Bang*. He encounters Face Spiders, creatures with the head of a tiny baby and the body of a spider (as envisioned by Father Dougall MacGuire in the first episode of *Father Ted*), which sleep in mattresses, but have a preference for the backs of bedroom cupboards. He sends newly married companions Amy and Rory Pond to a number of romantic honeymoon locations, including a doomed galaxy-class starliner (well, he wasn't to know that he was placing them in deadly peril once again).

> *A Christmas Carol*. The Eleventh Doctor admits that he compares very poorly with the celebrated governess (and references actor Dick Van Dyke's notorious cockney accent when meeting his former self in *The Day of the Doctor*). The Eleventh Doctor short story *Magic of the Angels* implies that he and Miss Poppins actually met. Einstein appears onscreen for the first time in the Seventh Doctor's début story *Time and the Rani*. The Seventh Doctor's companion Ace discovers and wears a fez in the vaults below Windsor Castle during episode one of *Silver Nemesis*. It is not too much of a stretch, is it, to suggest that the same fez is later transported to the Under Gallery for safekeeping and is subsequently hurled backwards in time by the Eleventh Doctor? By the standards of this book's speculations, it's positively mundane. The Second Doctor considers purchasing a fez in both the comic book *Prisoners of Time* and the short story *The Anti-Hero*. In the audio *Maker of Demons*, the Seventh Doctor claims to have attempted to duet with Ol' Blue Eyes.

The Doctor meets former companion Jo Grant's 13th grandchild, a dyslexic and an excellent swimmer. In South Africa, he discovers the properties of the oil of the Buchu shrub. Dropping companions Amy and Rory Pond off on a honeymoon planet (which is to say, a planet recently married to an asteroid), the Eleventh Doctor sets off to investigate a battlefield on the Wasteland of the Crimson Heart, only to end up stranded 10,000 light years from Earth when his TARDIS is stolen by the Shansheeth. He uses the available wreckage to build a device capable of keying into Clyde Langer's residual Artron energy.

The Sarah Jane Adventures story *Death of the Doctor*. The Eleventh Doctor uses Buchu oil on the machine he has constructed.

Prior to *The Impossible Astronaut*

The Eleventh Doctor asks companion Rory to help him with repairs to the TARDIS as they enter conceptual space (which, before you ask, is nothing like a banana).

The two-part Comic Relief special *Space* and *Time*.

He later drops Amy and Rory off on 21st Century Earth before embarking on a series of escapades, which include failing to escape from a prisoner-of-war camp, dancing with Stan Laurel and Oliver Hardy on the set of their 1939 film *The Flying Deuces*, and breaking out of the Tower of London in a mysterious sphere. He acquires a special straw that adds extra fizz, and finds that the year 1482 is full of glitches. He meets Founding Fathers John Quincy Adams and Alexander Hamilton, at least one of whom fancied him. He either sees the movie *The Graduate* or reads Charles Webb's novel of the same name. At some point before he is reunited with Mr and Mrs Pond in America, he turns 909 years old.

The Impossible Astronaut. Companions Amy and Rory have a home of their own. The Eleventh Doctor introduces River Song to Richard Nixon as 'Mrs Robinson,' a reference to the famous seductress in *The Graduate*. She, in turn, calls him Benjamin (the gauche young protagonist of that film, played by Dustin Hoffman) in *Let's Kill Hitler*. Amy says that the last time she saw the Doctor, he was 908. The version of the Doctor she, Rory and River meet in the diner which may be a disguised TARDIS, is 909. Alexander Hamilton also appears in the comic strip *The Long Con*, and, less famously, in some musical that very few people other than the Thirteenth Doctor are talking about.

The Doctor watches the Richard Nixon and David Frost interviews on TV.

Day of the Moon. The Eleventh Doctor tells Nixon to say hello to Frost. The Time Lord is accidentally the cause of Nixon's eventual downfall, encouraging him to record all conversations in the Oval Office. But the disgraced Prez attempts to nuke the UK in the comic strip *In With the Tide*, so it's the very least the Doctor could do for him. The Twelfth Doctor mimics Tricky Dick's famous double peace-sign gesture when boarding his Presidential jet in *The Zygon Invasion*.

In the Gamma Forests, he makes a tremendous impression on a young Lorna Bucket when he tells her to run (always good advice around the Doctor). He brings dishonour upon Sontaran Strax and his six-million-strong clone batch, causing Strax to seek penance by serving as a nurse at the Battle of Zaruthstra in the year 4037.

> *A Good Man Goes to War.* It is implied that the Doctor himself devised Strax's penance. Companions Rory and Amy don't know the Sontaran, so this is the last possible date for his association with the Doctor. The short story *Lorna's Escape* describes the young Miss Bucket's first encounter with the Eleventh Doctor.

The Doctor is impressed with the sunsets, spires and silver colonnades of the planet Apalapucia, Number Two in the Top Ten destinations for the discerning intergalactic traveller. He is less impressed with Number One, which is overrun by coffee shops. He is distressed to hear about Chen-7, a pathogen deadly to species with two hearts, such as Gallifreyans or Dulcians.

> *The Girl Who Waited.* Presumably, he visited Apalapucia during a period when the quarantine was not enforced.

Assisting with the drafting of the US Declaration of Independence, he discovers that Thomas Jefferson has a great love of tomatoes. In 1911, the Eleventh Doctor is about to take lessons in either knitting or flying when he receives a summons to Lake Silencio, sent by his future self.

> *The Impossible Astronaut.* The Thomas Jefferson recollection appears in a deleted scene from *The Lazarus Experiment*; the Eleventh Doctor mentions him again here, as do the Sixth and Seventh in the audios *The Guardians of Prophecy* and *Survival of the Fittest*, respectively. In *The Wedding of River Song*, the Eleventh Doctor is seen reading *Knitting for Girls.* The Eighth Doctor asks for knitting in *The Night of the Doctor*, so perhaps that particular skill is one of the many things lost to the Time War. Damn you, Time War!

Prior to *Day of the Moon*

The Doctor invents a nano recorder, which fuses with the cartilage in the hand. During the three months following the end of *The Impossible Astronaut*, the Eleventh Doctor formulates a plan to deal with the Silence, sending his companions Amy and Rory and River Song across America to investigate on his behalf. His plan involves being taken prisoner by former FBI agent Canton Everett Delaware III. He designs a hologram of one of the Silence, based on the image recorded on Amy's phone.

Day of the Moon

Prior to *The Curse of the Black Spot*

The Time Lord reads the story of Goldilocks. While travelling in the TARDIS, the Eleventh Doctor picks up a distress signal that appears to emanate from Captain Avery's ship in the 17th Century.

The Curse of the Black Spot. The Eleventh Doctor asks 'Who's been sleeping in my Gun Room?'

Prior to *The Doctor's Wife*

The warning lights in the TARDIS become unreliable, causing the Doctor to consider removing them. He purchases an umbrella which he repairs many times until it no longer resembles the item he originally owned (it is probably the one partially vaporised by the Krotons). Seemingly for the heck of it, the Doctor materialises the TARDIS in very, very deep space. At this point, it is 700 years from his perspective since the events of *100,000 BC*.

The Doctor's Wife. The episode begins with the TARDIS parked in space. The Eleventh Doctor complains that the warning lights never stop blinking. While in human form, the TARDIS states that it took on the appearance of a Police Box 700 years earlier.

Prior to *The Rebel Flesh*

The Eleventh Doctor takes companions Amy and Rory Pond to the Eye of Orion. Probably. He makes them a new bedroom in the TARDIS. Whether or not it still has bunk beds is unknown.

The Eye of Orion is the Eleventh Doctor's intended destination at the end of *The Doctor's Wife*, though writer Neil Gaiman has stated that he doubts they ever reached it. Given that the Amy in this story is merely the Flesh duplicate of the real one, the bunk beds are presumably the Doctor's way of preventing any hanky-panky in the TARDIS.

During the 19th Century, the Eleventh Doctor meets female Silurian Vastra in the London Underground as she attempts to avenge her sisters by attacking tunnel diggers. He tells her 'anger is always the shortest distance to a mistake.' In the 52nd Century, he makes the acquaintance of black marketeer Dorium Maldovar.

A Good Man Goes to War. There is no indication of whether or not Rory and Amy were with the Doctor when he met either Dorium or Vastra. The latter encounter was seemingly with the Eleventh Doctor, since he states in *The Hungry Earth* that the Silurians in that story are a branch of the species he has not encountered before, and Madam Vastra appears to belong to that species. Then again, the comic strip *The Lost Dimension* states that it was the Ninth Doctor who first encounters Vastra. By 1888, she considers her debt to the Doctor 'very old.'

He explains the concept of regeneration to his Silurian friend, and she is with him when he forms an historical supergroup with Roman Emperor Marcus Aurelius on bass.

Deep Breath. Upon meeting the Twelfth Doctor shortly after his regeneration, Vastra comments – as the Brigadier did in *Planet of the Spiders* - 'Here we go again,' implying some familiarity with Time Lord physiognomy.

In addition to all its other amazing features, the Doctor installs a dartboard in the TARDIS' Control Room. He has an adventure in which he uses the phrase 'I've got to get to that cockerel before all hell breaks loose,' never imagining that he would have cause to repeat it under (one would imagine) different circumstances. He acquires a snowglobe.

The Rebel Flesh. Companions Amy and Rory Pond are playing darts at the start of the episode. The Fourth Doctor is revealed to be a skilful darts player in *The Android Invasion.*

The TARDIS takes him to a planet where everyone is all ears (the Ninth Doctor would have been quite at home). In order to win a bet, he plugs his brain into the core of a planet and halts its orbit. He is given a vial containing a red substance that tastes of burnt onions and can cure blood clots. He places several inflated red balloons in the TARDIS.

The Almost People. He has red and blue balloons in *Hide.*

The Almost People

Prior to *A Good Man Goes to War*

The Eleventh Doctor makes preparations for his attack on Demons Run, which include transporting several World War Two fighter planes and the spaceship containing Captain Avery's crew into the future. He materialises the TARDIS in the quadrant monitored by the 12th Cyber Legion.

A Good Man Goes to War

Prior to *Let's Kill Hitler*

The Doctor builds a sonic cane to compliment his screwdriver. He visits the Sisters of the Infinite Schism, which he proclaims the greatest hospital in the Universe. The Eleventh Doctor picks up a copy of the *Leadworth Chronicle*, which reports the discovery of a crop circle made in the shape of his name.

> *Let's Kill Hitler*

Prior to *Night Terrors*

The Doctor studies pantophobia, the fear of everything (and not a fear of pants, except insofar as pants are a part of everything). He develops a hatred of Rubik's cubes, finds himself in situations where he bumps into people he can't remember and is forced to address them as Brian, and meets the species known as the Tenza. He reads the story of Ali Baba.

> *Night Terrors*. The Eleventh Doctor is familiar with the Tenza and their abilities.

The Girl Who Waited

Prior to *The God Complex*

Attending a party with River Song, the Eleventh Doctor finds himself at the heart of a potential galactic conflict when Her Majesty the Queen is turned into a fish.

> *Bad Night*, a short scene included on the Season Six DVD. Rory and Amy are still travelling with the Eleventh Doctor. I'm treating this and the other extra scenes as relating to Season Six and no later, and I dare you to stop me.

On a particularly busy night, the Eleventh Doctor assists a possessed orchestra on a moonbase (with the aid of a euphonium), prevents a couple of supernovas, pens an entirely joke-based history of the universe (that's one in the eye for Oolon Coluphid), and helps out as a locum at a short-staffed medical practice in Brixton. He also attends a party with River Song and, it would seem, Marilyn Monroe.

> *Good Night*, another Season Six DVD extra. The Eleventh Doctor may have gone through a wedding ceremony with Norma Jean. *The Husbands of River Song* seems to confirm that assertion.

The Doctor visits Alderaan Beta ('planet of the chip shops') on September 21, 2360, where, from the top of a 400-foot tree, more stars are visible at 12 minutes past midnight than at any other moment.

First Night, another Season Six DVD extra. The Eleventh Doctor plans to take River there (and does so more than once, it seems). Great, now I want chips.

The Eleventh Doctor has now overcome his dislike of apples. He and companion Amy have a row about the washing-up in the TARDIS. He promises to takes her and Rory to Ravenscala, but the TARDIS materialises instead in the lobby of a faux English hotel.

The God Complex. When the Doctor drops his companions off at the end of the story, Amy suggests it is due to the washing-up. Having declared apples 'rubbish' moments after his regeneration, he munches on one that he finds in a bowl in the lobby. Then again, it's not a real lobby, so maybe it's not a real apple either (although he does produce an apple from his pocket in *Under the Lake*). According to *Hell Bent, Twice Upon a Time* and a deleted scene from *Human Nature*, he's not that fond of pears either, reducing his chances of getting his five a day even further.

Prior to *Closing Time*

If the Time Lord is to be believed (and River Song insists that he isn't), then a gap of 195 years in the Doctor's timeline occurs here. The Eleventh Doctor and River visit Easter Island, where he finds himself worshipped by the local population. They meet a being named Jim the Fish. Before his 1,103rd birthday, the Doctor visits him again. On more than one jaunt with River, he makes the TARDIS invisible, despite his habit of bumping into the craft when it's in this state.

The Impossible Astronaut. At Lake Silencio, the Eleventh Doctor says he's 1,103, and Amy notes that the last time she and Rory saw the Time Lord, he was 908. Given that he is travelling alone by this stage, the missing years must accumulate here. The Doctor tells River that Jim the Fish – later mentioned in *The Husbands of River Song* – is '*still* building his dam' (my italics), suggesting more than one meeting, and that River was not present at the second. When he bumps into the cloaked TARDIS, River sighs 'Every time!' The Second Doctor turns the TARDIS invisible in episode one of *The Invasion* and the Fourth in a scene deleted from *Terror of the Zygons*. The novel *Eye of Heaven* sees the Fourth Doctor visit Easter Island.

The Doctor discovers the telephone number of Brigadier Lethbridge-Stewart's nursing home. He develops a hatred of rats.

The Wedding of River Song. The Doctor worries that there might be rats in the crypt in which Dorium's severed head is stored. One might think that his distaste for the rodents occurs as a result of his fourth incarnation's encounter with Magnus Greel's mutations, but in episode one of *Paradise Towers*, his seventh self praises them as highly intelligent creatures. The Eleventh Doctor telephones the nursing home during *The Wedding of River Song*.

Several people mention the planet Trenzalore to him, but he makes a point of avoiding it.

The Name of the Doctor. Seemingly, it isn't news to the Eleventh Doctor when Dorium mentions Trenzalore. The point at which he begins to suspect that it is his ultimate resting place must come after this story, since he is content for much of *Closing Time* and *The Wedding of River Song* that he is destined to die at Lake Silencio.

The Eleventh Doctor learns the precise date of the Alignment of Exodor - 17 galaxies in perfect unison locked in a time stasis field - but ends up missing it.

Closing Time

Prior to *The Wedding of River Song*

The Eleventh Doctor confronts and overcomes the Daleks in order to obtain information about the Silence. After River Song fails to kill him at Lake Silencio, he spends an indeterminate period inside the Teselecta (which has grown a beard and long hair, because ... well, why not?) in a disintegrating timestream.

The Wedding of River Song. Technically, River marries not the Eleventh Doctor but rather the Teselecta and its entire crew, but this point is never pursued onscreen.

Prior to *The Doctor, the Widow and the Wardrobe*

For the Eleventh Doctor, this is the start of the passage of 93 years between the incident in Utah and his arrival at a town called Mercy.

In *A Town Called Mercy*, the Eleventh Doctor says that he is 1,200 years old.

The Doctor visits Fairyland. I know. He gains an appreciation of the music of 1980s power rock band Poison. He uses a dimensional portal to visit an unnamed planet 'many times.' For reasons known only to the Doctor, he acquires a copy of the Magna Carta. On Christmas Eve, 1938, the Eleventh Doctor foils an apparent attempt by an unknown humanoid species to destroy the Earth. How he manages to get on board without the TARDIS (which is parked on the planet below) is unclear. Very likely, the Doctor arrives in the TARDIS, which is then set adrift and locks onto the nearest centre of gravity (the Earth), just as it does in *Voyage of the Damned*. Upon hearing Madge Allsop's wish (what the hell, it's Christmas), he takes the job as caretaker in the Dorset home owned by Madge's Uncle Digby.

> *The Doctor, the Widow and the Wardrobe*. The Eleventh Doctor quotes the Poison song *Every Rose Has Its Thorn*. Given the multi-dimensional nature of the TARDIS, the portal may well be one of its components. The alien species in the pre-titles sequence are never seen, but their spacesuits have the standard number of limbs for a humanoid. In *The End of the World*, Cassandra also has a copy of the Magna Carta, the document around which the plot of the Fifth Doctor adventure *The King's Demons* revolves.

Prior to *Asylum of the Daleks*

The Doctor's progress through space and time is tracked by the species known as the Elders. They dub him 'the traveller from beyond time.'

> *The Savages*. There is no reason to suppose that the Elders are tracking merely the First Doctor. It probably, however, occurs before the events of *Asylum of the Daleks*, when Oswin Oswald deletes all recorded information about the Doctor (which presumably includes this book, so if it is nothing but blank pages, be certain to ask for a refund).

Similarly, word of his adventures reaches the Tractators.

> *Frontios*. Gravis tells the Fifth Doctor in episode four that they've heard of him.

The Doctor sees the Parliament of the Daleks. He plays the triangle on a recording of *L'Amour Est un Oiseau Rebelle* from *Carmen*, but gets lost in the mix. He hears the legend of the Dalek Asylum, but doesn't believe it, and attempts to hack the Daleks' Path Web, but finds it impossible.

> *Asylum of the Daleks*. The Doctor recognises the Parliament.

A busy time for the Eleventh Doctor follows: He eludes the Sontarans by surfing the Fire Falls of Galgathon 9, enjoys a nice bit of crumpet in a Paris hotel room when he encounters Mata Hari, lays down backing tracks for Dizee Rascal and crashes the TARDIS in ancient Greece (the latter incident caused by the continually faulty Helmic Regulator). He rescues an Ood from the Androvax conflict, and accidentally leaves him in Amy and Rory's house. After he returns the Ood to its home, the Helmic Regulator is struck by an arrow at Hastings Hill (no date is given, but I think we can guess). He rides a horse through 17th Century Coventry and introduces the Mongols to pasta.

> *Pond Life,* the online miniseries. The Fourth Doctor also refers to the Battle of Hastings in the audio *The Final Phase,* and mention of it is made in the Eighth Doctor audio *Mary's Story.* The Tenth Doctor complains about never having been able to find a good parking spot there in the audio *Backtrack.* The Seventh Doctor describes Hastings as 'lovely' in the audio *Bang-Bang-A-Boom!* The Doctor displays his horse-riding skills in *The Masque of Mandragora, The Girl in the Fireplace, The Pandorica Opens, The Day of the Doctor* and *The Woman Who Lived.* He finds it good for the liver. A being named Androvax the Annihilator shows up in several episodes of *The Sarah Jane Adventures,* so the conflict from which he extracted the Ood might well have been something to do with him. According to the First Doctor audio *Quinnis,* he's met Mata Hara once before, though hopefully without Susan in tow.

To celebrate her birthday, the Eleventh Doctor breaks River Song out of the Stormcage facility to take her ice skating at the last great frost fair in 1814, to musical accompaniment provided by singer Stevie Wonder. On another birthday, she meets two incarnations of the Time Lord.

> *A Good Man Goes to War.* River is freed from Stormcage as a result of the Doctor's actions in *Asylum of the Daleks.*

On one of his visits to the Stormcage facility to free/return River, the Eleventh Doctor sees the identifier mark apparently tattooed onto the wrists of certain criminals, and the insertion of neural restrictors into the craniums of offenders due to be released.

> *Rosa*

While in the TARDIS, the Eleventh Doctor receives a psychic summons to Skaro.

> The online prequel to *Asylum of the Daleks.* It's unclear why, in *The Magician's Apprentice,* the Twelfth Doctor should be so surprised that Skaro is back in existence following the Time War. The building-sized Dalek seen onscreen is apparently the same one featured in the Seventh Doctor audio *We Are the Daleks.*

Prior to *Dinosaurs on a Spaceship*

The Doctor provides two of the hands in Franz Schubert's Fantasia in F Minor for four hands, despite the composer's attempts to tickle him in order to put him off. He visits the Commerce Colony of the Roxbourne Peninsula, witnesses the Identify and Value (IV) system, shops at Argos, and meets the indigenous species of Earth's moon. The Eleventh Doctor is of assistance to the Indian Space Agency. He shares an adventure on the African Plains in 1902 with big-game hunter John Riddell, before departing in the TARDIS in order to get some liquorice - and doesn't return for seven months (by Riddell's time). In 1334 BC, Queen Nefertiti becomes enamoured of the Doctor when he saves Egypt from an attack of weapon-bearing giant locusts.

> *Dinosaurs on a Spaceship*. The Eleventh Doctor likens the IV system to the British chain store Argos. He says nothing of there being a species living on the moon during *The Moonbase* and *The Seeds of Death*, so he doubtless learned of their existence later (or else he's referring to the spiders seen in *Kill the Moon*). He is consulted by the ISA about the spaceship en route to Earth.

The Doctor meets and becomes fond of the inventive species known as the Kahler. He is surprised when he discovers what became of the monkeys sent into space by Earth Space Agencies in the 1950s and '60s.

> *A Town Called Mercy*

Prior to *A Town Called Mercy*

The Eleventh Doctor deposits the dinosaurs from the previous adventure on Siluria, wherever that might be.

> In the final scene of *Dinosaurs on a Spaceship*, companions Amy and Rory receive a postcard from Rory's father Brian.

He becomes a follower of the long-running BBC radio serial *The Archers*. His companion Rory almost causes a temporal incident when he leaves his phone charger in Henry VIII's en-suite. Rory causes even more problems when he drops toast crumbs on the TARDIS console, sending the craft away from the Day of the Dead festival in Mexico.

> *A Town Called Mercy*. In *The Power of Three*, they return to Henry's court (presumably to pick up Rory's charger), only to end up hiding from the monarch when Amy accidentally accepts his proposal. The First Doctor also gets on the wrong side of Henry VIII (see *The Sensorites*).

Prior to *The Power of Three*

The Doctor runs several restaurants, and invents the Yorkshire pudding. In order to play a tennis match, he borrows Fred Perry's shorts and never returns them. He hears the story of Little Red Riding Hood, and disapproves.

> *The Power of Three.* The Twelfth Doctor addresses Clara as 'Red Riding Hood' during *In the Forest of the Night*, while the Fifth quotes from the tale in the audios *The Land of the Dead* and *Loups-Garoux*, and the Eighth mis-quotes it in the audio *Immortal Beloved.*

Prior to *The Angels Take Manhattan*

The Eleventh Doctor changes the bulb on top of the TARDIS, not long before taking Amy and Rory to New York in 2012, and discovering a private eye novel in his jacket.

> *The Angels Take Manhattan.* The Doctor responds to River Song's suggestion that he change the TARDIS light. The subject originally arises in the Season Five DVD extra *Meanwhile in the TARDIS*, and is broached again in the Season Six DVD extra *Last Night.*

Prior to *The Snowmen*

Distraught following the loss of the Ponds, the Eleventh Doctor sets about deleting all information about himself, wherever it is stored. He sabotages the records of the Inforarium, the greatest source of illicit information in history.

> The Season Seven DVD extra *The Inforarium*, in which the Doctor appears as a recording.

On an unnamed planet, the Doctor carefully picks up several worms capable of deleting an individual's memory with a single touch. On Earth, he acquires a tin with a map of the 1960s London Underground on the lid, and sees a Punch and Judy show. Following the loss of his companions the Ponds, the Eleventh Doctor goes into self-imposed retirement in 1890s London, where he makes contact with Madam Vastra and her associates (including the Sontaran Strax, despite his apparent death at the conclusion of *A Good Man Goes to War*). In addition to redesigning the TARDIS' interior and adding an antifreeze setting to his sonic screwdriver, he purchases a deerstalker and Inverness cape (of a different design to the ones worn by his fourth incarnation in *The Talons of Weng-Chiang*) and takes to using the spectacles given to him by former companion Amy Pond in *The Angels Take Manhattan.* He also – horror of horrors – stops wearing a bow tie.

The Snowmen. The Eleventh Doctor impersonates Mr Punch, and the icy governess, in turn, impersonates him. It seems from *The Day of the Doctor, In the Forest of the Night, Empress of Mars* and the Eleventh Doctor novel *The King's Dragon* that the sonic screwdriver still doesn't work on wood (or turkeys, we find out in *The Time of the Doctor*). In *The Name of the Doctor,* he describes this period of his life as 'the dark times.' It is stated, in the online sequel to *A Good Man Goes to War,* that rather than dying, Strax simply fainted. A Punch and Judy show is performed on Manussa during *Snakedance,* but there's no suggestion that the Fifth Doctor watched it. *The Time of the Doctor* features a Punch and Judy-like show involving puppets of the Eleventh Doctor and what appears to be a Monoid. The Doctor has four more memory worms in *Time Heist.*

Prior to *The Bells of Saint John*

The Eleventh Doctor searches for Clara Oswin Oswald (mostly by not really searching at all). He finds that he is no longer able to pilot the TARDIS on short hops quite so well any more.

The Bells of Saint John. In episode four of *State of Decay,* the Fourth Doctor declares short hops very tricky, but claims he is getting better in *Logopolis.* Despite having successfully made the same brief journey three times during episode three of *Full Circle,* he surprisingly finds them tricky once more in the very next story. The Thirteenth Doctor complains in *Resolution* that the TARDIS is not designed for short hops.

In 1927, the Doctor enjoys scones in the Lake District.

The Rings of Akhaten

Encountering his old foes the Ice Warriors, he learns their salute and hears the ancient Martian Code 'Harm one of us and you harm us all' - bad news for a man who tricked their entire warfleet into flying into the sun. He learns of Mars' greatest hero, Grand Marshal Skaldak, Sovereign of the Tharsisian caste and vanquisher of the Phobos Heresy.

Cold War

The Eleventh Doctor eventually gives up looking for Clara and takes the TARDIS to a British playground in the early 21st Century.

The online prequel to *The Bells of Saint John.*

The Doctor meets several empaths, whom he considers the most compassionate and lonely people he has ever met. On Earth, several hundred years after the 20th Century, he learns of the disappearance of time travel pioneer Hila Tacorian. Researching her family tree, he discovers that she is the descendant of wartime spy and supernatural investigator Major Alec Palmer and empath Emma Grayling. In the 1970s, he is enthusiastic about the ACR 99821 device, particularly its toggle switches.

Hide

He places a manual typewriter in the TARDIS, sees the outlawing of Magno-Grabs in several galaxies, and imagines his own ship safe so long as its field oscillators are functioning.

Journey to the Centre of the TARDIS. Companion Clara discovers the typewriter. The comic strip *The Last Word* implies that the Seventh Doctor wrote all the New Adventures books on it. It also shows up in the novel *The Room With No Doors*.

On Hedgewick's World, the universe's largest and best amusement park, the Doctor enjoys himself on the Spacey Zoomer ride, and receives a golden ticket entitling him to, among other things, free ice cream. Battling an early model of the Cybermen, he finds that their operating systems can be scrambled by the application of cleaning fluid.

Nightmare in Silver

UNIT sets up a 'Doctor channel,' through which they may contact him in time of need.

The Magician's Apprentice. Clara has never heard of this method of communication, suggesting that it predates her travels in the TARDIS (unless her knowledge of it was wiped at the Black Archive). Kate Stewart thinks the Doctor has forgotten about it.

Frustrated by his failure to locate 'the impossible girl,' the Eleventh Doctor withdraws to a Cumbrian monastery in the year 1207. He is with them long enough to gain the nickname 'the mad monk.'

The Bells of Saint John

Prior to *The Rings of Akhaten*

Travelling to the Earth year 1981, the Eleventh Doctor buys a copy of *The Beano Summer Special*.

The Rings of Akhaten. The Doctor is seen reading the comic as the episode begins.

Prior to *Cold War*

Tinkering with the TARDIS, the Doctor resets the Hostile Action Displacement System (HADS) for the first time in several incarnations. He acquires a Sindy doll, a ball of string and a toffee apple. The Eleventh Doctor promises to take companion Clara to Las Vegas, but they instead wind up on a Soviet submarine at the North Pole in 1983.

> *Cold War*. The HADS is last seen functioning in *The Krotons,* and is put into action in the novels *Mission: Impractical, SLEEPY* and *Dead of Winter* and the audios *The Mutant Phase, Last of the Cybermen, Faith Stealer, The Girl Who Never Was* and *The Lost Magic*. In *The Witch's Familiar,* the acronym stands for Hostile Action Dispersal System. The Thirteenth Doctor puts the string to good use in *It Takes You Away*. The Twelfth Doctor eventually gets Clara to Vegas in the comic strip *Gangland*. The Sixth and Seventh Doctors both travel there, in the short stories *Priceless Junk* and *Too Rich for My Blood,* respectively.

Prior to *Hide*

The Eleventh Doctor and Clara journey to the South Pole by Russian sub to pick up the TARDIS.

> *Cold War*. In the final scene, the Eleventh Doctor learns that he and the TARDIS are literally poles apart, something Clara is still complaining about during *Kill the Moon*.

The Doctor hears the song *Let's Do It, Let's Fall in Love,* by Cole Porter, and returns to the planet Metebelis 3 (which is now pronounced differently) and collects another blue crystal. He becomes fond of carrier pigeons.

> *Hide*. The Eleventh Doctor quotes from the song. Clara might well have been with him on Metebelis 3; there is no way to know for certain. The Seventh Doctor has several crystals in the audio *Mask of Tragedy*.

Prior to *Journey to the Centre of the TARDIS*

More than 900 years have passed since the Doctor stole the TARDIS from Gallifrey. He ensures that the ship's own gravity functions permanently. The Eleventh Doctor's companion Clara complains to him that the TARDIS is looking at her funny.

> *Journey to the Centre of the TARDIS*. The Second Doctor has to climb out of the TARDIS when it lands on its side in *The Ice Warriors,* as does the Eleventh in *The Eleventh Hour*. His fifth self has to be lowered into the ship to reset the gravity manually in episode one of *Time-Flight*.

Prior to *The Crimson Horror*

The Time Lord develops a fondness for pontefract cakes. Perhaps hoping to investigate the similarities between companion Clara and a deceased governess of the same name (and appearance), the Eleventh Doctor promises to take her to London in the year 1893.

The Crimson Horror

Prior to *Nightmare in Silver*

The Eleventh Doctor's companion Clara persuades him to take her charges Angie and Artie on a trip in the TARDIS.

Immediately prior to *Nightmare in Silver.*

Prior to *The Name of the Doctor*

The Eleventh Doctor mentions River Song to Clara, but neglects to specify the professor's gender, among other things.

The Name of the Doctor

Speaking of River, the Eleventh Doctor arranges a dinner date with the archaeologist, and winds up taking them to the planet of the Rain Gods by accident, where they're held at spear-point by the superstitious natives.

Rain Gods, a Season Seven DVD extra.

Prior to *The Day of the Doctor*

After somehow (emphasis on the 'somehow') rescuing Clara from his own timeline, the Eleventh Doctor returns his companion to 21st Century Earth, where he is able to use his connections to get her a teaching job at Coal Hill Secondary School in Shoreditch. Some unspecified time later, he leaves a message for her to meet him, that they might spend a few weeks in ancient Mesopotamia and on future Mars, prior to enjoying cocktails on the moon. Four hundred years have passed since the Doctor imagines he activated the Moment and destroyed Gallifrey. He is introduced to the joys of Cup-a-Soup, picks up a copy of *Advanced Quantum Mechanics,* and makes a minor adjustment to the TARDIS' outer shell, ensuring that the telephone behind the door panel can now be used. The Eleventh Doctor, Clara and possibly River Song assist UNIT, and the Time Lord is given the contact telephone numbers of Kate Lethbridge-Stewart and scientists Petronella Osgood and McGillop. Whatever crisis he is called upon to solve, he must enter the Black Archive, where he spots the frequently late Captain Jack Harkness' Vortex Manipulator. He places some confetti in his pocket.

The Day of the Doctor. The Eleventh Doctor telephones both Kate and McGillop (who does not appear in *The Power of Three*) during the episode. Osgood attempts to call the TARDIS at the beginning of *The Zygon Invasion.* Companion Clara's recollection of visiting the Black Archive, and of meeting Kate, has been wiped by the memory filters - if Kate thinks the Doctor is similarly affected, she is wrong. He later takes advantage of the devices to create a stalemate situation in the battle between humanity and the Zygons. River Song's chunky red shoes from *The Time of the Angels* are seen in a glass case, along with the Vortex Manipulator, which the Doctor knows is held by UNIT. There's also a picture of River posing with Kate in the Black Archive. Clara throws confetti at the wedding of the Tenth Doctor and Elizabeth I. The Eleventh Doctor likens the freezing of the Zygons within Gallifreyan artwork to Cup-a-Soups. The War Doctor has never heard of them, and the Tenth Doctor doesn't express a view either way, although the Seventh is said to have several packets on his person in the novel *Parasite.* The figure of 400 years is mentioned by the Eleventh Doctor several times during the course of the episode. The sign outside the school gives the name of the Chairman of the Board of Governors as I Chesterton. And if you're really prepared to argue that it might be a different I Chesterton, then, frankly, I don't care to talk to you. When first seen, the Eleventh Doctor is reading a book on quantum mechanics. In both *The Empty Child* and *The Bells of Saint John,* he is adamant that the door phone should not work. Here, he uses it twice to put calls through to UNIT. In *The Time of the Doctor,* he asks to be reminded to patch the telephone back through the console unit, though he still hasn't done so in *Time Heist.*

For reasons one would imagine too complicated to go into, the Doctor invents an android friend, whom he then finds it difficult to dump.

The Time of the Doctor. The audio story *Death Comes to Time* sees the Seventh Doctor travelling with an android named Antimony.

Upon learning that UNIT has supplies of Z-67 nerve gas capable of unravelling Zygon DNA, the Doctor steals it.

The Zygon Invasion. Kate Stewart says it was manufactured by the Doctor's former companion Harry Sullivan some time after the original Zygon attack in either the 1970s or '80s (evidently she doesn't know about the one thwarted by the Eleventh

> Doctor at the Savoy Hotel in 1890 during *The Power of Three*). Presumably, the gas was taken before the events of *The Day of the Doctor*, or else UNIT would have used it then, instead of resorting to the nuclear option.

Prior to *The Time of the Doctor*

By some unknown means, the Valeyard comes into existence - a distillation of all that is evil in the Doctor, an amalgamation of the dark side of his nature, who gets to know the Master well.

> *The Ultimate Foe*. It is stated that the Valeyard exists somewhere between the Doctor's twelfth and final incarnation, but how that actually works remains a mystery. The fresh set of regenerations bestowed upon the Doctor by the Time Lords means that he is now nowhere near his final incarnation, true - but in *The Name of the Doctor*, the Great Intelligence states that before his death on Trenzalore, the Doctor is known as, among other things, the Valeyard. That particular timeline is nullified by the events of *The Time of the Doctor*.

Following the truce agreed upon by humans and Zygon settlers on Earth, the Doctor presents UNIT with the Osgood Box, which is only to be used in the event of a breakdown in relations between the species. Kate Stewart agrees to the safeguard, but her memory of the nature of that safeguard is then wiped from her memory by the Doctor.

> *The Zygon Invasion*. The box (or boxes, for there are two) is/are kept in the Black Archive, beneath the Tower of London. Only Clara, both Osgoods and the Doctor - who says he devised the plan on what was, for him, a very important day - have access.

The Doctor and River Song picnic at Asgard. He tells her what becomes of Donna.

> Asgard is first mentioned in *Silence in the Library*, and has been entered in the archaeologist's diary in *The Husbands of River Song*. The events of the picnic at Asgard are described in the short story *Picnic at Asgard*, which is handy, because otherwise the title would have to be changed.

The Doctor plays a game of Twister, possibly clothed, possibly not. He stores some Christmas crackers in the TARDIS, the sort with the jokes and the hats inside. The Eleventh Doctor witnesses the popularity of the genetically engineered confessional priests unpopularly known as the Silence. He helps companion Clara out on several instances, by taking her back in time to ensure that she doesn't miss any birthdays or TV programmes, and so that she is able to make restaurant bookings in good time – the hell with Blinovitch.

> *The Time of the Doctor.* The sort-of naked Eleventh Doctor suggests a game of Twister at the Oswalds' Christmas party, and expresses his fondness for it in the audio *The Ring of Steel.* He still isn't any wiser about the nature of the Silence by the end of *The Wedding of River Song,* so this knowledge must have been acquired since then. He tells Clara he has crackers in the TARDIS, and expresses a preference for the sort with jokes. He notes in *Last Christmas* that anything seems funny when wearing a paper hat.

He sees Walt Disney's animated feature *Snow White,* learns the story of murderous London barber Sweeney Todd and reads the poetry of Walt Whitman.

> *Deep Breath.* Upon being reunited with Strax, the slightly confused Twelfth Doctor addressed the Sontaran as 'Sleepy, Bashful, Sneezy, Dopey' before settling on 'Grumpy' (there's another reference to the dwarves in the Fourth Doctor comic strip *Black Destiny*). He likens the organ-harvesting robots to Todd's pie-making operation, and calls the Cyborg known as Half-Face Man 'Captain, my Captain,' in reference to Whitman's extended metaphor poem.

He watches the movie *Fantastic Voyage* and sees a moleculon nanoscaler reduce the size of living tissue.

> *Into the Dalek.* The Doctor tells Colonel Morgan Blue that shrinking a surgeon and injecting them into a patient is a 'fantastic idea for a movie.' It's entirely possible that a moleculon nanoscaler was used to shrink the Eleventh Doctor in *The Wedding of River Song;* in *The Invisible Enemy,* his fourth incarnation uses the TARDIS' relative dimensional stabilizer.

After a big fight with River, the Doctor lives among otters for a month, which mostly involves sulking.

> *The Caretaker.* The Doctor cites his otter experience as proof of his ability to blend in.

He learns both sign language and semaphore. Without Clara in tow, he sees a Faraday cage at work.

> *Under the Lake.* Following his regeneration, his knowledge of sign is completely deleted. The Sixth Doctor knows of, but has

not met, Michael Faraday during *The Mark of the Rani*. Faraday cages are mentioned, though not by the Doctor, in *Planet of the Dead*, while the Second Doctor makes use of one in the audio *The Great Space Elevator*.

The Eleventh Doctor orders a replacement fez from the online retailer Kerblam!

Kerblam! It's a couple of incarnations and several hundred years before the Doctor's purchase finally arrives.

At the Maldovar Market, the Doctor comes away brandishing a Cyber head which he christens 'Handles' and which serves as a K-9 stand-in (although it's tough to stand when you're basically just a head) and a symbol of his bravery, as does a detached Dalek eye stalk, which he may have come across under different circumstances. Like members of so many other species, he is drawn to the planet Trenzalore, having received a mysterious and apparently indecipherable message. Knowing that the planet has been shielded by the Church of the Papal Mainframe (and perhaps because he is a tiny bit bored), he shaves his head and places a spare TARDIS key under a wig he wears. Sporting a hooded cloak, he attempts to make contact with the other species surrounding Trenzalore - an enterprise that proves hazardous, given that there are very few of them he hasn't annoyed over the centuries.

The Time of the Doctor. In the comic strip *Four Doctors*, the Tenth Doctor is extremely proud of the Cyberman head he's just received in Paris - but that was during an Earthbound battle with the Cybermen and has nothing to do with the Maldovar Market.

The Twelfth Doctor
Peter Capaldi
2014-2017

Prior to *Deep Breath*

After his sudden regeneration and apparent amnesia, the Twelfth Doctor manages to regain some control of the TARDIS, landing it on prehistoric Earth, where it is swallowed by a *Tyrannosaurus*. He then dematerialises, taking the dinosaur with him, and sets the co-ordinates for Victorian London, home to his old friend Madam Vastra. Some eight hundred years have passed since the TARDIS deposited the Eleventh Doctor on Trenzalore.

> *Deep Breath.* The *T-Rex* coughs up the TARDIS as the episode begins. The question of how reliable this new Doctor's memory is crops up throughout his début season, causing endless problems for honest, hard-working, reference book authors. The only thing to have gone for definite is, according to *Under the Lake,* his knowledge of sign language. The Doctor is 'twelve hundred and something' during *The Day of the Doctor,* and here claims to be 'over two thousand.'

Prior to *Into the Dalek*

Having arrived in Glasgow with Clara, the Twelfth Doctor goes to fetch coffee. Becoming distracted, he abandons his companion and takes the TARDIS into the far future, where he observes a space battle between the Daleks and ships of the Combined Galactic Resistance.

> *Into the Dalek.* Pilot Journey Blue finds herself aboard the TARDIS after her vessel is destroyed. Three weeks pass for Clara before the Doctor contacts her again, but it's not revealed whether the coffee has gone cold during his time away from Earth.

Prior to *Robot of Sherwood*

The Doctor protects the Ice Warrior hives on Mars, and is granted an honorary title as a reward. He meets the hard-drinking Tumescant Arrows of the Half-Light, who are capable of fracturing more than a dozen levels of reality. He fences with King Richard I, Cyrano de Bergerac and Errol Flynn.

> *Robot of Sherwood.* He thinks he might have a polaroid of the

Arrows, probably taken with the camera his fourth incarnation carries in *City of Death*. His duelling sessions with Richard the Lionheart must have taken place after the events of *The Crusade*, and also after the fencing lessons he received from Cleopatra's bodyguard prior to his second regeneration. In *Empress of Mars*, the Doctor claims to hold the title of Honorary Guardian of the Tythonian Hive. Cyrano de Bergerac is a character summoned by the Second Doctor to do battle against the Master of the Land of Fiction in *The Mind Robber*. He is also name-checked in the Seventh Doctor novel *Christmas on a Rational Planet*.

Prior to *Listen*

The Doctor spends years looking for Wally (the British equivalent of Waldo) in non-*Where's Wally?* books.

Listen

Prior to *Time Heist*

The Doctor's travels take him to the Satanic Nebula and the Lagoon of Lost Stars. He sees a Neophyte circuit, capable of rebooting any system or replacing lost data.

Time Heist. The Doctor states that he's only seen one Neophyte circuit before.

Prior to *The Caretaker*

He visits the giant crocodile-worshipping Egyptians of ancient Crocodilopolis (it's the crocodile that's giant, not the worshippers), and the frost fairs held on the Thames in 1800s. The Twelfth Doctor gives Clara his vibro-cutters, which she places in her jacket pocket. Later, they find themselves chained up on a bone-strewn desert world where they are to be fed to the sand piranhas. To the Doctor's chagrin, Clara isn't wearing the jacket with the vibro-cutters in the pocket. Having somehow escaped from that particular sticky situation, they pay a call upon a society of fish people, and come away drenched. Later still, they are in their natural element - running through corridors, pursued by soldiers armed with lasers. One incident doesn't even give Clara enough time to remove a space helmet before her date with Danny Pink. The Doctor reads *Pride and Prejudice* by Jane Austen and hears *Another Brick in the Wall* by Pink Floyd, and the traditional hymn *Oil in My Lamp*. Travelling alone through the Olveron Cluster, he encounters the deadly robotic Skovox Blitzers and later learns that one has been drawn to Earth, specifically to the vicinity of Coal Hill

High School, by the high concentration of Artron energy (probably the result of a police box constantly materialising and dematerialising in the supplies cupboard). He develops a plan to suck it off into the time vortex, with the aid of some unstable chronodyne generators. Having apparently seen too many episodes of the 1970s TV show *The Gemini Man* (and one is easily too many), he invents a watch capable of reversing light waves and making the wearer invisible.

> *The Caretaker*. Fragments of three separate adventures are depicted at the beginning of the episode, and the incident with the space helmet is mentioned by Danny. The fish people might well be the Atlanteans featured in *The Underwater Menace*. He whistles the classic Pink Floyd song while carrying out his caretaking duties, and later announces 'Oh, sing Hosanna.' He plans to use his newfound gift of invisibility to confuse the Blitzer, before rendering it harmless and returning it to the Olveron Cluster. Danny Pink is the last person to wear the watch, and subsequently returns it to the Doctor. Despite being mentioned in *The Zygon Inversion*, this useful gadget is never seen again. Maybe it turned itself invisible, and the Doctor just couldn't find it? The First Doctor encounters the divine Miss Austen in the audio *Frostfire* (at which point he claims to have read her complete works), and her unfinished novel *Sandition* is mentioned by Romana in the Fourth Doctor audio *Babblesphere*. The Twelfth Doctor takes companion Bill Potts to the very last frost fair in *Thin Ice*, and confirms that he has been there 'a few times.' One such instance might be the birthday party described by River Song in *A Good Man Goes to War*. By the time of *The Magician's Apprentice*, the Twelfth Doctor has introduced Clara to Jane Austen.

Prior to *Kill the Moon*

The Twelfth Doctor and Clara pay a visit to Crocodilopolis, and perhaps even another frost fair. They dine at a Berlin restaurant in the year 1937.

> *The Caretaker*. He promises to take her to Egypt and London in the past once the Skovox Blitzer has been dealt with. Later, he reminds her of their time in Berlin. The novel *Silhouette* confirms that the Twelfth Doctor and Clara did indeed visit a frost fair, as he hinted that they might.

The Doctor visits Earth shortly after 2049, where he sees a prototype Bennett Oscillator and, somewhat more impressively, that humankind has resumed its space exploration program following an incredible event seen worldwide.

He acquires several of the DVDs that, when inserted in the TARDIS console, initiate Security Protocol 712. After he callously tells her that she is not special (which isn't remotely true), Clara's pupil Courtney Woods steals the Twelfth Doctor's psychic paper.

> *Kill the Moon.* The Doctor retrieves the psychic paper offscreen; he has it back in *Mummy on the Orient Express.* He has a shelf full of DVDs that will bring the TARDIS to him. It's impossible to know just how much prior knowledge he has of the moon/egg incident of 2049. By way of explanation, he simply says he has 'grey areas' (and not all of them in his hair). The hatching of the moon is mentioned again during *Before the Flood,* which makes it odd that the same incarnation of the Doctor would use the phrase 'dead as the moon' in *The Pyramid at the End of the World.* The Fourth Doctor identifies a far more advanced model of Bennett Oscillator in *The Ark in Space.* The First or Second Doctor previously encountered an adult Courtney Woods, serving as President of America, and in the company of Aaron Blinovitch.

Prior to *Mummy on the Orient Express*

The Doctor hears the legend of the Foretold, a galactic mummy that kills within a strict time limit of sixty-six seconds and can only be stopped by the uttering of a specific phrase, one that no-one has yet divined. Thousands of years before the route of the *Orient Express* is established, he visits several of the worlds destined to be be lost over the event horizon of the Magellan black hole: Obsidian, which is shrouded in perpetual darkness, an unnamed planet of shrubs, and Thedion Four, where he picnicked in a gas mask as protection against the effects of the acid rain. He acquires a cigarette-case, in which he stores jelly babies.

> *Mummy on the Orient Express.* The Doctor is familiar with the Foretold, stating that the myth dates back five thousand years, which would only be helpful if we knew when this story is set. He's back on the jelly babies for the first time since *Doctor Who – The TV Movie.* By the time of *The Doctor Falls,* he's dispensed with the cigarette-case and returned to the traditional paper bag.

The Doctor invents a device which, when inserted in the ear, hacks the user's optic nerve, enabling him to see what they see on the TARDIS scanner. He encounters a gaseous race who communicate via fireball, and multi-stomached aliens for whom disembowelment is viewed as a friendly greeting.

Flatline. The Doctor explains away the gadget's functions with the one word 'nanotech.' This technology is never mentioned again, and the next time he needs to see the world from Clara's point of view - during *Face the Raven* - he has her wear his sonic shades.

Prior to *Flatline*

In the company of Clara Oswald, the Twelfth Doctor returns to the planet of shrubs, presumably before it becomes a victim of the Magellan black hole. Their travels together occur over a period of three months.

His stated intention at the end of *Mummy on the Orient Express.* The next episode begins with the Doctor intending to return Clara to her proper time and place, but it's highly probable that there are several unseen adventures between Shrubworld and the TARDIS materialising in Bristol; in *Dark Water,* one of the post-it notes Clara has prepared prior to her declaration of love for Danny reads 'three months.'

He acquires a hammer, watches *The Addams Family,* and reads several theories regarding two-dimensional universes.

Flatline. He hands the tool to Clara while trapped inside the shrinking TARDIS. He understands Clara's reference to the classic TV series, and is able to manoeuvre the tiny time machine by sticking his hand through the door, in an impersonation of the bodyless appendage Thing.

Prior to *In the Forest of the Night*

The Doctor hears of Victor Hugo's *Les Miserables,* but has no interest in reading or seeing it. He observes the explosions at Tunguska in 1980 and in Curuçá, Brazil.

In the Forest of the Night. He tells Clara that even his life is too short for ... Well, it's not clear whether he's referring to *Les Mis* the book, *Les Mis* the musical or *Les Mis* the movie, or *Les Mis* the BBC miniseries. Pick the one you like the least and go with that. The Third Doctor attempts to witness the Tunguska event in the novel *The Wages of Sin.* The Seventh Doctor novel *Birthright* reveals a TARDIS time-ramming to have been the cause of the explosion.

Prior to *Dark Water*

The Doctor dances a memorable foxtrot with Sylvia Anderson. Having minted seven TARDIS keys over the centuries, he stores one in a paperback copy of *The Time Traveller's Wife* by Audrey Niffenegger, and has to retrieve it from there at least once during his journeys with Clara. He tells her that it would take the power of a volcano to destroy one (or seven). He shows her the dream patches he purchased in New New York and says that they are for inducing sleep. Or maybe he has patches for both purposes. On an unidentified world, the Twelfth Doctor finds something to occupy his attention. That has to be the vaguest entry in the entire book, doesn't it? At this stage, the Doctor has been married four times.

> *Dark Water/Death in Heaven.* When finally responding to Clara's phone call, he simply says that he has been busy. Clara plans to use a sleep patch to incapacitate the Doctor, but it's actually a dream patch, which he proceeds to use on her. If you're wondering why the Doctor even needs a TARDIS key when he can snap his fingers to open the doors, I recommend you look to 'The Future.' Of the Doctor's four wives we can positively identify the original Mrs Who, Elizabeth I and River Song. The fourth might or might not be Marilyn Monroe, though the Doctor questions the validity of the service.

He hears the story of the Tooth Fairy and learns of the Kantrofarri, colloquially known as Dream Crabs, which alter perception via a telepathic field. He discovers the Helman-Zeigler test, which he considers the only reliable method of judging whether an individual is dreaming, and finds out about Facebook.

> *Last Christmas.* The Doctor jokingly suggests that Santa Claus might be either the Easter Bunny or the Tooth Fairy. He tells Father Christmas that he's never seen a Kantrofarri before he and Clara experience a nasty attack of the crabs, and warns his companion about getting attached to other people, likening their situation to the popular social networking site (which he mentions again in *Oxygen*). The unseen attack on the Doctor by the Kantrofarri evidently occurs during *Death in Heaven*, between saying his goodbyes to Clara and Santa surprising him in the TARDIS. Clara performs the Helman-Zeigler test on herself during *The Zygon Inversion.*

On several occasions, Clara tells the Doctor he has attention deficit something-or-other. He comes to appreciate the work of comedy magician of Tommy Cooper

> *The Doctor's Meditation*, the second online sequel to *The Magician's Apprentice.* The Doctor isn't really listening to his

companion, so he's not exactly certain what he's supposed to be suffering from, implying that her diagnosis may well be correct. He impersonates Cooper while performing a magic trick. Given the comedian's preferred headgear, it's a shame that this occurs after he's passed through his fez-wearing phase. The Eighth Doctor mentions Cooper in the audio *The Vengeance of Morbius.*

Death in Heaven

Last Christmas

Prior to *The Magician's Apprentice*

The Doctor makes two more trips to possible versions of Atlantis. Possibly.

The Magician's Apprentice. UNIT's algorithm places him in three possible versions of the fabled city, and while *The Underwater Menace* and *The Daemons* both touch upon the subject, he's only seen to visit Atlantis in *The Time Monster.*

On his way to a bookshop, the Twelfth Doctor takes a spectacular wrong turn and winds up on war-torn Skaro.

The Doctor's Meditation. He begins to relate his encounter with the young Davros, which occurred 'a little while' earlier, to Bors in the year 1138 at the end of this online prequel to *The Magician's Apprentice.*

Accompanied by Clara, the Twelfth Doctor meets famed novelist Jane Austen. He hears the music of both Roy Orbison and David Bowie, and experiences the uniquely British entertainment known as a pantomime. He acquires a tank (that's right, a tank). He also gets his hands on an electric guitar and an amplifier from Magpie Electronics.

This encounter with Austen, mentioned in *The Magician's Apprentice,* clearly occurs some time after their discussion of her works in *The Caretaker.* Clara informs her pupils that Jane was a 'phenomenal kisser.' Whether this knowledge is acquired first-hand, or she's just paying lip service, I leave up to you. Clara meets the author in the Eleventh Doctor audio *False Coronets.* The electric guitar appears in several Twelfth Doctor stories. Here, he serenades Clara with Orbison's most famous song, *Pretty Woman.* He references the song Bowie penned for Mott the Hoople, *All the Young Dudes,* and later quotes *Ashes to Ashes* during *Smile.* In the novel *No Future,* the Fourth Doctor is said to have played the card game Find the Lady with Bowie, while the Eighth recalls him in the audio *Horror of Glam Rock*. He uses the tank as a piece of prop comedy while in England in the year 1138. Presumably, he materialised the TARDIS around it in order to transport it back in time. The Magpie brand first appears in *The Idiot's Lantern*, and is seen onscreen in several stories. The amp shows up again in *Before the Flood*, although it's revealed in *Hell Bent* that he doesn't actually need it if he's wearing his shades (about which, read on). The Doctor encourages his medieval friends to hiss the wicked stepmother, meaning Missy.

He spends some time with a hungover Pythagoras and film star Audrey Hepburn. One or perhaps both of them lend him their sunglasses. Where the famous philosopher acquired them in the first place remains unclear.

The Ghost Monument. This would undoubtedly be before he took to packing his sonic shades (about which, read on). The Tenth Doctor mentions Audrey Hepburn in the novel *Wetworld*.

Having thrown his sonic screwdriver to the young Davros and neglected to retrieve it, the Twelfth Doctor creates a pair of sonic shades as a replacement.

The Doctor is first seen wearing the shades in *The Magician's Apprentice*, but their true purpose is revealed in *The Witch's Familiar*. According to *The Zygon Inversion*, setting 137 unlocks van doors, which is handy if you see one where tools are locked inside overnight.

The Twelfth Doctor revisits the Sisterhood of Karn, possibly after receiving word that he is being sought by a dying Davros. He realises that Missy's apparent death was faked.

The untitled online prequel to *The Magician's Apprentice* sees the Doctor on Karn. Ohila is visited by Davros' messenger Colony Sarff in the episode itself, at which point, the Doctor is already present, but in hiding. It's not clear whether he knows Davros is looking for him before Colony Sarff's announcement. It's equally unclear precisely when the Doctor realises that Missy is still alive, but he gives Ohila his confessional dial which she somehow passes on to his old enemy. Not Davros, his *other* old enemy.

He takes to carrying a fresh cup of tea in his pocket (which, remember, is bigger on the inside) and sees a hyperspace relay in operation.

The Witch's Familiar. The Fourth Doctor pops a hot drink into his pocket in *The Power of Kroll*. He also has a glass of water about his person in *The Return of Doctor Mysterio*. He's the Doctor, just accept it. He recognises the relay to which Davros is attached.

The Witch's Familiar

Prior to *Under the Lake*

Accompanied by Clara, the Doctor visits the planet Quantifer, where, perhaps as the result of some unspecified temporal distortion, New Year's celebrations have been underway for two centuries. He visits a small settlement at the edge of the known universe. To the Doctor's embarrassment, Clara gets into an argument with Mahatma Gandhi. Following incidents in which he shows little sympathy for a captive, shows little sympathy in general, fails to do anything to reassure individuals facing imminent death, fails to be compassionate in the face of someone's loss, and bumps into former companion Sarah Jane Smith, Clara has the Twelfth Doctor prepare a set of cards to which he can refer and thus seem more relateable. He's a nervous wreck when he meets Welsh songstress Dame Shirley Bassey. He's less of a fan of Peter Andre, however, and after two weeks of being woken up by his song *Mysterious Girl*, the Doctor turns his radio into a clockwork squirrel (the mechanical companion we all wanted but never got). He places an apple in his pocket.

Under the Lake. One of the Doctor's cards reads 'It was my fault, I should have known you didn't live in Aberdeen,' which is where his fourth incarnation dumped his companion at the conclusion of *The Hand of Fear*. Another card, bearing the phrase 'I could be wrong, let's try it your way' is seen in *Face the Raven*. The New Year's Eve planet is eventually identified as Quantifer by the Thirteenth Doctor in *Resolution*.

The Doctor places a bust of Beethoven and a recording of his Fifth Symphony on vinyl in the TARDIS. He learns about time travel conundrum known as the Bootstrap Paradox, and discovers Google. He re-records the message that notifies TARDIS passengers of the activation of Security Protocol 712.

Before the Flood. He produces both his bust and his 12 inch record during his explanation of the Bootstrap Paradox, which he advises, um, *someone* to Google. Exactly who the Doctor is talking to is anybody's guess, but if you're reading this over the festive season, I'd just like to say 'A happy Christmas to all of you at home.' He mentions Google again in *The Pyramid at the*

End of the World, and plays Beethoven's Fifth on the guitar both here and in *The Pilot*.

Travelling alone, he sees a wing-shaped nebula with green fringes, but forgets where it is.

The Girl Who Died

The Doctor visits Earth in the year 1348, when the Black Death reaches England.

The Woman Who Lived. He tells the immortal Ashildr that he meant to warn her about it. The Tenth Doctor witnesses the outbreak in the comic strip *Black Death White Life*.

Before the Flood

Prior to *The Girl Who Died*

After an encounter with the warrior race known as the Mire, the Doctor jots down all he needs to know about them in his 2000 year diary. He sees the popular children's series *Noggin the Nog* and the comedy of Benny Hill. He reads Johanna Spyri's novel *Heidi*, rocks out to the music of ZZ Top, and finds out about the social network known as the Galactic Hub. He traps his finger, which causes him to shout. He reads Clarke's third law, which states that any sufficiently advanced technology is indistinguishable from magic. At a later date, the Twelfth Doctor and his companion find themselves in a whole heap of trouble, when the TARDIS comes under attack from four and-a-bit battle fleets and a space-suited Clara visits a spider mine, then somehow winds up floating in deep space with a creature capable of removing her brain crawling up her leg. This is all done in the name of saving a race known as the Velosians,

The Girl Who Died. The episode opens with this particular predicament already in progress. The Velosians are first mentioned in the Seventh Doctor audio *Starlight Robbery*. The Doctor nicknames three of the Vikings he trains Noggin the Nog, Heidi and ZZ Top. He seems to recognise Benny Hill when Clara mentions him, and threatens to upload footage of Odin's defeat to the Galactic Hub. Upon hearing the Doctor shouting, she assumes that the Doctor has trapped his finger again. He recites the third law to Clara in *The Girl Who Died*, to James I in *The Witchfinders*, and to Ace in a deleted scene from *Battlefield*.

Prior to *The Woman Who Lived*

Having seen them broken in two by a Viking, the Twelfth Doctor either repairs his sonic shades or makes himself a new pair. Or maybe he built more than one in the first place. Feeling a certain responsibility for bestowing immortality upon Ashildr, he tracks any mention of her in Earth's history, keeping his records in a secret room inside the TARDIS. He looks in on her as she founds a leper colony. He either reads the Zorro stories of Johnston McCulley or else watches one of the many screen adaptations, enjoys the work of ventriloquist Terry Hall, studies the habits of the mayfly, develops a fondness for both sherbet lemons and Ferraris, sees the protective Greek talisman known as the Eyes of Hades (never suspecting that it originated on the planet Delta Leonis), and goes on record regarding his feelings about banter. He's at the Battle of Dunbar in 1650. He builds a device called a curio scanner, capable of tracking exoplanetary energy. The Twelfth Doctor assists one of Clara's pupils, Evie Hubbard, with her homework assignment concerning his old pal Winston Churchill. When his companion is otherwise occupied taking her pupils to a Taekwondo class, he uses his curio scanner to locate a particular piece of alien technology which resembles the Eyes of Hades. After a couple of weeks on its scent, he materialises the TARDIS on Earth in the year 1651.

> *The Woman Who Lived.* He addresses Ashildr, who is posing as notorious highwayman the Knightmare, as Zorro, and her leonine companion Leandro as Lenny the Lion (Hall's famous puppet). The location of the leper colony, and the date upon which Ashildr founded it are never stated, though it is mentioned in passing in the short story *The Ghosts of Branscombe Wood.* Obviously, it is some time between 851 (which is roughly when *The Girl Who Died* is set) and 1651. Clara reveals in *Face the Raven* that she discovered his secret room. The Doctor claims that his psychic paper is the Dunbar Victory Medal. Whether he was awarded such a thing or not, he certainly knows of the battle. Very probably, he either took Evie Hubbard back in time to interview Churchill, or else brought the great man forward to Evie's time. He tells Clara he'd prefer either a sherbet lemon or a Ferrari as reward for this task. The Second Doctor carried sherbert lemons in his pocket in *The Wheel In Space.*

Prior to *The Zygon Invasion*

Kate Stewart accidentally butt-dials the Doctor. He hears the 18th Century hymn *Amazing Grace* and the 1976 hit by Parliament entitled *Dr Funkenstein.* He sees the show *Monster High* and the animated Disney version of *Cinderella.* He becomes aware of multiple blobby factions within the hidden

Zygon community on Earth, and learns that the leaders of the main blobby high command are disguised as two British schoolgirls, Jemima and Claudette.

> *The Zygon Invasion.* He's playing John Newton's famous piece on the guitar at the beginning of the episode. Maybe he plays it in tribute to his eighth incarnation's first companion. He refers to himself as 'Dr Funkenstein' when meeting Colonel Walsh in Turmezistan. He addresses the Zygons disguised as schoolgirls by the cartoon designs on their backpacks. When receiving a call from Kate, he asks if she's phoning him with her backside again. The Fifth Doctor references *Cinderella* in the audio *Circular Time: Autumn.*

Using his sonic shades, the Twelfth Doctor has visited some really weird websites. He sees the long-running TV talent show *Opportunity Knocks.* The truce between humanity and Zygons comes perilously close to breaking down on fifteen occasions. Each time, the Doctor is present when Kate Stewart uncovers the secret of the Osgood Box(es), and each time he wipes her memory.

> *The Zygon Inversion.* The Doctor impersonates the programme's unctuous American-accented host, Hughie Green, even using his famous catchphrases 'It's make-your-mind-up time' and 'I mean that most sincerely.' The sites listed on his sunglasses' browser history (mentioned again in *Smile,* and queried by the First Doctor in *Twice Upon a Time*) might well be found on the Galactic Hub.

The Zygon Inversion

Prior to *Sleep No More*

The Doctor sees the musical *Oliver!* He witnesses the Great Catastrophe that causes a merging of India and China. On Earth in the 38th Century, he sees cloned human soldiers grown in hatcheries. Later, the Twelfth Doctor and Clara arrive on Le Verrier Station near Neptune in the same time period. On a Tuesday.

> *Sleep No More.* The TARDIS is not seen or heard materialising as the episode begins. The Doctor sings part of a line from the song *Consider Yourself,* which features in the Lionel Bart show. Author Mark Gatiss has suggested the the Great Catastrophe might well be the same one described by Turlough in *Frontios.*

Prior to *Face the Raven*

Accompanied by Clara and Commander Nagata, the Twelfth Doctor travels to Triton, with the intention of destroying the sleep devices known as Morpheus machines.

> *Sleep No More.* This is the Doctor's intention at the end of the story. Since it turns out that the machines have nothing to do with the spread of the creatures known as Sandmen, that particular course of action is fruitless. Hopefully, he realises that at some point before all the people of Triton are consumed.

In a solo encounter with Torchwood, the Doctor sees their amnesia drug Retcon do its thing. He hears stories of hidden London streets containing alien beings, but chooses not to believe them. He makes a collection of annoying brass instruments, meets members of the psychic two-faced Janus species, and sees the targeted weapon/being known as a quantum shade. Having followed Ashildr's movements as far as the early 1800s, he finally loses track of her. The Twelfth Doctor and Clara have a disagreement over the assignment of roles in the good cop/bad cop scenario. It's agreed that the Doctor should be Bad Cop on account of his face. They encounter Jane Austen on several other occasions; Jane and Clara enjoy pranking one another.

> *Face the Raven.* The Doctor identifies the drug given to Rigsy as Retcon, its first mention outside *Torchwood.* It is a quantum shade that takes the life of the Doctor's companion.

The Doctor studies the properties of Azbantium, a substance four hundred times harder than diamond.

> *Heaven Sent.* The Doctor spends four and a half billion years attempting to break the Azbantium wall between his confession dial prison and Gallifrey.

They visit the most beautiful garden in all of time and space - probably on the planet Zaakros - where the Time Lord is almost forcibly married to a giant sentient plant, but escapes when his companion jumps to the side, apparently.

> Immediately before *Face the Raven.*

Heaven Sent

Hell Bent

Prior to *The Husbands of River Song*

During a visit to the Halassi vaults, the Doctor sees the tiny but impossibly valuable diamond known as the Androvar. He defeats giant robot fish from the ninth dimension.

> *The Husbands of River Song*. When River fails to recognise him, he suggests battling robot fish as an example of something the Doctor might be getting up to.

The TARDIS takes the Twelfth Doctor to the beautiful planet Rhodia just in time to rescue the crown prince and his unwilling Quill bodyguard from an invasion by the Shadow Kin. He drops off the Prince and the Quill - now posing as humans - along with a Rhodian weapon known as the Cabinet of Souls on Earth, outside Coal Hill Academy, where he's made arrangements for them to pose as a student and member of the staff. Encountering a race of giant centipedes known as the Lothan, he comes away with a selection of spare prosthetic limbs, which he stores in the TARDIS medical bay.

> The *Class* episode *For Tonight We Might Die*. He provides student Ram with a replacement leg after his own is cut off during a skirmish with the Shadow Kin. He says in *Oxygen* that he also has a set of replacement eyes, but they're not particularly suitable, unless he regenerates into a reptile.

He gets his hands on a rare gemstone, one of only four such crystals in existence, formed in a red hole. This one is known to the Monks of the Andorax as Hazandra, the ghost of love and wishes.

> *The Return of Doctor Mysterio*. The young Grant (whose surname is never stated) swallows the gem, thinking it to be medicine.

He visits an unnamed world, 23 million years after the 21st Century, as it is measured on Earth. He witnesses the Dalek-Movellan war at its height.

> *The Pilot*. The Doctor takes Bill and Nardole to the distant planet in an attempt to escape the water-being that pursues them. Nardole is unequivocal about his dislike for the conflict between the inhabitants of Skaro and their dreadlock-sporting foes, which appears to suggest he might have been in the Doctor's company when he witnessed it. It's possible, of course, that Nardole was there on his own - there's a lot about him we don't and will never know, including what colour his invisible hair is, and how he styles it.

The Doctor sees the hard-working minuscule robots referred to as Vardy, and is told of the Earth colony on Gliese 581 D where the settlers have seemingly discovered the secret of happiness. He meets an amorous emperor composed of algae. On various colony planets, he finds that the Scottish contingent insist upon declaring independence.

> *Smile.* The name Gliese 581 D appears on the series' official website, and originates in the Fourth Doctor short story *All Snug in Their Beds.*

He enjoys watching zero-gravity wrestling, which involves tentacles and magic spells.

> *Thin Ice*

He gets his hands on a set of spare eyes. Unfortunately, they're lizard's eyes.

> *Oxygen*

In the year 1045, he bumps into Pope Benedict IX, who casts a spell on the Doctor with her castanets. She considers him more in need of confession than anyone alive, but it's the only proposition he doesn't take her up on. Her Holiness ends up writing him a letter of recommendation. Whether or not it mentions the castanets is known only to the Vatican. On one of his return trips to Gallifrey, the Doctor comes away with a piece of technology that will enable him to borrow qualities from his future selves. Or possibly kill him.

> *Extremis.* A blind Twelfth Doctor attempts to use a Time Lord device to borrow sight from his future incarnations. Granted, this all happens in a computer simulation, but it seems very likely that there's an equivalent in the real world. Given what happened when he and Clara were last on his home planet in *Hell Bent,* it's unlikely that he'd go back there any time during the same incarnation, but one has to ask why, if he had this future incarnation device much earlier, he didn't use it?

Though he has yet to encounter or do battle with them, the Doctor learns of worlds upon which the aliens known only as the Monks have ruled for thousands of years.

> *The Lie of the Land.* He tells Missy that the Monks have been engaging in their bad habits for millennia.

Roman-occupied Britain provides the Doctor with a lot of distractions, quite apart from the presence of the Pandorica. He spends time there as a governor, a farmer, a juggler and a vestal virgin (second class). He chats with crows.

> *The Eaters of Light*

The Doctor discovers to his horror that – rather than all originating from Mondas, as he had supposed – Cybermen have a tendency to emerge on many planets with a human population, his beloved Earth included. Marinus, the world on which he battled the Voord, is another example, as is Telos.

> *The Doctor Falls.* The Sixth Doctor comic strip *The World Shapers* ends with the Doctor believing Marinus and Mondas to be one and the same. If that story can be considered canonical (and this onscreen reference appears to suggest that it can), then at some point, he realises his error and understands this to be a case of parallel evolution.

The Twelfth Doctor learns that the only good Dalek, commonly referred to as Rusty is, several billions of years after their first meeting, entrenched on the planet Villengard. It is still, however, linked into the Dalek hive mind, an even larger database than the Matrix on Gallifrey.

> *Twice Upon a Time.* Rusty first appears in *Inside the Dalek.*

The Twelfth Doctor has a very long day, during which everyone around him transforms into a lizard, and a piano falls on him. Disheartened, he goes for a haircut, then takes the TARDIS to the human colony of Mendorax Dellora during the festive season. Despite being keen not to be cheered up, the TARDIS provides him with a set of novelty hologramatic antlers.

> *The Husbands of River Song*

Prior to *The Return of Doctor Mysterio*

The Twelfth Doctor and River spend the night together (the nights on Darillium lasting twenty-four years). He has sufficient free time over the course of the night to somehow reassemble his wife's assistant Nardole, last seen as a severed head. He's forced to cut a few corners, however, which means purchasing lungs of dubious provenance.

> The Twelfth Doctor and his wife are last seen eating out in *The Husbands of River Song*. Nardole shows up in reassembled form during *The Return of Doctor Mysterio*. The Doctor breaks the news about his dodgy lungs to him in *The Pyramid at the End of the World.*

News that the Twelfth Doctor has, at long last, settled down, reaches the Daleks, and through them, Missy. When he learns that his arch-enemy is about to be put to death – not for the first time – the Doctor does not leave at once. Instead, he waits until River has departed for the Library, fully aware of her fate. It is not until he receives word that she has died that he sets off to play his part in Missy's execution.

> *Extremis.* Nardole states that he has followed the Doctor from Darillium, as per River's instructions. He must, however, have

made a stop at the Library to pay his respects and withdraw her diary, which he hands to the Doctor at Missy's execution.

Having rescued Missy from her fate, the Twelfth Doctor takes her quantum fold prison to Earth, where he puts Nardole to work as his assistant - it's evidently easier than building himself another K-9. Nardole's main duty is to ensure that the Doctor keeps his oath to guard Missy and not to go off-world. He takes a non-specific post at St Luke's University in Bristol, and installs the vault beneath the university, in which Missy is imprisoned. Only he and Nardole have access to it (and her).

The Pilot

He is befuddled by the furniture and meatball emporium known as Ikea. The Twelfth Doctor receives a call from 'Miss Quill,' advising him that the leader of the Shadow Kin, Corakinus, has tracked his prey to Coal Hill.

The *Class* episode *For Tonight We Might Die*. When Corakinus demands the Cabinet of Souls, the Doctor refers him to Ikea. This trip in the TARDIS, as well as the one to New York, are not technically in contravention of his vow, which was not to leave the Earth.

He puts a glass of water in his pocket. The right way up, obviously, otherwise it'd spill. He reads the story of the Sword of Damocles. In an attempt to repair some of the time distortion experienced by New York during *The Angels Take Manhattan*, the Twelfth Doctor sets up a device on the roof of an apartment building, of which the gem Hazandra is a vital component. He sets a trap to prevent anyone from stealing his machine, and foolishly decides to test it.

The Return of Doctor Mysterio. The Doctor likens the freighter in orbit over Earth to the Sword of Damocles.

Prior to *The Pilot*

The Doctor hears the story of the Magic Haddock, and tests his own blood pressure, only to find it worryingly high.

Smile

He reads Heinrich Hoffman's *The Story of Little Suck-a-Thumb*. He places a couple of diving suits inside the TARDIS.

Thin Ice. He recites the German children's story to a group of urchins, thirty-one years before its first publication.

He installs a macaroon dispenser in the TARDIS. Over the course of seventy years at St Luke's, he builds up a collection of sonic screwdrivers, which he keeps in his office, along with framed photographs of Susan and River Song.

The Pilot

He is obliged to shop for women's clothing.

The Woman Who Fell to Earth. The Thirteenth Doctor says it's a long time since she's done so. Male incarnations of the Doctor are seen wearing female attire in *The Highlanders* and *The Green Death*. The Second and Sixth Doctors are similarly disguised in the audios *The Glorious Revolution* and *The Vanity Box*, respectively, while the Seventh Doctor dresses as a nun in the novel *Just War*.

He notices non-student Bill Potts attending his lectures, and has Nardole bring her to his office.

The Pilot. It's unclear precisely how long he's been guarding Missy by the time he meets Bill, but it's evidently less than the thousand years he vowed to keep her imprisoned; in *Thin Ice*, he simply says he's 'over two thousand,' which is how old he told Clara he was in *Deep Breath*. One of his sonic screwdrivers is destroyed in *Oxygen*.

Smile

Thin Ice

Prior to *Knock Knock*

The Twelfth Doctor checks on Greenland, to make certain it hasn't been destroyed by the creature he freed from its chains beneath the Thames.

Thin Ice. He promises Bill he'll do this.

He helps out Quincy Jones when his usual bassist is discovered to be a Klarj neon death voc bot, and an untalented one, at that.

Knock Knock. This incident is likely to have involved the Twelfth Doctor, but just imagine how awesome it would be if it had occurred to the First.

Prior to *Oxygen*

The Twelfth Doctor informs Nardole that the TARDIS is unable to travel anywhere following the removal of the fluid link. He's lying. He changes his mind about whether it's possible to die well.

Oxygen. Not having a fluid link handy certainly disables the ship

> during *The Daleks*, but the Doctor has evidently fixed that problem over the centuries. He previously stated that in the *Class* episode *For Tonight We Might Die* that it was not possible to die well. Here, he describes it as 'winning.'

He explains the concept of regeneration to Bill, and reveals to her that he is the last of his race, what with Gallifrey hanging out at the end of time, and Missy's presence in the vault remaining a deep, dark secret.

> He mentions regeneration in *Knock Knock*, but doesn't go into further details. But in *The Lie of the Land*, he expects her to believe she's witnessing the process, and reminds her in *The Eaters of Light* that he regenerates instead of dying. Bill does get to meet several previous Doctors in the comic strip *The Lost Dimension*, so perhaps that accounts for it. He introduces Missy to Bill as 'the other last of the Time Lords.'

He plays Super Mario.

> *Extremis*. His computerised avatar likens his experience in the phoney world designed by the Monks to Mario discovering that he's not real.

He sees the British TV show *The Pyramid Game*, a version of the American game show *The $10,000 Pyramid*.

> *The Pyramid at the End of the World*. He thanks the alien Monks for 'playing the big pyramid game.'

After inventing a device capable of unscrambling signals and providing map co-ordinates for their source, the Doctor stores it in the TARDIS, along with several takeaway menus and fifty Danish krone.

> *The Lie of the Land*

Extremis

The Pyramid at the End of the World

Prior to *The Lie of the Land*

Following the Monks' conquest of planet Earth, the Twelfth Doctor is taken to a prison boat, from which he broadcasts propaganda for humanity's new masters. Over the course of six months, in part at Nardole's suggestion, he recruits and de-programs his guards while he waits for Bill to come and find him.

> *The Lie of the Land*

Prior to *Empress of Mars*

The Doctor draws up a list of movies he must get around to watching. He at least manages to see Disney's *Frozen*.

Empress of Mars. He tells Bill he'll add *The Terminator* to the list.

Prior to *The Eaters of Light*

Following Missy's rescue of the Twelfth Doctor and Bill from the surface of Mars in the 19th Century, she's set to work checking the TARDIS engines, a fact the Doctor neglects to mention to Nardole. As a precautionary measure, though, he bio-locks her out of the ship's controls. Shortly thereafter, a row erupts between the Time Lord and his companion as to who knows the most about the Romans (the nationality, not the four-part First Doctor serial). He mislays his teacakes.

The Eaters of Light. The Doctor takes Bill and Nardole to Aberdeen in the 2nd Century in order to settle the dispute over the fate of the Ninth Legion. Nardole points out to the Doctor that he's the only one who knows where the teacakes are.

Prior to *World Enough and Time*

The Twelfth Doctor plays a part in the complex Operation Cup-a-Soup, in which thirteen TARDISes are positioned equidistantly (such a grown-up word) around the planet Gallifrey, in order to save it from the Dalek onslaught.

The Day of the Doctor

Encouraged by Missy's gradual rehabilitation, the Twelfth Doctor relaxes his self-imposed rule about not leaving Earth, making it a habit to answer distress calls on a weekly basis.

World Enough and Time. The Doctor describes the response to distress signals as 'our usual Saturday.'

He sees the comedy of Richard Hearne in his guise as the doddering Mr Pastry, the extraordinarily popular entertainment show *The Great British Bake-Off* and the long-running BBC sitcom *Dad's Army*.

Twice Upon a Time. He addresses his first incarnation first as 'Mr Pastry,' then as 'Mary Berry' (one of the original judges on *Bake-Off*) and finally as 'Corporal Jones,' a character from the beloved comedy. The actor who played Mr Pastry, Richard Hearne, was considered for the role of the Fourth Doctor.

Some time between 1978 and 2008, he is a spectator during the famous Dakar rally. He watches the popular television programme *Antiques Roadshow*, and spends three weeks as a hologram, during which time he picks up some juicy gossip.

> *The Ghost Monument*. The Thirteenth Doctor states that Epzo's spacecraft belongs on the *Roadshow*, and likens the Rally of Twelve Galaxies to the Paris-Dakar.

In early December 1955, he meets Elvis in New York. On this on another occasion, he provides the singer with a mobile phone. He becomes a big fan of civil rights activist Rosa Parks, watches the film *The Wild One*, and either meets or *is* the mysterious graffiti artist Banksy. He sees an information brick, a temporal displacement weapon and a multi-intercept and surveillance device in operation

> *Rosa*. As the TARDIS arrives in Alabama, the Thirteenth Doctor says she believes Elvis is in New York. In fact, he's on his way there for a meeting with RCA executives, but close enough. She addresses the leather jacket-clad Krasko – who has amassed all the equipment she discovers – as 'Brando.' The Doctor has definitely heard of Banksy, but is cagey about whether or not they are one and the same.

The Doctor briefly becomes a sister in an aqua-hospital, which turns out to be a training camp for the Quiston Calcium Assassins. He and aviatrix Amelia Earhart are forced to weave dragline spider silk to a thickness necessary to stop an aircraft in flight. Circa 2018, he hears a lot of humans talking about Ed Sheeran.

> *Arachnids in the UK*. The Eighth Doctor novel *Seeing I* mentions an encounter with Amelia Earhart, while the Fifth Doctor has her flying jacket in the audio *No Place Like Home*. And, yes, Quiston Calcium Assassin *does* sound like an awesome brand of toothpaste.

Visiting the junk galaxies, he spends a month on either Seffilun 27 or Seffilun 59, searching for a big pile of components important for the continued functioning of the TARDIS. In the course of an adventure, he uncovers a sonic mine, but comes away uninjured. He spends less time than he'd like in the 67th Century, but enough to see that, though it might get tricky in the middle, everything eventually turns out all right. While there, he sees an antimatter drive in operation, discovers the properties of a sterilised MedBlanket, studies the symptoms of the illnesses known as Corton Fever and Pilot's Heart, hears of the Tsuranga Quadzone rescue craft, and learns to perform the traditional death incantation. He reads the Book of Celebrants, and takes particular interest in the entry regarding legendary neuro-pilot's General Eve Cicero defeat of the Army of the Aeons at the Battle of the Underkind. Unsurprisingly, an entire volume has been dedicated to the actions of the Doctor, who has become such a fan of the musical *Hamilton* that he has seen performances by all 900 casts. He meets the Gifftan and witnesses the rapidity and intensity of male pregnancies.

> *The Tsuranga Conundrum*. The Doctor deduces that Cicero is suffering from Pilot's Heart, and not, as she claims, Corton Fever.

In India, he witnesses the horrendous results of partition. He measures Korian waves, which usually indicate a nearby octonic engine, and meets Lord Mountbatten. He hears of the ancient race of assassins known as the Thijarians.

> *Demons of the Punjab*. The Thirteenth Doctor instantly recognises the significance of the date, August the 13th, 1947. She's quite certain she has never met the Thijarians before, which, given their rep, is quite surprising, really.

He meets someone named Roger Wilco.

> *Kerblam!*

The Doctor visits Mary, Queen of Scots during her imprisonment in Fotheringay Castle in the early months of 1587. In 17th Century England, he witnesses the savage work of the Witchfinder General. The Milk Wars of Keston Five leave him with a terrible hangover.

> *The Witchfinders*. The Thirteenth Doctor says that she knows the reason for the construction of the ducking stool. She tells King James that his mother lamented his unwillingness to see her prior to her execution. The Eighth Doctor sees the witch trials in the audio *The Witch from the Well*, while the First Doctor visits Salem in the novel *The Witch Hunters*. Maybe the Milk Wars are connected to the Quiston Calcium Assassins.

The Doctor visits Norway. In the year 2211, he witnesses the terrifying Woolly Rebellion, where sheep and mankind finally face off in a bloody, baa-filled conflict.

> *It Takes You Away*. The Thirteenth Doctor is able to identify Norway by tasting the soil.

He is partially responsible for the invention of the wellington boot. On his travels, he hears of the long-lived duo-species known as the Ux, dimensional engineers who are only to be found on three planets in the entire universe.

The Battle of Ranskoor Av Kolos

In either the late 18th or early 19th Century, he befriends Italian astronomer Giuseppe Piazzi. He takes on a Dalek reconnaissance scout, and discovers that it possesses abilities not granted to the average Skaro mutation. At a party, the Doctor either consumes or sees taken a particular medicine that, when mixed with alcohol, results in the growing of an additional head.

Resolution. Yaz calls Piazzi the Doctor's 'mate' when she is introduced to him in 1801, implying some previous association.

The Doctor Falls

Twice Upon a Time

The Thirteenth Doctor
Jodie Whittaker
2017-

Prior to *The Woman Who Fell to Earth*

As she tumbles towards glamorous Sheffield, the newly-regenerated Thirteenth Doctor loses her TARDIS key.

> *The Ghost Monument.* She no longer has her key when finally reuinted with her craft, but the TARDIS lets her inside anyway, without so much as a click of her fingers.

The Ghost Monument

Prior to *Rosa*

Like most sensible people, the TARDIS is keen to avoid Sheffield, and takes the Thirteenth Doctor and her friends to thirteen alternate destinations.

> *Rosa.* The Doctor says that Alabama represents their ninth failed attempt; Graham says it's their fourteenth.

Prior to *Arachnids in the UK*

The Doctor reads the novels of Edith Wharton. She finds her trusty psychic paper.

> *Arachnids in the UK.* The Doctor complains in her first two adventures about her empty pockets, so presumably her previous incarnation left the paper somewhere in the TARDIS, along with the stethoscope she uses in *The Tsuranga Conundrum.*

Prior to *The Tsuranga Conundrum*

Having acquired three human friends, the Thirteenth Doctor sets an alarm on the TARDIS console to notify her of any noteworthy activity on Earth.

> *Resolution.* The Doctor makes it plain that she's done this for the benefit of Yaz, Ryan and Graham (although when isn't she keeping an eye on our planet, to be honest?), so it must be after all three volunteer for Team TARDIS.

The Thirteenth Doctor takes her fam rainbathing in the upward tropics of Kinstarno. In need of vital components for the TARDIS, she travels to Seffilun 27, and provides everyone with pre-programmed detectors, in the sure and certain hope of finding the necessary parts within a month. After four hours, Graham has given up hope.

The Tsuranga Conundrum. The Doctor is uncertain whether she ought to be on Seffilun 27 or 59, most of the planets in the junk galaxies looking the same.

Prior to *Demons of the Punjab*

Following quarantine and a debriefing on Resus One medical station, the Thirteenth Doctor and her friends teleport back to Seffilun 27, where they recover the TARDIS.

The Tsuranga Conundrum. The Doctor is informed that it's four days flight back to the planet on which they were injured, but that teleport facilities are available at their destination. It's uncertain whether she eventually found the important components for the TARDIS, or simply learned to live without them, but she's seen conducting repairs to the console at the start of *Demons of the Punjab*.

In another mishap, the Thirteenth Doctor introduces her friends to the Death Eye Turtle Army, an incident for which she is forced to apologise profusely.

Demons of the Punjab

Kerblam!

Prior to *The Witchfinders*

As per Yaz's request, the Thirteenth Doctor takes the TARDIS to the planet Kandoka, in order to track down the daughter of her late colleague, Dan Cooper.

Kerblam! Immediately after the conclusion of the episode.

The Doctor develops a fondness for apple bobbing. She promises to show her friends the coronation of her infamous ex, Elizabeth I, but the TARDIS instead sets them down in 17th Century Lancashire.

The Witchfinders

It Takes You Away

The Battle of Ranskoor Av Kolos

Prior to *Resolution*

Needing to grease the TARDIS' geo-feudal locks, the Thirteenth Doctor sends her friends out to pick up peanut butter. Later, she takes them to nineteen New Year's Eve celebrations in a row, including ancient Mesopotamia, the top of Sydney Harbour Bridge in 2000 (which must have been a bit of a trial for Ryan), Italy in 1801, and, finally, to a sun in the process of going supernova.

> *Resolution.* The Doctor later returns to the supernova in order to destroy the Dalek mutant controlling Ryan's dad, Aaron. She sends Graham on what she refers to as an 'emergency peanut butter run,' suggesting this isn't the first time the geo-feudal locks have been playing up lately.

The Future?

The Doctor's adventures in ancient Egypt become immortalised in hieroglyphics.

> *Love & Monsters.* Bridget's slide show includes a hieroglyph of the TARDIS. This may refer to a previous Egyptian escapade, or one yet to come.

At a significant moment, River Song hears the Doctor's true name.

> *The Forest of the Dead.* Although the Eleventh Doctor appears to tell River his name in *The Wedding of River Song,* a later scene in the same episode reveals that he whispers something entirely different. Like many events concerning River Song, it is impossible to say whether or not, from the Doctor's perspective, this is yet to occur. Although the Twelfth Doctor states that it is necessary to draw up a flow chart to understand their relationship, unless he suffers some frequent bouts of amnesia, they don't officially meet until *Silence in the Library.* Nevertheless, she has photographs of all previous incarnations, including the War Doctor, in *The Husbands of River Song,* and several audios include encounters between River and several previous incarnations, including a threesome involving the Sixth and Seventh Doctors.

The Doctor's actions at a convent in the 1300s become the stuff of legend, when the 'sainted physician' smites a demon who falls from the sky. As a result, the TARDIS is immortalised in stained glass.

> *The End of Time.* The exact details of this incident (as well as which incarnation of the Doctor is involved) remain unknown. It might be something to do with the Eleventh Doctor's time as a monk, as seen in *The Bells of Saint John.* But equally, it might not.

The Doctor shares an adventure with River Song in the Bone Meadows.

> *The Time of the Angels.* In *The Husbands of River Song,* King Hydroflax is referred to as 'the butcher of the Bone Meadows,' but none of that particular adventure occurs there, wherever 'there' is.

More than one incident ends with River Song in handcuffs.

Flesh and Stone. River indicates that this is not the only time an encounter with the Doctor has ended in this fashion. She, of course, handcuffs the Tenth Doctor at the climax of *The Forest of the Dead*, but as that occurs in her future, there is no way she can know about it. The Fourth Doctor has a pair of handcuffs in *Genesis of the Daleks*, so make of that what you will. It's the Seventh Doctor who claps the missus in irons in the audio *The Eye of the Storm*.

The Doctor eventually redesigns the Control Room a total of thirty-one times.

The Doctor's Wife. The TARDIS, in human form, states that in the future, she will have stored thirty versions of the Control Room.

At some point after dropping off Amy and Rory at the end of *The God Complex*, the Doctor purchases a car for the couple.

The God Complex. This might well have happened during the gap between this story and *Closing Time*. Or it might not. There's just no way of knowing for certain. Maddening, isn't it?

On several occasions, River Song steals the TARDIS and later returns it without the Doctor's knowledge.

The Husbands of River Song. River has her own key.

The Doctor becomes known as both the Storm (no longer oncoming, it seems), the Beast of Trenzalore, The Imp of the Pandorica, the Shadow of the Valeyard, the Butcher of Skull Moon, the Last Tree of Garsennon, and The Destroyer of Worlds.

The Great Intelligence lists the names by which the Doctor will come to be known in *The Name of the Doctor*. Others are given by Testimony in *Twice Upon a Time*.

In later years, the Doctor takes on the form of some of his earlier incarnations. As an older version of his fourth self, he assumes the mantle of curator of the Under Gallery, and acquires the Time Lord painting titled *Gallifrey Falls No More* under 'unusual circumstances.'

The Day of the Doctor

In another dimension, a future incarnation of the Doctor takes on the role of Merlin. That Doctor carves a note in stone at Carbury, knowing that it will be discovered by their seventh self, thus leading him to the spaceship containing King Arthur's body and a note warning him of Morgaine's plan to detonate a nuclear missile a thousand years in the future. Morgaine and the Doctor play many games of chess (literally?), but despite his casting her down at Baden, she eventually seals him in the ice caves for all eternity.

Battlefield

The Also-Rans

The Sixth Doctor: *A Fix With Sontarans*

Written by Eric Saward for the popular BBC children's series *Jim'll Fix It*, this brief adventure reunites the Doctor with his former companion Tegan Jovanka (who, going by her uniform, appears to have got her air stewardess job back). The format of the show saw the wishes of young viewers granted by popular DJ and tireless charity worker Jimmy Savile. In this instance, 8-year-old viewer Gareth Jenkins asked to meet actor Colin Baker and see the interior of the TARDIS. The rather sweet sketch that resulted sees Gareth assist the Doctor in disposing of a few Sontarans who have invaded the Time Lord's ship. The fact that the Sixth Doctor seems to be travelling alone places this incident sometime after *The Trial of a Time Lord*, when he has relieved himself of the chronologically inconvenient Mel.

Following Savile's death in 2011, allegations of sexual abuse on an horrific and almost unimaginable scale came to light, robbing this segment and any other fond memories of the show (on which Tom Baker had earlier guested, handing out live terrapins and fragments of his scarf) of their charm. Samantha Baker penned a sequel, *Fixing a Hole*, featuring the Sixth Doctor and Tegan. Eric Saward's story *CHAOS* implies that the whole incident might have been a hallucination - which, given how badly the revelation of Savile's activities have sullied the recollections of an entire generation, is perhaps just as well.

Prior to *A Fix With Sontarans*

In the impossibly far-flung year of 2001, the Doctor sees a Sontaran fleet attack the planet Earth.

> The attack is, apparently, rebuffed by adult Gareth Jenkins, making the John Connor-esque presence of his 8-year-old self in the TARDIS a big deal for the Doctor's enemies.

During a skirmish with the Sontarans, he finds himself menaced by a vitrox bomb.

> As the scene begins, he is attempting to cut power to the TARDIS, hoping to disable the device.

Two of the aforementioned Sontarans from the Tenth Battle Brigade somehow manage to get inside the Sixth Doctor's TARDIS armed with the aforementioned vitrox bomb.

> How exactly Group Marshal Nathan and his subordinate (referred to in the script as "Turner," but never addressed by name onscreen) got through the doors that withstood the hordes of Genghis Khan is never revealed, not that it's really important.

The Seventh Doctor: *Search Out Space*

This episode of the BBC's educational children's programme *Search Out Science* was broadcast a year after the cancellation of *Doctor Who*.

Prior to *Search Out Space*

The Seventh Doctor winds up as host of the universe's biggest game show, *The Ultimate Challenge*, in which companions Ace and K-9 (who is initially on his own in the TARDIS) are contestants.

> Which model of K-9 this might be is anyone's guess (though we hear the theme for failed pilot *K-9 and Company* as the tin dog muses over different colours of smartie). The story *Storm in a Tikka* fills the gap between *Dimensions in Time* (recorded three years later) and *Search Out Science*.

The Seventh Doctor, et al: *Dimensions in Time*

Recorded for the BBC's Children in Need charity appeal, this 1993 two-parter, written by David Roden and John Nathan-Turner, featured multiple Doctors and companions interacting with the cast of popular soap opera *EastEnders* (which the Tenth Doctor watches during *Army of Ghosts*) in spectacular 3-D, on the occasion of *Doctor Who*'s 30th anniversary – by which time the series had been off the air for almost four years. *The Discontinuity Guide* suggests that the various Doctors are not, in fact, different incarnations, but rather a single Doctor whose perspective has been 'juggled.' Since this author hasn't the faintest idea what is going on for any of the story's sixteen minutes, he is in no position to argue, or to work out where it might take place within the series' continuity.

Prior to *The War Machines*

The First Doctor finds himself 'pickled in time' by fellow Gallifreyan the Rani.

As episode one begins, the First and Second Doctors' disembodied heads are seen spinning around the control room of the Rani's TARDIS.

Prior to *The War Games*

The Second Doctor also gets the *Futurama* treatment from his old enemy.

See above. It looks great in 3-D.

Prior to *Logopolis*

Trapped in the void yet again, the Fourth Doctor attempts to get word through to his other incarnations regarding the Rani's intentions.

The Fourth Doctor is sporting his burgundy ensemble. Strangely, he seems to be lacking his curls - perhaps, like the Eleventh Doctor, he was forced to shave his head when dealing with the representatives of the Church of the Papal Mainframe. What other rational explanation could there be?

Prior to *Dimensions in Time*

The Doctor sees a Megaluthian Slime Skimmer 'bounding around.' The Seventh Doctor plans to take companion Ace to see the Great Wall of China before his vessel is drawn off-course by the Rani. Her actions do not, this time, result in regeneration.

The Third Doctor likens himself to a Slime Skimmer. His seventh incarnation is surprised to find himself in London rather than China.

The Tenth Doctor: *The Infinite Quest*

This animated serial, originally broadcast in three-minute segments during the 1997 children's programme *Totally Doctor Who,* was written by the former editor of *Doctor Who Magazine,* Alan Barnes (who, in case you skipped over it, graciously provided this book's forward - see page 9). There are no gaps between Martha's first five adventures with the Doctor, so that would place this tale somewhere between *42* and *Utopia*.

Prior to *100,000 BC*

Researching the Dark Times, the First Doctor comes across mention of the starship known as the *Infinite*, and dismisses it as legend, which almost always proves to be a bad idea. He views examples of Dark Time technology.

> This story confirms the placement of the Racnoss and the Great Vampires within the Dark Times, but also adds the Nestenes.

Prior to *Smith and Jones*

The Doctor meets Boadicea, and hears of the fearsome reputation of Baltazar, the 40th Century Corsair King of Triton. In the same time period, he sees a planet heated by artificial suns, and is on Earth when oil supplies run out, and humanity is forced to drill on other worlds. He acquires a golden spoon once wielded by Earth's greatest chefs, both genuine and fictional, and forged by an unnamed alien species which specialises in turning hydroxiding fungus into kitchen implements. He visits the prison planet Volag-Noc - which, despite being the coldest place in the galaxy, seems to be of less interest to the Ice Warriors than good old Earth. Later, the Tenth Doctor has amassed 3,005 outstanding convictions, including 250 unpaid library fines. The TARDIS takes him to worlds in the Hesperus Galaxy and the Ceres System, as well as to Asteroid 7574B (at a point before its collision with the *Infinite*).

> In the opening scene, the Tenth Doctor likens villain Baltazar to Boadicea, as well as to Napoleon Bonaparte - whom he met in Venice during either his first or second incarnation - and Blackbeard, whom the Second Doctor conjured up while doing battle in the Land of Fiction, as seen in *The Mind Robber*. He knows Baltazar's biography and that he successfully destroyed Earth's defence force, though the two have never met, and claims that his spoon once belonged to Fanny Craddock, Delia Smith and Womble cook Madame Cholet. Delia is mentioned again in the Tenth Doctor novel *Shining Darkness*. On the planet Bouken, he identifies both the oil rigs and artificial suns. If there were no doubts as to the canonicity of *The Infinite Quest*, this would be a good reason for placing the Eleventh Doctor's very similar recollection of the depletion of Earth's fossil fuels in *Dinosaurs on a Spaceship* a little earlier. In fact, in honour of Mr Barnes' foreword, why not? The computer on Volag-Noc (a planet

mentioned in the Eleventh Doctor novel *Night of the Humans*) instantly imprisons the Doctor, suggesting that he was relatively guiltless upon his first visit, which must have been before the robot warden Locke was installed. When viewing an intergalactic map, he recognises the Ceres System, the Hesperus Galaxy and the asteroid instantly.

Prior to *The Infinite Quest*

Deciding that he will challenge Baltazar before the Corsair King turns the inhabitants of Earth into diamonds, the Tenth Doctor tinkers with his fungus spoon, adding the important element of zing, also known as va-va-voom.

Companion Martha Jones notes that the rust that destroys Baltazar's hand-forged craft is by no means ordinary.

The Tenth Doctor: *Dreamland*

Broadcast in six short episodes during 2009, Phil Ford's *Dreamland* sees the Tenth Doctor travelling on his own, placing this adventure somewhere after *The Runaway Bride* but before *The End of Time*. There is possibly (but not definitely) some conflict between this story and *Dalek*, in which the Ninth Doctor identifies a piece of the Roswell space ship, despite the Tenth never having been to Nevada's Area 51 before. However, the fact that Mr Dread and his android team reappear in the live-action *Sarah Jane Adventures* story *The Vault of Secrets* lends it a certain degree of credibility.

Prior to *The War Games*

In China during the Ming Dynasty, the Doctor enjoys the best dim sun this side of infinity.

The Eleventh Doctor mentions his fondness for this dish at the story's end. He visits China on more than one occasion before his fellow Time Lords strand him on Earth during his third incarnation.

Prior to *Planet of the Spiders*

He follows the fortunes of Manchester United. Illusionist and stunt performer Harry Houdini teaches him how to free his limbs from tight restraints.

When Cassie mentions 'the Reds,' the Tenth Doctor assumes she's talking about Man U. His fourth incarnation has a football rattle about his person in *The Masque of Mandragora*. Houdini is mentioned in several live-action stories, including *Planet of the Spiders, Revenge of the Cybermen* and *The Vampires of Venice*.

Prior to *Dreamland*

The Doctor experiences chili, served in an American diner both before and after 1962, and concludes that the pre-'62 version is preferable. He observes the fashions of the 1950s (when he watched Elvis Presley perform on *The Ed Sullivan Show*, perhaps?). He tangles with a swarm of very hungry Skorpius flies and a Viperox Battle Drone, but also sees the Viperox at a point in time when they have developed and become peace-loving. He is on Earth in 1994 when the US government admits the existence of Area 51. In the early 21st Century, he witnesses humanity finally perfecting a targeted amnesia drug (*Torchwood*'s famed Retcon?). He once again exhausts his supply of matches, and enjoys the *Die Hard, Alien* and *Star Wars* film franchises, as well as Bugs Bunny cartoons. In 1972, he witnesses an android mop-up team of Men in Black sent to a primitive planet by the Alliance of Shades, and notes how poor they are at blending in – accordingly, the Alliance pulls the plug on the androids (not literally, one imagines … although, then again …). Drifting by the Earth, circa 1958, he gets another chili jones.

The Tenth Doctor likens the '50s UFO mania with other trends of the day. He recognises the Viperox from their snarl, and knows about their combat habits and sensitive hearing. He also knows a Skorpius Swarm Brain when he sees it/them. He references the movies and the famous wascally cartoon wabbit when attempting to escape Area 51 by ventilation shaft. In the mining town of Solitude, he asks Jimmy for a match with which to light a lantern (and then, moments later, uses his sonic screwdriver as a torch). He informs both Lord Azlok and Colonel Stark that the Viperox will eventually change their ways. The Eighth Doctor comic strips *The Keep* and *Fire and Brimstone* contain mentions of *Star Wars* and *Alien*, respectively. In *Last Christmas*, the Twelfth Doctor claims never to have heard of the Ridley Scott film. There's a reference to *Star Wars* in the Fifth Doctor audio *Cobwebs*. In *Empress of Mars*, the Twelfth Doctor says 'I have a bad feeling about this,' which may be a quote, or he may just have a bad feeling about this.

Prior to *The End of Time*

The Eleventh Doctor returns to the Ming Dynasty for some more dim sum.

This is the Doctor's stated intention at the end of the story.

The ?th Doctor: *Scream of the Shalka*

The six-part animated drama *Scream of the Shalka* appeared on the BBC's *Doctor Who* website in 2003, at a period when it seemed unlikely that the Time Lord would ever return to television. Scripted by Paul Cornell, it starred Richard E Grant (who had previously portrayed one of the Doctor's ill-fated incarnations in the *Comic Relief* special *Doctor Who – The Curse of Fatal Death,* and who later played the Great Intelligence during several Eleventh Doctor stories) as the Ninth Doctor. Of course, that title was ultimately taken from him by Christopher Eccleston - who, thanks to a bit of retconning involving John Hurt's War Doctor, is now technically the Tenth Doctor - but there is little doubt that the serial's creators intended Grant's Doctor to be the next incarnation following McGann's take on the character.

Prior to *100,000 BC*

The First Doctor discovers the delights of the D'Oyly Carte.

In *Inside the Spaceship,* the First Doctor mentions being presented with an Ulster by Gilbert and Sullivan. Here, the ?th Doctor, makes a passing reference to their opera company in episode one.

Prior to *The Faceless Ones*

Dame Nellie Melba gives the Doctor a few singing lessons.

The ?th Doctor demonstrates the skills he picked up from the famous opera singer in episode four. She is mentioned by the Fourth Doctor in *The Power of Kroll,* while the Second Doctor recalls her ability to smash wine glasses using only her voice in *The Ice Warriors.*

Prior to *Scream of the Shalka*

The Doctor once again patches the TARDIS telephone through to the outer shell, the difference being that this time, he is able to remove the phone and use it remotely. While on Earth, he enjoys watching a number of eclipses, grows fond of the compositions of Johann Pachelbel, hears good things about the Mersault '96 and makes a study of whalesong. He meets the actor Lon Chaney - whom he considers wonderful, despite his hairy hands - and architect Antoni Gaudi. He sees the musical *Cabaret* and the Eurovision Song Contest. He assembles a fair amount of small change, including Atraxian semble seeds, Euros and Zornic groats (which give new meaning to the phrase 'money talks'). He also opens for Elvis Presley, making the mistake of treating the singer's fans to a poetry recital. By this point, his first nine incarnations have all met pop artist Andy Warhol.

The Doctor hears of the species known as the Soltox, the Duprest and the Valtanus, and believes each responsible for its own destruction, never realising that the Shalka are actually to blame. Following his regeneration, the ?th Doctor finds that he is somewhat asthmatic. In his new body, he meets the Secretary General of the United Nations. During his travels, he picks up an unnamed female companion, who is with him when he records a message for the TARDIS' answerphone. But tragedy strikes, and this companion is lost. The responsibility weighs heavily upon the Time Lord, who considers himself worn-out, and promises never to place himself or anyone else in another life-endangering situation. Redemption comes in the unlikely form of the Master (or, at least, an android version of his old arch-nemesis - it is unclear whether the Doctor has built him, as he did Antimony). The ersatz Master is of aid to the Doctor, and accepts a last chance for salvation. As he heads for Bognor Regis, his TARDIS is drawn off-course by the Time Lords and sets down in a Lancashire town in 2003.

> The ?th Doctor's first words upon arriving on Earth are, 'No, it's not where we're supposed to be.' The Eleventh Doctor uses the ship's exterior phone in both *The Day of the Doctor* and *The Time of the Doctor*, despite his earlier protestations, in *The Empty Child* and *The Bells of Saint John*, that it is not an actual communication device. In episode one, he complains that there is no Pachelbel on the jukebox in Alison Cheney's pub. He asks her if she is any relation to Lon Chaney (Jr, one presumes, judging by the Doctor's recollection of his hairy hands), and later offers her his asthma inhaler. The ?th Doctor never bothers to identify himself beyond saying 'It's me' when on the phone to the Secretary General. In episode three, he tells the Shalka leader Prime that he visits Earth merely for the eclipses and the wine. Evidently, this incarnation doesn't expect it to taste like the gums. In the final episode, he likens the titular scream to the song of Earth's whales, and says that Warhol - as wonderful as Lon Chaney, apparently - wanted to paint all nine of him. In his final confrontation with the Shalka, he sings the show-

stopper *Cabaret* and references the famously tacky international television event. In conversation with Alison after the crisis has passed, the Master reveals to her that the Doctor has, for some reason, promised to take his former arch-enemy to Bognor Regis. Are semble seeds used by the Atraxi, of *The Eleventh Hour*?

Musings

Victims of the Time War

Would that everything in the Whoniverse fit together seamlessly. But with numerous production teams throughout the past 50-plus years, the show has never had any kind of master plan (unlike the Master, who is full of them), thus affording hacks the opportunity to produce entire volumes of wild speculation based on passing references the writers never imagined anyone in their right mind to pick up on. There are thus bound to be a few things that are just never going to fit. If you like, you can blame them on the Time War. Except the last one. That one's just out there, and we all have to live with it.

Alternative Universes

The Third Doctor seems ignorant of the existence of alternative dimensions in *Inferno*, so this is clearly his introduction to the concept. But ...

Well, for starters, the First Doctor, in the unscreened pilot episode, mentions multiple universes. Admittedly, that's not conclusive, but during *Inside the Spaceship* he speaks of travelling to the Planet Quinnis in 'the Fourth Universe,' and the Second Doctor considers taking Victoria and Jamie to another universe in the final episode of *The Evil of the Daleks*. The Time Lords apparently have access to such realms - during *The Invasion of Time*, the Fourth Doctor frets about the Sontarans rampaging through any and all universes. The Eleventh Doctor mentions other universes in passing at the end of *Night Terrors* - it seems, according to *Rise of the Cybermen*, that there was a period when journeys between the dimensions were quite common. Speaking of Cybermen, they also seem to know about other universes in *The Pandorica Opens.*

The Dalek Invasion of Earth

The precise date of the Dalek occupation of our world is the subject of some debate. The calendar the Doctor discovers in episode one of *The Dalek Invasion of Earth* is from 2164, but as the factory in which it is found is disused, it is hardly likely to be recent. In *The Space Museum*, companion Vicki claims to have been taught that the invasion occurred 300 years before her time - which, according to *The Rescue*, is the year 2493. The First Doctor, in *The Daleks' Master Plan*, states that the invasion occurred in 2157, so it's good to know that we didn't allow such alien incursions to hamper our resilient calendar-printing industry. The Seventh Doctor novel *Lucifer Rising* puts the invasion a year later, in 2158.

In *Genesis of the Daleks,* the Fourth Doctor tells Davros that it happened in the year 2000 (a 1964 BBC TV trailer also sets the date as 2000). If that is indeed the case, I think I must have dozed off and missed the entire invasion. Also, in describing the invasion, the Doctor seems to be remembering the plot of a Peter Cushing movie he once saw rather than his own experiences. In *Remembrance of the Daleks,* the Seventh Doctor simply states that it occurred in the 22nd Century, while the Fifth Doctor audio *The Mutant Phase* notes that the Earth was occupied in 2158 and that the Doctor vanquished his foes in 2167, though the audio *Masters of Earth* sets the invasion between 2152 and 2164. So that's that cleared up, then.

The Doctor and Drink

Throughout *The Gunfighters,* the First Doctor insists that he never touches alcohol (preferring a glass of milk), and turns down an offer of brandy in episode one of *The Smugglers* (though he keeps some in the TARDIS by the time of *The Ark in Space,* for medicinal purposes only). This doesn't stop him from raising a celebratory glass to the kids at home in *The Daleks' Master Plan.*

In *The Impossible Astronaut,* the Eleventh Doctor declares wine 'horrid,' seemingly never having tasted it before. He at least knows what it smells like, insisting in his third incarnation that the planet Metebelis 3 has the same odour. But he is seen to drink wine in several earlier stories, including *The Evil of the Daleks, Day of the Daleks, The Green Death* and *The Time Warrior.* It is also worth noting that the Doctor at Lake Silencio isn't technically the Doctor at all, but rather the Teselecta taking the form of the Doctor (with the real Doctor inside), so that only adds to the complications.

In the *Class* episode *For Tonight We Might Die,* the Twelfth Doctor recommends darts as a pastime for the manner in which it combines skill and the consumption of alcohol.

Nursing a hangover in the radio drama *Slipback,* the Sixth Doctor claims naïveté when it comes to matters of drink.

The Bard

The Doctor claims to have known William Shakespeare in *Planet of Fear, City of Death* and *The Mark of the Rani,* but has never met him before in the much later story *The Shakespeare Code,* even though he is quite familiar with his life and works. Also in that adventure, the Doctor says that he has never seen a death like Lynley's (who appears to have drowned on dry land), but during his third incarnation, he witnesses a very similar demise in *The Mind of Evil.*

The Doctor's Age

It's clear from his first incarnation that the Doctor's lifespan is longer than that of mere humans - for instance, he ages about a hundred years when the Daleks activate the Time Destructor in *The Daleks' Master Plan*. It's not until *The Tomb of the Cybermen* that we learn his age. In response to Victoria's oddly phrased query, he states that he is 450 years old. So that's that. But ...

The Third Doctor's life 'covers several thousand years' in *Doctor Who and the Silurians.* Additionally, he seems about to say that he has been a scientist for several thousand years before stopping himself in episode one of *The Mind of Evil.* Though 'something like' 750 (which, in Time Lord terms, is approaching middle-age) in *Pyramids of Mars,* the Fourth Doctor is only 749 during *The Brain of Morbius* and *The Seeds of Doom*. Romana thinks he has become confused about his age when they first meet in *The Ribos Operation.* She claims he's 759, but he insists he is three years younger than that. A few stories later, however (during *The Power of Kroll*), he admits to being nearly 760. In *The Creature from the Pit,* though, Romana says that he was born around 750 years prior.

The Doctor admits to 750 again in *The Leisure Hive,* in which he ages 500 years and becomes 1,250. In both *Revelation of the Daleks* and *The Mysterious Planet,* the Sixth Doctor is 900 years old. Fifty-three years pass before he regenerates at the start of *Time and the Rani*. He has grown slightly younger in *Aliens of London,* in which the Ninth Doctor mentions '900 years of time and space' before confirming that as his age. In *The End of Time,* the Tenth Doctor is only 906.

In *Flesh and Stone, Amy's Choice* and the Season Five DVD extra *Meanwhile in the TARDIS,* the Eleventh Doctor gives his age as 907. When he drops Amy and Rory off sometime after *A Christmas Carol,* he is 908, and he's a year older in *The Impossible Astronaut* when he shows up at the diner (Clara's TARDIS?), unaware that his 1,103-year-old self has apparently just been killed. Nearly a Century has passed by *A Town Called Mercy,* in which he offers his age as 1,200. He loses 200 years by *The Bells of Saint John,* but regains them in *The Day of the Doctor,* which he is 'twelve hundred and something.' Another 300 years elapse by the mid-point of *The Time of the Doctor,* and following his regeneration, he states in *Deep Breath* that he is 'over two thousand.'

In *Doctor Who - The TV Movie,* the Eighth Doctor appears to suggest that he has been piloting the TARDIS for 700 years (he says no one has opened the Eye of Harmony in that time). But we learn in *The Doctor's Wife* that 700 years have elapsed since the TARDIS first took the form of a Police Box. In *The Pirate Planet,* it is stated that he has been piloting the TARDIS for 523 years. He refers to '900 years of phonebox travel' in *The Empty Child* (an assertion he makes again in *Journey to the Centre of the TARDIS*), but also states that he has been known as the Doctor for nine centuries.

In *Twice Upon a Time,* the Twelfth Doctor tells the First that they are separated by a gap of 1,500 years. Assuming that he's rounding his own age down to the nearest two thousand, that would mean that the First Doctor is 500 at the time of his regeneration, fifty years younger than his second incarnation admits to being.

And we haven't even considered the length of a Gallifreyan year. The novel *The Eight Doctors* states that a day on Gallifrey lasts 24 hours. Now we just need to know how long a Gallifreyan hour lasts.

Oh, and there's also the fact that the Doctor spends four and a half billion years trapped inside a confession dial in *Heaven Sent.* And is the the Doctor who emerges from the trap really the Doctor, or a copy of a copy of a copy of a copy of a copy of (continued in volumes 2 to 10 billion)?

Language

The Ninth Doctor tells Rose, in *The End of the World,* that the TARDIS generates a telepathic field, translating all foreign languages (the first suggestion that the TARDIS is telepathic occurs in *The Time Monster*). In episode three of *The Masque of Mandragora,* the Fourth Doctor describes it as a Time Lord gift. Whatever the reason, it should mean that we never hear dialogue in any language other than English. But ...

In *The Parting of the Ways,* the Doctor says he has five billion languages (if they're all translated for him, what's the point?). He recognises French in *The Moonbase,* but has to ask Gulliver to speak English in episode two of *The Mind Robber.* Soldiers in *The War Games* speak German - like French, a language of which the Second Doctor seems to have little understanding. He speaks Latin first in *The Daemons,* and again in *The Masque of Mandragora,* leading companion Sarah Jane Smith to question how she can understand Italian (but not, mind you, why she can't understand Latin). The Thirteenth Doctor translates the Latin motto on James I's garter in *The Witchfinders.* The Third Doctor converses in Chinese in *The Mind of Evil* and Tibetan in *Planet of the Spiders,* while the Fourth says in *The Talons of Weng-Chiang* that he speaks 'Mandarin, Cantonese, all the dialects.' In *Four to Doomsday,* the Fifth Doctor doesn't understand Aboriginal dialects and must ask Tegan to translate for him. The Tenth Doctor often uses French and Italian phrases (it's an important plot point in *Midnight*), and Missy speaks both French and

Spanish during *The Lie of the Land*. In *Flatline,* the TARDIS is incapable of translating the language of the Boneless.

Regarding alien languages, the Sixth Doctor recognises Ycarnos' Krontep swear words in *Mindwarp*. In *The Waters of Mars,* the Tenth Doctor speaks North Martian, despite the fact that all the Martians he has ever encountered speak English. He addresses the Judoon in their own tongue during *The Stolen Earth.* The Atraxi's warning to Prisoner Zero in *The Eleventh Hour* is heard by the Eleventh Doctor in multiple languages.

The Third Doctor is only able to understand the language of *The Ambassadors of Death* because of their own translation devices. The Mogarians of *Terror of the Vervoids* have similar devices, and neither the TARDIS nor the Matrix can comprehend their native tongue - which is useful, given that it proves important to the story. The Fourth Doctor and Romana cannot tell what the Foamasi are saying in *The Leisure Hive.*

The communication barrier presented in *Planet of the Dead* may occur because the TARDIS is too far away to translate, even though, in *The Angels Take Manhattan,* River Song tells companion Rory that the gift 'hangs around.' It certainly doesn't work for Martha Jones, who encounters German-speaking Daleks in *Journey's End.*

The Pope requires a translator when speaking to the Twelfth Doctor in *Extremis.* However, it turns out not to be the real Pope, the real Doctor, or the real world, so none of it counts, probably.

The TARDIS' inability to translate the written word in *The Impossible Planet* is treated as a rarity (although Rose has to ask the Ninth Doctor to explain a Welsh sign in *Boom Town*), and in *The Fires of Pompeii,* the signs at the Roman market are seen in English. But in *The Massacre,* the First Doctor knows that the TARDIS has brought him to Paris because the road signs are all in French. In *The Stones of Blood,* the Fourth Doctor and Romana are unable to decipher the writing on the seal of the Megaran capsule. We see Viking and Russian writing in *The Curse of Fenric* - and the Seventh Doctor also speaks Russian in that story. The TARDIS won't translate the writing of the Fisher King in *Under the Lake/Before the Flood.* Presumably, the translation function applies to numbers as well as words, but in *Logopolis,* Alzarean companion Adric explains that the Fourth Doctor taught him to read Earth numbers.

The Doctor speaks Baby (*A Good Man Goes to War, Closing Time* and *The Girl Who Died*), Horse (*A Town Called Mercy*), Dinosaur (*Deep Breath*), Tree, in the First Doctor audio *O Tannenbaum,* Tree, and Sheep in the novel *Scratchman,* but the TARDIS chooses not to provide a translation for anyone else. *Carnival of Monsters* makes it abundantly clear that he doesn't speak chicken. As recently as the Eleventh Doctor story *The Rings of Akhaten,* he is forced to speak the native language of the Terraberserkers and Dor'een the moped saleswoman. In *Under the Lake,* he believes he knows sign language, but it may actually be semaphore.

This question could drive a sane man crazy, so it's best to remember the words of the theme song for *Mystery Science Theater 3000*: 'Just repeat to yourself, it's just a show, I should really just relax.'

The Doctor's Vegetarianism

Many novel writers have made a big deal out of the fact that, at the end of *The Two Doctors*, the Sixth Doctor appears to be considering becoming a vegetarian. But …

In *World War Three*, Rose says that the Ninth Doctor eats shepherd's pie (or that he is, at least, *prepared* to eat shepherd's pie). He eats meat in *The Empty Child*, and the Eleventh Doctor eats either chicken or steak (possibly both) in *Midnight*. He expresses a love of hot dogs in *The Age of Steel*, and chops and gravy in *Planet of the Dead*. In *Amy's Choice*, the Dream Lord - an aspect of the Doctor's own personality - twice calls the Eleventh Doctor a vegetarian, even though he eats fish (in finger form) within minutes of regenerating. The Twelfth Doctor asks for sausages and claims not to like liver in *Deep Breath*. He carries a burger and some sushi during *The Return of Doctor Mysterio*, despite claiming in *Smile* that he's not fond of eating fish. In *Thin Ice*, he munches on something that might very well be an intestine on a stick, and declares it his favourite. In the audio *Seasons of Fear*, the Eighth Doctor says he rarely eats meat - which might mean that he doesn't often eat it, or that he prefers it rare. Or both.

The Indestructibility of the TARDIS

The TARDIS' safety features are evidently as unreliable as its steering mechanism, despite the Third Doctor's insistence, in the first and last episodes of *The Curse of Peladon*, that the craft is indestructible.

In episode one of *The Sensorites*, the First Doctor treats breaking down the door of the TARDIS as a definite possibility, although it would disturb the field dimensions inside. A few stories later, during episode two of *The Web Planet*, he insists that the interior of the ship is inviolable.

In episode six of *The Daleks' Master Plan*, he says that the vessel is protected by a force field (which he built himself, according to *Galaxy 4*). It must, however, protect only the exterior, for in the very same scene, he chides Steven for conducting an experiment that might blow up the ship. The force-field generator is destroyed along with Omega's antimatter universe in *The Three Doctors*. Presumably, he builds a new one.

In episode one of *The Invasion*, the Second Doctor seems concerned that the missile fired at them from the dark side of the Moon is capable of destroying them.

In *The Time Monster*, the Master is quite content that his arch-enemy's TARDIS can't be destroyed, and the Third Doctor is in agreement, explaining that it is as indestructible as Kronos' crystal because 'it has its being outside time.'

Susan is unnerved by the Cybermen's attempt to blow up the ship in *The Five Doctors*, though as a Gallifreyan (and, seemingly, the one who coined the term TARDIS), she should know that she and the Fifth Doctor's companion Turlough aren't in any real danger.

The Fifth Doctor never doubts for a moment that his vessel has been destroyed in *Frontios*, though he's remarkably sanguine about the fact throughout the story.

In *Timelash*, the Sixth Doctor isn't certain that the TARDIS will survive the collision with the Bandril missile, despite always telling Peri that the TARDIS is indestructible. In *Attack of the Cybermen*, several stories earlier, he talks about the shell of the TARDIS being punctured.

The Ninth Doctor's ship is not protected by any force field until the Slitheen extrapolator, confiscated during *Boom Town*, is installed during *The Parting of the Ways*. The device is seen again briefly during *The Runaway Bride*, and the force field is still in operation during *The Witch's Familiar* and *Resolution*.

The Daleks of *Journey's End* have no difficulties in taking down the TARDIS' defences, and the Tenth Doctor has no doubt that his craft will be torn apart by the Crucible's Z-Neutrino energy. His next incarnation is less concerned about the effects of acid in *The Almost People*, though.

When Davros announces his intention to destroy the TARDIS in *The Magician's Apprentice*, Missy disabuses Clara of the notion that such an act would be impossible. Then again, Missy's a pathological liar, so that's not particularly helpful.

In *Bad Wolf*, the Ninth Doctor claims (incorrectly) that the TARDIS cannot be penetrated by Transmat beams, ignoring the unavoidable fact that the Daleks have managed to do just that. He later does the same thing himself in *Asylum of the Daleks*. When he materialises the TARDIS around Brian Williams in *Dinosaurs on a Spaceship*, the Eleventh Doctor instantly assumes he boarded the craft by Transmat. (Incidentally, why Brian wasn't at Rory and Amy's wedding remains a mystery.)

The Krotons marks the first mention of the Hostile Action Displacement System (HADS) - seen again many years later, in *Cold War* - which causes the TARDIS to dematerialise if it is in danger. The Second Doctor says he doesn't always remember to set the HADS, but the question remains: If the ship is indestructible, why does it even need the HADS? By the time of *The Witch's Familiar*, the acronym now stands for Hostile Action Dispersal

System. Either that, or it's a different but very similar-sounding function, which is just confusing.

The Doctor's Hearts

The novelization of *Galaxy 4* mentions the Doctor's two hearts, but this fact is not established onscreen until *Spearhead From Space*. It's worth noting that in *The Dominators*, the titular villains decide not to perform an examination of the Second Doctor, assuming that his biology would be the same as Jamie's, and not like that of the two-hearted Dulcians. Perhaps the idea of a second heart was in the minds of the producers even at this stage.

It has been suggested that the additional heart doesn't grow until after a Time Lord's first regeneration because, in *Inside the Spaceship*, companion Ian Chesterton feels only a single pulse, meaning either that he has just one heart at this stage, or that Ian is really lousy at taking a person's pulse. Oddly, in *The Hungry Earth*, the Eleventh Doctor refers to his heart in the singular. Kim Newman's story *Time and Relative* and the First Doctor audio *The Beginning* both state that the Doctor's granddaughter Susan has two hearts, so make of that what you will.

The Doctor's Doctorate

In episode three of *100,000 BC*, the First Doctor announces grumpily 'I'm not a doctor of medicine!' and he repeats this assertion in the penultimate chapter of *Marco Polo*. By the time of *The Moonbase*, however, the Second Doctor claims to have earned his Doctorate studying under Lister in 1888, which must have occurred sometime after the events of *The Ark*, if it occurred at all. There's reason to suppose that it did not, although the Seventh Doctor novel *White Darkness* says that it did, but in the year 1875. During *Into the Dalek*, he claims that during his first incarnation the term Doctor was 'just a name.'

The Second Doctor states, in episode one of *The Enemy of the World*, that his Doctorate is not of any medical significance, and in *The Krotons* he tells companion Zoe that he is not a medical doctor.

In *The Ark in Space* the Fourth Doctor claims his title is purely honorary. Companion Sarah Jane Smith confirms this in episode one of *Seeds of Death*, after he refuses to perform an amputation. During *The Brain of Morbius*, he is not in a position to say whether her blindness is permanent, and is thus forced to consult the despicable Mehendri Solon.

In the dream world of *Amy's Choice*, 'Dr' Rory teases the Eleventh Doctor by saying 'Unlike you, I've actually passed some exams.' A few stories later, however, during *The God Complex*, the Doctor claims to have degrees in both medicine and cheese-making. The Twelfth Doctor states in *Mummy on the Orient Express* that his doctorate is in intestinal parasites.

The Doctor displays his medical skills in several stories, including *The Sensorites, The Highlanders, The Daemons, Frontios, The Twin Dilemma* and *Terror of the Vervoids*. In the Season Six DVD extra titled *Good Night*, he says he has helped out at as a locum at a medical centre in Brixton, so one hopes he has at least a bit of experience, for his patients' sake.

In *The Tsuranaga Conundrum*, the Thirteenth Doctor states that she has doctorates in medicine, science, engineering, candyfloss, Lego, philosophy, music, problems and, mostly, hope.

Finger-Clickin' Good

In *The Forest of the Dead*, River Song states that the Doctor she knows is able to open the TARDIS doors with a click of his fingers, which the Tenth Doctor actually does at the end of that story, as well as in the novel *Autonomy* and the short story *The Sontaran Games*. The Eleventh is seen to do so in *The Eleventh Hour*, which does not feature River. He is unable to open the TARDIS without the key in *The Sarah Jane Adventures* story *Death of the Doctor*, which occurs after *The Eleventh Hour*.

Clara closes the doors with a click in both *The Day of the Doctor* and *The Caretaker*, but she, too, needs a key in *The Time of the Doctor, In the Forest of the Night* and *Sleep No More*. In *Dark Water*, she threatens to send all seven keys to doomsday if he refuses to prevent Danny Pink's death. Granted, it all turns out to be a dream, but if both she and the Doctor are capable of opening the TARDIS doors up with just a snap, why would she think that destroying the keys would be a big deal to him?

Rassilon's scheme in *Face the Raven* concerns depriving the Doctor of his key. This, despite the fact that Clara would retain hers, and that whole finger-clicking thing, of course.

In *The Ghost Monument*, the Thirteenth Doctor has to beg the TARDIS to let her in after she loses her key somewhere over Sheffield. She could always click her fingers, but that no longer seems to be a thing.

Clara and the Doctors

Unleash the Continuity Nightmare Child!

So, at the climax of *The Name of the Doctor*, companion Clara leaps into the late Doctor's timeline in order that she might protect all of his former selves from the actions of the Great Intelligence. So she knows every detail of the

Doctor's life, including his true name, which she first discovered in *Journey to the Centre of the TARDIS*, forgot, and then heard again from the mouth of River Song. With the exception of the details of the War Doctor's life - which he somehow continues to repress, despite the fact that he's dead - there is literally nothing Clara doesn't know about the Doctor's life ...

... except for his relationship with Tasha Lem of the Papal Mainframe. Oh, and the nature of the beings known as the Silence, which he learns during his final (official) incarnation. And everything about his childhood, which she later witnesses in *Listen*. And the fact that River Song isn't a man. Of course, with the fresh set of regenerations bestowed upon the Doctor at the end of *The Time of the Doctor*, the events of *The Name of the Doctor* never actually happen, and Clara, therefore, does not enter the Doctor's timestream ...

... except that she remembers the Tenth Doctor and her brief meeting with the War Doctor in *The Day of the Doctor*, and has detailed knowledge of his past, which she related to the Cybermen during *Death in Heaven*. And without Clara, the events of *Asylum of the Daleks* and *The Snowmen* would have occurred very differently, if at all. And Oswin Oswald would not have been around to delete all records of the Doctor's existence ...

... except that in *The Time of the Doctor*, the Daleks still have no knowledge of his identity, until they drain the mind of Tasha Lem. Is anyone else's brain dribbling out of their ears?

About the Author

Matthew J Elliott is the writer of several *Doctor Who* audio titles, including *Maker of Demons, Zaltys, The Silurian Candidate* and *The Lure of the Nomad*. His published works include the authorized sequels to the cult Fox movie *Big Trouble in Little China*: *Big Trouble in Mother Russia* (2016) and *Big Trouble in Merrie Olde England* (2017). He is also the author of *Sherlock Holmes on the Air* (2012), *Sherlock Holmes in Pursuit* (2013), *The Immortals: An Unauthorized Guide to* Sherlock *and* Elementary (2013) and *The Throne Eternal* (2014). His articles, fiction and reviews have appeared in the magazines *Scarlet Street, Total DVD, SHERLOCK,* and *Sherlock Holmes Mystery Magazine*.

Matthew has also contributed stories to the collections *The Game's Afoot, Curious Incidents 2* and *Gaslight Grimoire* and essays to *A Galaxy Far, Far Away: Exploring* Star Wars *Comics, Bright Eyes, Ape City: Examining the* Planet of the Apes *Mythos* and *Somewhere Beyond the Heavens: Exploring* Battlestar Galactica. His short story *Art in the Blood* appeared in *The Mammoth Book of Best British Crime 8* in the UK, and *The Mammoth Book of Best British Mystery 8* in the US. He is the editor of the collections *The Whisperer in Darkness, The Horror in the Museum, The Haunter of the Dark* and *The Lurking Fear* by H P Lovecraft, *The Right Hand of Doom* and *The Haunter of the Ring* by Robert E Howard, and *A Charlie Chan Omnibus* by Earl Derr Biggers.

For radio, he has scripted episodes of *The Twilight Zone, Vincent Price Presents, Wrath of the Titans, Logan's Run: Aftermath, Fangoria's Dreadtime Stories, The Further Adventures of Sherlock Holmes, The Classic Adventures of Sherlock Holmes, Jeeves and Wooster, The Perry Mason Radio Dramas, Raffles the Gentleman Thief, The Father Brown Mysteries, Kincaid the Strangeseeker, The Adventures of Harry Nile, The Enchanted Story Emporium, The Thinking Machine, Allan Quatermain, The Prince and the Pauper, The New Adventures of Mickey Spillane's Mike Hammer, The Enchanted Story Emporium* and the Audie Award-nominated *The War of the Worlds* and. He is the creator of *The Hilary Caine Mysteries*, which first aired in 2005.

His stage play *An Evening With Jeeves and Wooster* was performed at the Palace Theatre, in Grapevine, Texas, in 2007.

Matthew is probably best-known (if at all) as a writer and performer on RiffTrax.com, the online comedy experience from the creators of cult sci-fi TV series *Mystery Science Theater 3000* (*MST3K* to the initiated).

He lives in the North-West of England with his wife and daughter.

Other *Doctor Who* Titles From Telos Publishing

Howe's Transcendental Toybox: Merchandise Guide
David J Howe and Arnold T Blumberg

Talkback Vols 1, 2, 3
Ed. Stephen James Walker

Back to the Vortex: *Doctor Who* 2005
J Shaun Lyon

Third Dimension: *Doctor Who* 2007
Stephen James Walker

Monsters Within: *Doctor Who* 2008
Stephen James Walker

End of Ten: *Doctor Who* 2009
Stephen James Walker

Cracks in Time: *Doctor Who* 2010
Stephen James Walker

River's Run: *Doctor Who* 2011
Stephen James Walker

Time of the Doctor: *Doctor Who* 2012 and 2013
Stephen James Walker

The Comic Strip Companion Vol 1
Paul Scoones

The Barry Newbery Signature Collection
Barry Newbery

Wiped! The History of the Missing *Doctor Who* Episodes
Richard Molesworth

Now on the Big Screen: *Doctor Who* at the Movies
Charles Norton